Cells Tissues Organs

in vivo, in vitro

Founded 1945 as 'Acta Anatomica' by R. Chambers, G. Glimstedt, T. Peterfi and G. Wolf-Heidegger
Continued 1962–1974 by E.A. Boyden, 1955–1980 by A. Delmas, 1972–1980 by F. Walberg, 1945–1980 by G. Wolf-Heidegger, 1981–1988 by R. O'Rahilly, Davis, Calif., 1989–1990 by G.E. Goslow, Jr., Providence, R.I., 1981–1992 by W. Lierse, Hamburg

KARGER

Printed in Switzerland on acid-free paper by Reinhardt Druck, Basel

Appears monthly: 3 volumes per year (12 issues)

Guidelines for Authors

Cells
Tissues
Organs

Aims and Scope
Cells Tissues Organs is an international forum for communication among scientists interested in current research on functional morphology and morphogenesis at all levels of organization, from subcellular to macroscopy, with emphasis on humans and higher vertebrates. The journal offers rapid exchange of novel and significant information gained from experimental and theoretical investigations on all aspects that are pertinent to the formation and transformation of biological structure.

Topics of special interest include
Developmental and reproductive biology, cell biology, tissue engineering, artificial organs, in vitro systems and transplantation. Papers highlighting the links between structural and functional aspects are preferred.

Types of Papers
The journal publishes: (1) Original papers on experimental research. (2) Theoretical contributions. These will appear in the section 'Hypotheses and Concepts' and may include provocative hypotheses, provided that they are innovative, well founded and show promise for new avenues of research. (3) Short reviews/perspectives. While (1) and (2) are submitted contributions, reviews/perspectives (3) are invited. Suggestions concerning reviews on current topics of high interest are welcome.
All manuscripts must be accompanied by a cover letter signed by all authors. Assurance should be given that the manuscript is not under simultaneous consideration by any other publication. Reported studies using animal and human subjects must have been approved by the appropriate institutional review boards.

Submission
Manuscripts from North and South America should be sent to:

Prof. A.W. English, PhD
Emory University School of Medicine
Dept. of Cell Biology
Whitehead Biomedical Research Building, 4th Floor
Atlanta, GA 30322 (USA)
Fax +1 404 727–3677
E-Mail cto@cellbio.emory.edu

Manuscripts from all other countries to:
Prof. H.-W. Denker
S. Karger AG
Editorial Office 'Cells Tissues Organs'
PO Box
CH–4009 Basel (Switzerland)
Tel. +41 61 306 13 57
Fax +41 61 306 14 34
E-Mail l. haas@karger.ch

Mailing address for courier deliveries only:
Allschwilerstr. 10
CH–4055 Basel (Switzerland)

All manuscripts are subject to peer review. Submission of an article for publication implies the transfer of the copyright from the author to the publisher upon acceptance. Accepted papers become the permanent property of Cells Tissues Organs and may not be reproduced by any means, in whole or in part, without the written consent of the publisher. It is the author's responsibility to obtain permission to reproduce illustrations, tables, etc. from other publications.

Format and Arrangement
Manuscripts should be written in English and be as concise as possible. They should be submitted in quadruplicate (with four sets of original illustrations), typewritten double-spaced on one side of the paper, with a wide margin. *Lines should be numbered in the margin.* It is mandatory to include an electronic version of the entire manuscript, either on a 3,5-inch disk or CD-ROM.

Title page: The first page of each paper should indicate the title, the authors' names, the institute where the work was conducted, and a short title for use as running head.

Full address: The exact postal address of the corresponding author complete with postal code must be given at the bottom of the title page. Please also supply phone and fax numbers, as well as e-mail address.

Key words: For indexing purposes provide a list of up to 5 key words.

Abstract: Each paper needs an abstract of up to about 20 lines summarizing the essential new information communicated.

Subheadings: Introduction; Materials and Methods; Results; Discussion.

List of Abbreviations: Provide a list of the abbreviations used in your paper. Please list them on a separate page of the manuscript. The list will be printed as a footnote at the bottom of the first page of your article.

Footnotes: With the exception of the list of abbreviations, footnotes should be avoided. When essential, they are numbered consecutively and typed at the foot of the appropriate page.

Nomenclature: The nomenclature used should conform, wherever possible, to the current edition of the Nomina Anatomica (Terminologia Anatomica), Nomina Anatomica Veterinaria, or to the Nomina Anatomica Avium.

Tables and illustrations: Tables and illustrations (both numbered in Arabic numerals) should be prepared on separate sheets. Tables require a heading and figures a legend, also prepared on a separate sheet. For the reproduction of illustrations, only good drawings and original photographs can be accepted; negatives or photocopies cannot be used. Please only use scale bars to indicate magnifications of the illustrations. Due to technical reasons, figures with a screen background should not be submitted. When possible, group several illustrations on one block for reproduction (max. size 180 × 223 mm) or provide crop marks. On the back of each illustration, indicate its number, the author's name, and 'top' with a soft pencil. Electronically submitted b/w half-tone and color illustrations must have a final resolution of 300 dpi after scaling, line drawings one of 800–1200 dpi.

Color illustrations: During the review process, the decision will be made as to which color illustrations of a manuscript can be reproduced free of charge. Authors will be informed of this at the time of acceptance of their paper. Otherwise, these illustrations will be reproduced at the author's expense. Up to 6 color illustrations per page can be integrated into the text at the special price of CHF/USD 660.00 per page.

References: References in the text should be made by author's name followed by the year of publication, arranged chronologically, then alphabetically. When there are more than two authors, use the first author's name and et al. When references are made to more than one paper by the same author, published in the same year, designate them as a, b, c, etc. The list of references should include only those publications which are cited in the text. Material submitted for publication but not yet accepted may be cited in the text as 'unpublished data' but must not be included in the reference list. In the list of references, arrange references alphabetically listing all authors, then year of publication. Preferably, please cite all authors. Abbreviate journal names according to Index Medicus.

Digital Object Identifier (DOI)
S. Karger Publishers supports DOIs as unique identifiers for articles. A DOI number will be printed on the title page of each article. DOIs can be useful in the future for identifying and citing articles published online without volume or issue information. More information can be found at www.doi.org.

Examples
(a) Papers published in periodicals: Sun, J., H. Koto, K.F. Chung (1997) Interaction of ozone and allergen challenges on bronchial responsiveness and inflammation in sensitised guinea pigs. Int Arch Allergy Immunol *112:* 191–195.
Hadler, W.A., S.R. Silveira (1981) Técnica histoquímica que permite discriminar o colesterol de substâncias afins e de seus ésteres. Cienc Cult *33(suppl):* 586–587.
(b) Papers published only with DOI numbers:
Theoharides, T.C., W. Boucher, K. Spear: Serum interleukin-6 reflects disease severity and osteoporosis in mastocytosis patients. Int Arch Allergy Immunol DOI: 10.1159/000063858.
(c) Monographs: Matthews, D.E., V.T. Farewell (1996) Using and Understanding Medical Statistics, ed 3, revised. Basel Karger.
(d) Edited books: Parren, P.W.H.I., D.R. Burton (1997) Antibodies against HIV-1 from phage display libraries: Mapping of an immune response and progress towards antiviral immunotherapy; in Capra, J.D. (ed): Antibody Engineering. Chem Immunol. Basel, Karger, vol 65, pp 18–56.

Further details: Authors may consult the 'Guide to Writing Articles in English' by R. O'Rahilly (Acta Anat *131:* 1–2, 1988).

Galley proofs
Unless indicated otherwise, galley proofs are sent to the first-named author and should be returned with the least possible delay. Alterations made in proofs, other than the correction of printer's errors, are charged to the author.

Reprints
Order forms and a price list are sent with the proofs. Orders submitted after the issue is printed are subject to considerably higher prices.

KARGER

Fax +41 61 306 12 34
E-Mail karger@karger.ch
www.karger.com

The Guidelines for Authors are available at:
www.karger.com/cto_Guidelines

Cells Tissues Organs

General Information

Publication data: 'Cells Tissues Organs' is published 12 times a year. Volumes 179–181, each with 4 issues, appear in 2005.

Subscription rates: Subscriptions run for a full calendar year. Prices are given per year.

Personal subscription:

Print or Online	Print/Online combined
CHF 240.–	CHF 363.–
EUR 178.–	EUR 268.–
USD 218.00	USD 329.00

postage and handling (added to print and print/online)
CHF 65.40 Europe, CHF 97.20 Overseas
EUR 47.40
USD 88.20

Institutional subscription:

Print or Online	Print/Online combined
CHF 2889.–	CHF 3120.–
EUR 2139.–	EUR 2310.–
USD 2625.00	USD 2835.00

postage and handling (added to print and print/online)
CHF 81.60 Europe, CHF 121.20 Overseas
EUR 58.80
USD 110.40

Airmail surcharge: CHF 81.60 / USD 67.80

Microforms: Please direct all enquiries and orders to:
University Microfilms Inc.
300 North Zeeb Road, P.O. Box 1346
Ann Arbor, MI 48106-1346 (USA)

Subscription orders: Orders can be placed at agencies, bookstores, directly with the Publisher
S. Karger AG, P.O. Box
CH–4009 Basel (Switzerland)
or with any of the following distributors:
Deutschland: S. Karger GmbH, Postfach
D–79095 Freiburg
France: Librairie Luginbühl
36, bd de Latour-Maubourg
F–75007 Paris
Great Britain, Ireland: S. Karger AG
4 Rickett Street
London SW6 1RU, UK
USA: S. Karger Publishers, Inc.
26 West Avon Road, P.O. Box 529
Farmington, CT 06085, USA
India, Bangladesh, Sri Lanka:
Panther Publishers Private Ltd.
33, First Main
Koramangala First Block
Bangalore 560 034, India
Japan: Karger Japan, Inc.
Yushima S Bld. 3F
4-2-3, Yushima, Bunkyo-ku
Tokyo 113-0034, Japan

Change of address: Both old and new address should be sent to the subscription source.

Single issues and back volumes: Information can be obtained through the Publisher.

Advertising: Correspondence and rate requests should be addressed to the Publisher.

Bibliographic indices: This journal is regularly listed in bibliographic services, including *Current Contents*® and Index Medicus/MEDLINE.

KARGER
Fax +41 61 306 12 34
E-Mail karger@karger.ch
www.karger.com

The Journal Home Page is available at:
www.karger.com/cto

A useful compilation of up-to-date information

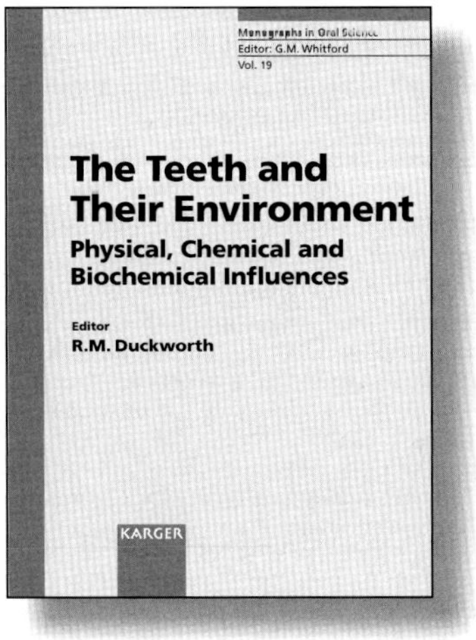

The Teeth and Their Environment

Physical, Chemical and Biochemical Influences

Editor
Ralph M. Duckworth

Dental Medicine; Clinical Chemistry; Caries Prophylaxis, Dental Hygiene, Preventive Medicine, Public Health

Providing a current overview of how physical, chemical and biochemical aspects of the oral environment influence tooth condition, this publication covers caries, calculus, tooth wear and erosion, and the roles of pellicle, saliva and plaque in inducing and/or moderating these conditions. It highlights topics such as new intra-oral and laboratory methods to assess tooth wear, the latest ideas on de- and re-mineralisation processes involving enamel and dentine, new insights into the tooth structure-function relationship and the site specificity of anticaries treatments. Reviews of pellicle function and of the inverse relationship between caries and calculus complete the volume.
This valuable book is highly recommended to all oral care scientists, laboratory and clinical researchers alike, and to lecturers in dental medicine.

Contents

KI 05448

www.karger.com/moors

Monographs in Oral Science, Vol. 19
Series Editor: Whitford, G.M. (Augusta, GA)
ISSN 0077–0892

The Teeth and Their Environment
Physical, Chemical and Biochemical Influences
Editor: Duckworth, R.M. (Cheshire)
X + 154 p., 36 fig., 5 in color, 13 tab.,hard cover, 2006
CHF 167.– / EUR 119.50 / USD 152.00
Prices subject to change
EUR price for Germany, USD price for USA only
ISBN 3–8055–7968–3

KARGER

Order Form

Please send: _____ copy/ies

Postage and handling free with prepayment

Payment:
☐ Check enclosed ☐ Please bill me

Please charge to my credit card
☐ American Express ☐ Diners ☐ Eurocard
☐ MasterCard ☐ Visa

Card No.: ________________

Exp. date: ________________

Orders may be placed with any bookshop, subscription agency, directly with the publisher or through a Karger distributor.

Fax: +41 61 306 12 34

S. Karger AG, P.O. Box, CH–4009 Basel (Switzerland)
E-Mail orders@karger.ch, **www.karger.com**

Name/Address: ________________

Date: ________________

Signature: ________________

Cells
Tissues
Organs

Extra-Cellular Matrix in the Craniofacial Complex

Guest Editors
Marian F. Young, Bethesda, Md.
Paul H. Krebsbach, Ann Arbor, Mich.

62 figures, 37 in color, 3 tables, 2005

KARGER

Basel · Freiburg · Paris · London · New York ·
Bangalore · Bangkok · Singapore · Tokyo · Sydney

S. Karger
Medical and Scientific Publishers
Basel • Freiburg • Paris • London
New York • Bangalore • Bangkok
Singapore • Tokyo • Sydney

Disclaimer
The statements, options and data contained in this publication are solely those of the individual authors and contributors and not of the publisher and the editor(s). The appearance of advertisements in the journal is not a warranty, endorsement, or approval of the products or services advertised or of their effectiveness, quality or safety. The publisher and the editor(s) disclaim responsibility for any injury to persons or property resulting from any ideas, methods, instructions or products referred to in the content or advertisements.

Drug Dosage
The authors and the publisher have exerted every effort to ensure that drug selection and dosage set forth in this text are in accord with current recommendations and practice at the time of publication. However, in view of ongoing research, changes in government regulations, and the constant flow of information relating to drug therapy and drug reactions, the reader is urged to check the package insert for each drug for any change in indications and dosage and for added warnings and precautions. This is particularly important when the recommended agent is a new and/or infrequently employed drug.

P.O. Box, CH–4009 Basel (Switzerland)
Printed in Switzerland on acid-free paper by
Reinhardt Druck, Basel
ISBN 3–8055–8109–2

KARGER

Fax +41 61 306 12 34
E-Mail karger@karger.ch
www.karger.com

Vol. 181, No. 3–4, 2005

Cells
Tissues
Organs

Contents

KARGER

Fax +41 61 306 12 34
E-Mail karger@karger.ch
www.karger.com

Access to full text and tables of contents, including tentative ones for forthcoming issues:
www.karger.com/cto_issues

Cells
Tissues
Organs

Cells Tissues Organs 2005;181:125–126
DOI: 10.1159/000091373

Introduction

In the context of living organisms, cells do not function as independent units. Instead, they interact with neighboring cells and receive physical and functional support from a solid-phase microenvironment called the extracellular matrix (ECM). The ECM is a complex structure harboring myriad structural proteins whose complex functions are now beginning to be unraveled. Using a host of experimental approaches ranging from classic protein chemistry, nanotechnology, molecular and cell biology to the creation of animal models, new and unexpected roles for individual ECM proteins are emerging. This special issue of *Cells Tissues and Organs* contains proceedings from a symposium held at the American Association of Dental Research on March 10, 2005. This volume consists of papers by key scientists in the area.

This special topics issue is divided into four general areas related to the control of the formation and function of the structures of the head and face. The first section focuses on the role of the ECM in craniofacial structures during development and aging. Dr. Opperman from Texas A&M University summarizes studies that reveal how the ECM environment controls the complex mechanisms of cranial suture morphogenesis and growth. Both collagen and non-collagenous protein functions are highlighted. In work carried out at the National Institute for Dental and Craniofacial Research, Dr. Wadhwa shows how the ECM controls the integrity of the temporomandibular joint post-natally. New data from an animal model in which two small proteoglycans called biglycan and fibromodulin are absent are described and indicate that matrix proteins can, in fact, affect the expression and localization of each other. This type of reciprocal interaction between ECM proteins sheds new light on our interpretations of simple loss of expression systems for analysis of protein function. These observations underscore the complexity of the ECM microenvironment and how it is regulated during development and aging of the head and face. Craniofacial disorders are important clinical problems; however, the biological basis for the defects is not well understood. The studies presented here provide a basis to further understand the mechanisms involved in these disorders.

The second broad topic of this issue probes the biophysical, genetic and molecular factors controlling craniofacial mineralization and turnover. Dr. Boskey from the Hospital for Special Surgery, New York, presents studies on the molecular interactions of mineral and matrix and describes new work using micro-computed tomography and Fourier transform infrared spectroscopy to examine molecular details of mineralization mechanisms in normal craniofacial structures and those depleted in ECM proteoglycans biglycan and decorin. Dr. Marc McKee from McGill University, Canada, describes exciting new data from genetic models lacking the ECM protein matrix Gla, revealing its critical roles in the mineralization of bones and teeth. Dr. Gopalakrisan from the University of Minnesota presents work where he identified new *cis-* and *trans-*acting nuclear factors that control matrix Gla protein. This section will also highlight work from the lab of Dr. Holmbeck from the National Institute

KARGER
Fax +41 61 306 12 34
E-Mail karger@karger.ch
www.karger.com

1422–6405/05/1814–0125$22.00/0

Accessible online at:
www.karger.com/cto

for Dental and Craniofacial Research who has uncovered the role of one of the key enzymes that controls matrix degradation: membrane type I (matrix metalloproteinase 14). By depleting the MT1 gene, Dr. Holmbeck developed a new animal model to demonstrate how the craniofacial complex is reliant on this matrix metalloproteinase and that a detailed analysis of these mutant mice reveals new paradigms about how this unique structure forms during development. The third section of the symposium explored the formation and function of dentin and enamel, two important mineralized tissues of the tooth. The first paper in this section is by Dr. Fukumoto from Kyushu University, Japan, who describes new data showing that ameloblastin may function as a cell adhesion molecule in developing teeth. Dr. Gibson from the University of Pennsylvania presents an overview of her studies on the role of amelogenin in enamel formation employing mouse and human models. Dr. Oldack from the University of Southern California continues on the topic of enamel and describes work on the interactions of amelogenin with mineral and her exciting work on the use of 'nano-technology' to probe amelogenin macro assembly.

For years, scientists have believed there is an intimate relationship between enamel and dentin, and the final section of this issue explores the role of the ECM in this latter tissue type. Dr. Feng from the University of Missouri, Kansas City, is a leader in efforts to define the role of the SIBLING (small integrin-binding ligand N-linked glycoprotein) dentin matrix protein (DMP) in the skeleton. Using knockout models, Dr. Feng shows the many essential roles DMP plays in craniofacial function. Dr. George from the University of Illinois at Chicago is a leading biochemist and molecular biologist in dentin matrix research and complements this in vivo work by showing biophysical roles for the DMPs in the cellular control of odontoblast function. Dr. Simmer from the University of Michigan details important structure function and evolutionary aspects of matrix biochemistry and presents his view of how structural domains of matrix proteins may have evolved and how this is important to understanding their function in the ECM craniofacial complex.

This special issue of *Cells Tissues and Organs* concludes with a paper by Martha Somerman from the University of Washington who explores the role of the ECM in cementum function, employing new approaches with unique animal models to uncover novel modes of regulation of mineralization including ankylosis protein. Dr. Somerman provides an overall commentary on her perspectives of ECM research over the years and her view of future possibilities in this area of investigation.

In spite of the fact that the ECM comprises the majority of the molecular mass of the craniofacial complex, for many years, it was simply not clear what its role was. Initial experimental approaches to study the ECM focused mainly on biochemical analysis. Although this initial approach was solid and informative, there are now new and exciting ways to deepen our understanding of the role of the ECM in the craniofacial complex. Papers presented in this issue reveal new concepts about the role of the ECM in controlling the structure, strength and function of the head and face. New emphasis on understanding the mechanism of ECM action as it relates to growth factor distribution and function as well as matrix microarchitecture are elaborated. The authors present a contextual background and new data, as well as perspectives for future work using experimental systems employing animal models, new tools for cell biology and imaging, molecular profiling and nanotechnology. As you will see from the papers contained in this issue, our current concept of the ECM in craniofacial biology has been 're-invented' and now integrates multiple fields focusing on suture biology, mineralization, tooth development, and temporomandibular joint form and function.

Marian F. Young, Bethesda, Md.
Paul H. Krebsbach, Ann Arbor, Mich.

Cells
Tissues
Organs

Cells Tissues Organs 2005;181:127–135
DOI: 10.1159/000091374

The Extracellular Matrix Environment in Suture Morphogenesis and Growth

Lynne A. Opperman Joseph T. Rawlins

Department of Biomedical Sciences, Baylor College of Dentistry, Texas A&M University System Health Science Center, Dallas, Tex., USA

Key Words
Extracellular matrix · Craniosynostosis · Cranial sutures · Intramembranous bone growth

Abstract
Sutures are the major bone growth sites of the craniofacial skeleton and form in response to developmental approximation of and interaction between two opposing osteogenic fronts. Premature obliteration of these craniofacial bone growth sites or craniosynostosis results in compensatory growth at other bone growth sites, with concomitant craniofacial dysmorphology. While much is now known about the growth and transcriptional factor regulation of suture formation and maintenance, little about the nature of the extracellular environment within sutures and their surrounding bones has been described. This review elucidates the nature of the sutural extracellular matrix and its role in mediating suture maintenance and growth through the regulation of cellular and biomechanical signaling.

Introduction

The Nature of Craniofacial Sutures

Cranial and facial sutures are the major intramembranous bone growth sites of the calvaria and maxilla, resulting in almost 70% of the bone surface area [Baer, 1954]. Sutures form relatively late in craniofacial morphogenesis and result from the developmental approximation of, and interaction between, two osteogenic bone fronts. These bone fronts arise from initial blastema formation within the craniofacial mesenchyme, as a result of the interaction of the mesenchyme with the overlying epidermis [Hall and Van Exan, 1982; Hall, 1987, 1991; Hall and Miyake, 1992, 1995, 2000]. In response to these interactions, condensations of mesenchymal cells differentiate into osteoblasts and start secreting an osteoid extracellular matrix (ECM). As the bone blastema increases in size, the edges of the blastema remain covered by osteo-

Abbreviations used in this paper

ALP	alkaline phosphatase
BGN	biglycan
BMP	bone morphogenic protein
COL	collagen
CSF	colony-stimulating factor
DCN	decorin
ECM	extracellular matrix
FGF	fibroblast growth factor
LTBP	latent TGF-β-binding protein
MMP	matrix metalloproteinase
NG2	neuron-glial antigen 2
OPN	osteopontin
TGF-β	transforming growth factor-β
TN	tenascin

KARGER

Fax +41 61 306 12 34
E-Mail karger@karger.ch
www.karger.com

1422–6405/05/1814–0127$22.00/0

Accessible online at:
www.karger.com/cto

Lynne A. Opperman, PhD
Department of Biomedical Science, Baylor College of Dentistry
Texas A&M University System Health Sciences Center, PO Box 660677
Dallas, TX 75266-0677 (USA)
Tel. +1 214 828 8134, Fax +1 214 828 8951, E-Mail lopperman@bcd.tamhsc.edu

progenitor cells and osteoblasts, which contribute to the increasing volume of bone. Several of these blastemas originate in the craniofacial skeleton. For example, each parietal bone in the cranial vault begins as two separate blastemas, while each frontal bone originates as a single blastema [Sperber, 2001]. How the different blastemas either fuse to create single entities (such as in the parietal bones), or create sutures remains unexplained. However, by birth, the individual calvarial bones are separated by sutures, which are at their widest at the confluence of three or more bones, and in these wide regions are called fontanels.

Craniosynostosis

Normally, patent sutures allow for expansive growth of the cranial vault and facial bones. Unlike cartilaginous growth plates in long bones, the sutures themselves have no intrinsic growth potential [Moss, 1960]. In the cranial vault, expansion of the bones is thought to occur in response to the expansion of the underlying brain, while in the face, the maxillary bones increase in size due to the driving forces derived from the growing nasal capsular cartilages. Premature obliteration of these bone growth sites (craniosynostosis) is associated with multiple pathological syndromes, or can occur in isolation [Cohen, 2000; Mooney and Siegel, 2002; Mooney et al., 2004]. Craniosynostosis can involve single or multiple sutures. Generally, the more sutures involved, the more severe the craniofacial dysmorphology. Several genes have been identified in which mutations have been associated with craniosynostotic disorders. Of these, the genes for several growth factor receptors or their downstream signaling molecules have been implicated in craniosynostosis. The first mutations were identified in genes for transcription factors *MSX2* and *TWIST* [Izumi et al., 1992; Jabs et al., 1993, 1994; Liu et al., 1994, 1995; el Ghouzzi et al., 1997; Howard et al., 1997]. Mutations in genes for fibroblast growth factor (FGF) receptors and transforming growth factor-β (TGF-β) receptor II have also been associated with craniosynostotic disorders [Muenke et al., 1994; Wilkie et al., 1995; Bellus et al., 1996; Loeys et al., 2005]. Several other factors have been implicated in the complex signaling networks that regulate suture patency, including bone morphogenetic proteins (BMPs), related proteins like Noggin, cartilage-derived morphogenetic protein 1, TGF-β-induced factor, and RUNX2 [Kim et al., 1998; Zhou et al., 1999; Massague et al., 2000; Muenke and Beachy, 2000; Ignelzi et al., 2003; Warren et al., 2003].

Tissue Interactions in Craniofacial Suture Morphogenesis

To establish the role of the surrounding tissues in regulating the formation and maintenance of sutures, several groups conducted experiments in which developing sutures were cultured with or without their surrounding tissues. Initial overlap of the bone fronts during suture formation was found to be independent of the surrounding tissues [Opperman et al., 1993, 1995; Bradley et al., 1996; Roth et al., 1996; Kim et al., 1998; Adab et al., 2003], and maintenance of the newly formed suture did not require the presence of the overlying periosteum [Opperman et al., 1994]. However, maintenance of patent cranial sutures required the presence of the underlying dura mater [Opperman et al., 1993, 1995; Bradley et al., 1996; Roth et al., 1996; Kim et al., 1998], while maintenance of patent facial sutures required the presence of the underlying nasal capsular cartilages [Adab et al., 2003].

Regional differences in the composition of the dura mater were found to differentially affect suture patency [Levine et al., 1998], and these regional differences are seen clinically and experimentally by the ability of the dura mater of young individuals to regrow skulls complete with sutures [Mabbutt and Kokich, 1979; Mabbutt et al., 1979; Drake et al., 1993]. Yu et al. [1997] gave an excellent example of the regional differences in dura mater by showing that dura mater from beneath sutures was experimentally induced to make cartilage, while the same procedures induced dura mater from beneath parietal bones to make bone. More importantly, Mooney et al. [2000] using a rabbit model of spontaneously occurring craniosynostosis showed that dura mater from beneath normal sutures transplanted underneath craniosynostotic sutures was able to rescue these sutures from premature obliteration. Physical contact between the dura mater and sutures was not required for maintenance of sutures, as the dura mater secreted soluble heparin-binding factors capable of rescuing sutures from premature obliteration [Opperman et al., 1996]. However, the physical composition of the dura mater, i.e. the cellular content, ECM, and secreted growth factors would all be crucial in regulating the appropriate signals maintaining the patent suture. Since several reviews have described the role of growth and transcription factors in regulating suture patency [Cohen and Kreiborg, 1996; Wilkie, 1997; Opperman, 2000; Marie et al., 2002; Mooney et al., 2004], the remainder of this review will focus on the role of the ECM in regulating suture patency and function.

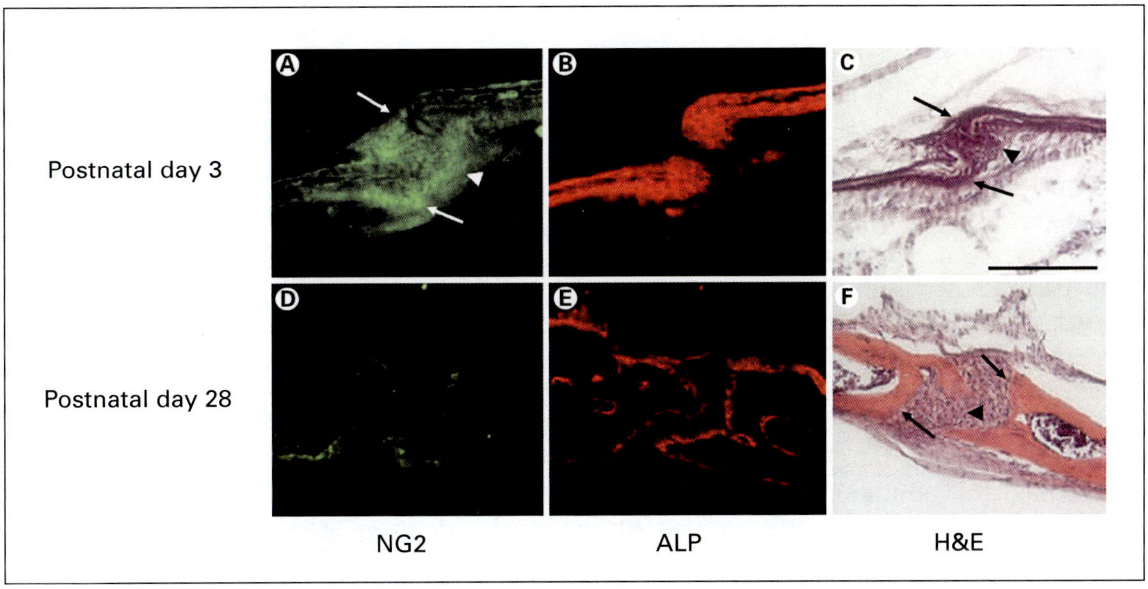

Fig. 1. Photographs of histological cross sections through mouse sagittal sutures at postnatal day 3 (**A–C**) and day 28 (**D–F**), immunoreacted with antibodies to NG2 (**A**, **D**) or ALP (**B**, **E**), or stained with hematoxylin and eosin (H&E; **C**, **F**). Note the decreased distribution of NG2 with age within the suture and of ALP with age within the bone margins. The distributions of NG2 and ALP appear to become non-overlapping with increasing age. Arrows denote the bone margins on either side of the suture, arrowheads denote suture matrices. Scale bar = 100 μm. Reprinted with permission from Fukushi et al. [2003].

ECM Molecules in Sutures

Sutures have a fibrous, cellular organization that includes continuations with the periosteum surrounding the margins of the adjacent bones, and a fibrous, cellular interzone [Persson, 1973]. Both type I (COL I) and type III (COL III) collagens are present in developing calvarial bones and periosteum [Sandberg et al., 1988; Yen et al., 1989b; Carter et al., 1991]. Yen et al. [1989b] showed that the ratio of COL III to total collagen in mouse sutures was age dependent, being high at birth and decreasing to undetectable levels after 12 weeks of age.

Tenascin (TN) and fibronectin are found adjacent to and within sites of active bone formation, and fibronectin is absent from mature lamellar bone [Carter et al., 1991]. Similarly, bone sialoprotein clearly labels calvarial bone plates, periosteal surfaces and bone margins adjacent to sutures, while osteopontin (OPN) is absent from the sutural ligament [Alberius and Johnell, 1990]. However, of the proteoglycans, only biglycan (BGN) was detected in the sutural area [Alberius and Johnell, 1990]. In recent studies, neuron-glial antigen 2 (NG2) proteoglycan, first detected as a cell marker for oligodendrocyte precursor cells, was also detected within the developing suture and in osteoprogenitor cells lining the bone fronts on either side of the suture [Fukushi et al., 2003]. While Fukushi et al. [2003] interpret the NG2 to colocalize with alkaline phosphatase (ALP), it is more probable that the domains of these two molecules are mutually exclusive, with ALP present in the mature bone and osteoid layers, and NG2 confined to the osteoprogenitor layers around the bones and to the midsutural mesenchyme (fig. 1). This latter interpretation fits with the putative role of NG2 in regulating cell proliferation [Grako and Stallcup, 1995; Nishiyama et al., 1996], most likely by retarding cell maturation [Larsen et al., 2003].

NG2 was also colocalized with TN [Mackie et al., 1998; Fukushi et al., 2003], which is an ECM ligand for NG2 [Burg et al., 1996]. Fukushi et al. [2003] postulate that NG2 could help mediate the differentiation of osteogenic cells in response to TN perhaps by inhibiting TN activity, since TN blocking antibodies inhibit ALP and COL I synthesis [Mackie and Ramsey, 1996]. It is interesting that both TGF-β_1 and FGF2 induced expression of different-sized TN molecules [Tucker et al., 1993], and that FGF2 binds to NG2 while TGF-β_1 does not [Goretzki et al., 1999]. Since the different-sized TN transcripts appeared to be associated with different developmental functions [Tucker et al., 1993], it would be intriguing to determine if NG2 binding to FGF2 mediates FGF2-induced TN expression.

A more direct role for the ECM in mediating normal craniofacial development has been demonstrated by Marks et al. [1999]. These researchers showed that retarded growth of the anterior facial skeleton of *toothless* rats was associated with the absence of expression of COL III mRNA within the premaxillary-maxillary suture (fig. 2). Sutures from these animals also showed decreased cell numbers, and the cells were less differentiated. Interestingly, the addition of monocyte-macrophage colony-stimulating factor (CSF)-I to cultures rescued the expression of COL III mRNA, and it has been determined that mutations in the CSF-I gene are responsible for the *toothless* phenotype [Marks et al., 1999; Van Wesenbeeck et al., 2002]. However, it has not been demonstrated that CSF-I directly regulates expression of COL III.

CSF-I knockout mice are severely osteopetrotic, due to an inability of osteoblasts to induce normal osteoclastogenesis [Van Wesenbeeck et al., 2002]. Loss of function mutations in the gene for heparan sulfate proteoglycan glypican-3 results in a marked reduction in the appearance of osteoclasts, correlated with a reduced response of osteoclast progenitors to CSF-I [Viviano et al., 2005]. This leads to the speculation that COL III is required for osteoclast formation in response to CSF-I, and therefore, is integrally involved in the pathological state of premaxillary-maxillary sutures in *toothless* rats, and is responsible for the rescue of normal suture morphology by CSF-I. Even more interesting is the finding that cell-surface-bound heparan sulfate proteoglycans are capable of binding Noggin, an inhibitor of BMP-induced suture closure [Paine-Saunders et al., 2002; Warren et al., 2003; Viviano et al., 2004]. Both cell-bound and free heparan sulfate bind Noggin, and this complex is capable of binding and inactivating BMP [Paine-Saunders et al., 2002]. Since Noggin is very specifically localized within the suture matrix [Warren et al., 2003], it is likely that heparan sulfate proteoglycans are responsible for maintaining this localization. If so, this indicates a direct role for ECM molecules in regulating suture patency.

The posterior frontal suture of rodents and humans fuses early in postnatal life [Moss, 1954; Cohen and Kreiborg, 1996]. Deficiencies in growth factors like TGF-β_2 result in delayed bone formation and delayed suture formation [Opperman et al., 1999; Dunker and Krieglstein, 2000]. Failure of the posterior frontal suture to close was also noted in decorin (DCN)/BGN double knockout

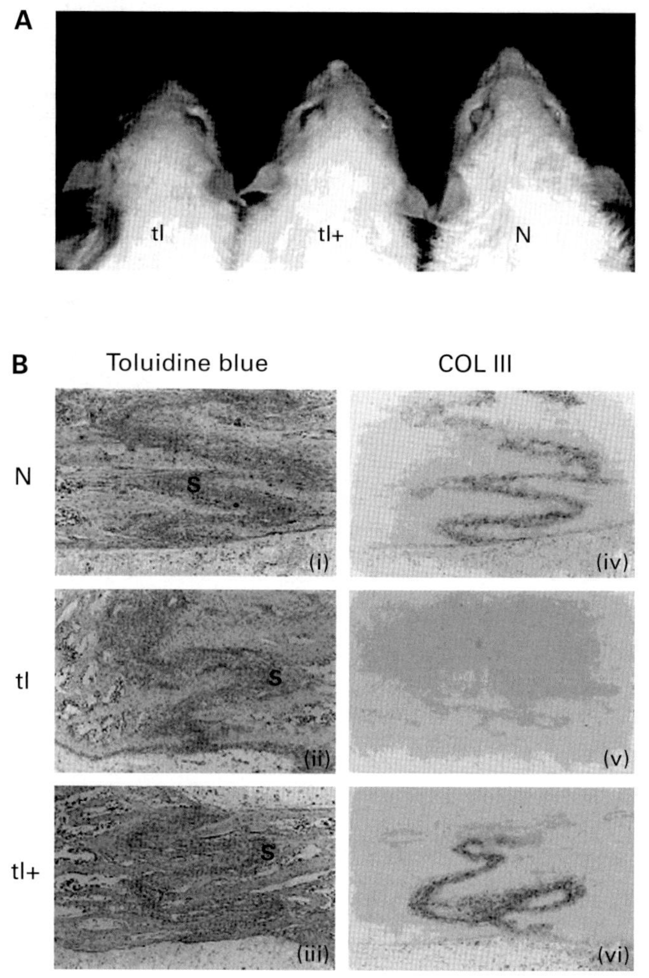

Fig. 2. A Photographs of the superior view of heads of 2-week-old toothless knockout (tl), toothless knockout treated with CSF-1 (tl+), and wildtype (N) mice. Note the shortened faces of the knockout mice, which are rescued by treatment with CSF. **B** Histological cross sections through the premaxillary-maxillary sutures of 2-week-old mice, showing sections stained with toluidine blue (i, ii, iii) and subjected to in situ hybridization for COL III (iv, v, vi). Note the absence of COL III in tl sutures and the reappearance of COL III in sutures of mice treated with CSF-1. S = Suture. Original magnification: ×100. Reprinted with permission from Marks et al. [1999].

Fig. 3. Histological frontal sections through internasal (**A**, **C**) and interfrontal (**B**, **D**) sutures of 4- to 6-month-old *Sus scrofa* pigs. **A**, **B** Sections of undecalcified tissues labeled with calcein (green) and tetracycline (yellow). Note the degree and orientation of interdigitation between the bone fronts lining the sutures. **C**, **D** Hematoxylin and eosin stained decalcified frontal sections through sutures showing the orientation of collagen fibers (arrows) to resist compression (**C**) or tension (**D**). C = Central network. Scale bars = 500 μm (**A**), 50 μm (**C**). Reprinted with permission from Rafferty and Herring [1999].

3

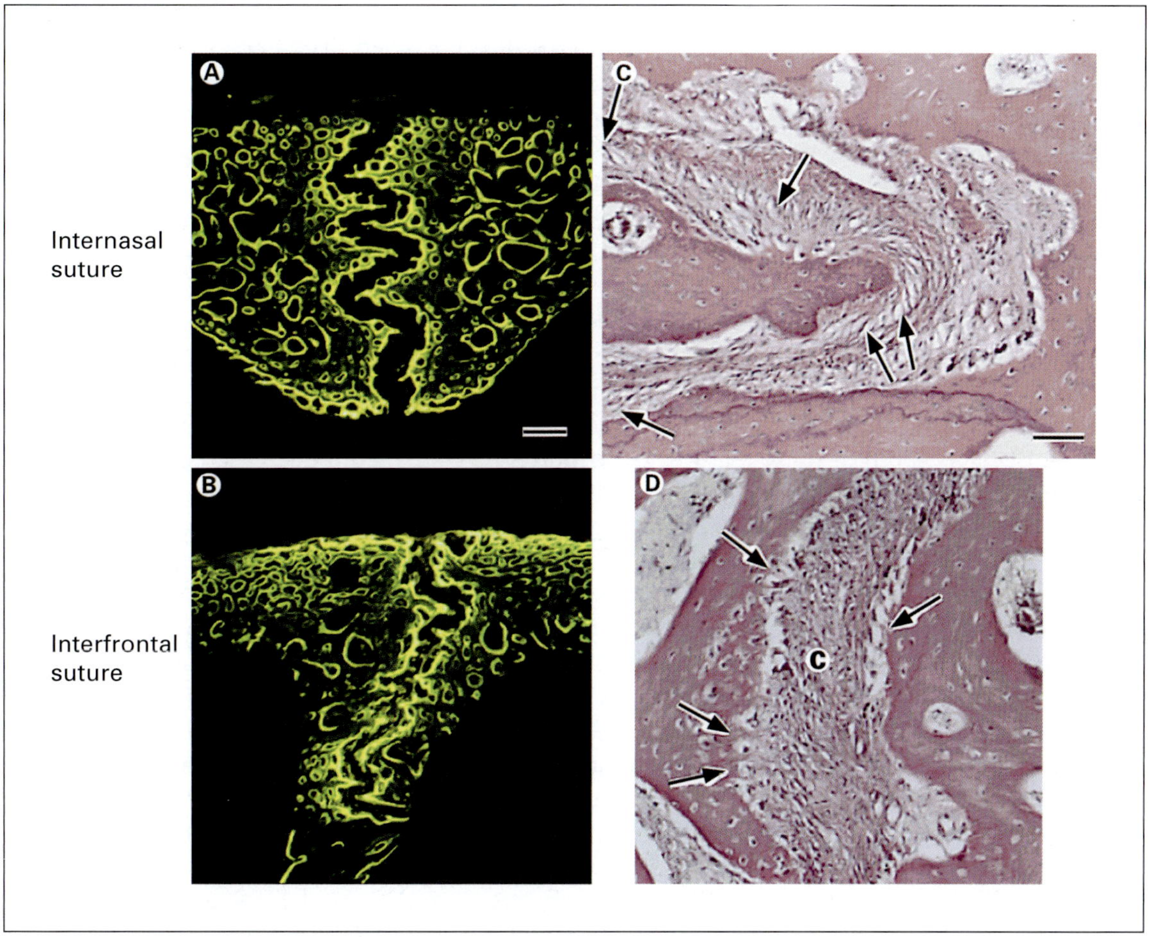

4

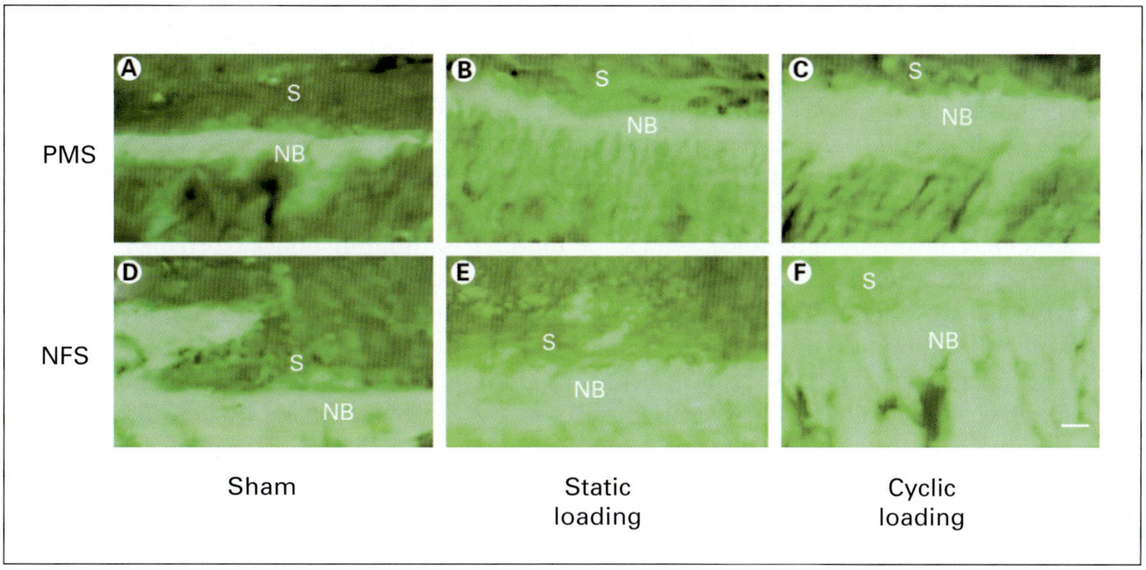

Fig. 4. Photomicrographs of newly formed sutural bone labeled with calcein (pale green) in the premaxillary-maxillary (PMS) and nasofrontal (NFS) sutures of 6-week-old New Zealand white rabbits subjected to sham (**A**, **D**), static (**B**, **E**) and cyclic (**C**, **F**) loading forces. Note the increased bone formation in the sutures subjected to cyclic loading forces compared with bone formation in static or sham-loaded sutures. S = Suture; NB = new bone. Scale bar =10 μm. Reprinted with permission from Kopher and Mao [2003].

mice [Wadhwa, pers. commun.]. The craniofacial malformations induced in these mice included demonstrably shortened faces and severe lateral displacement of the nasal region reminiscent of hemifacial microsomia. The mice also exhibited osteopenia with trabecular and cortical bone mass markedly reduced compared with wildtype mice and compared with DCN and BGN single knockout mice [Danielson et al., 1997; Xu et al., 1998; Corsi et al., 2002]. It is possible that the facial kyphosis is due to an edge-to-edge bite that would result from the facial shortening causing the teeth to deflect to one side or the other. It is unclear whether the patent posterior frontal suture resulted from the facial kyphosis from the reduced bone mass. Most likely, both of these features contributed to the persistently patent suture.

Deficiencies in all small leucine-rich proteoglycans result in abnormal collagen fibril structure [Ameye and Young, 2002], and some of these small leucine-rich proteoglycans can upregulate the expression of other ECM molecules. For example, expression of glycoproteins fibrillin 1 and fibrillin 2 are upregulated by DCN and BGN [Schaefer et al., 2004]. Furthermore, many of these small proteoglycans can also interact with growth factors such as TGF-βs and FGFs [Ruoslahti et al., 1992; Hildebrand et al., 1994; Kan et al., 1999; Richardson et al., 1999; Wang et al., 1999]. Fibrillins are closely associated with latent TGF-β-binding proteins (LTBPs), and complexes of these molecules are found in the ECM of bone [Dallas et al., 2000]. LTBPs appear to be a mechanism for storing TGF-βs in the ECM, keeping the TGF-βs in their inactive form by masking the receptor binding sites of TGF-β proteins [Dallas et al., 2002; Janssens et al., 2003]. This has been confirmed in vivo by the demonstration that matrix metalloproteinases (MMPs) can cleave LTBPs, releasing active TGF-β [Dallas et al., 2002]. In contrast, heparan sulfate proteoglycans called syndecans bind to FGF, upregulating FGF activity [Clasper et al., 1999; Richardson et al., 1999]. Since TGF-βs and FGFs play important and sometimes contrasting roles in regulating suture morphogenesis and patency, it is clear that ECM molecules have critical functional roles in this process by regulating the availability of biochemical signaling molecules within the suture.

The ECM and Suture Biomechanics

The ability of sutures to remain patent over several weeks in calvarial organ cultures is a clear demonstration that biomechanical forces are not required for maintaining suture patency [Foley and Kokich, 1980; Nappen and Kokich, 1983; Opperman et al., 1995; Bradley et al., 1996; Roth et al., 1996; Kim et al., 1998; Ignelzi et al., 2003]. This observation has received strong endorsement from biomechanical studies on growing sutures that the timing of sutural closure and patterns of transutural strain do not suggest that strain patterns contribute to the initial fusion of sutures in vivo [Shibazaki et al., 2005]. However, biomechanical forces may play a critical role in regulating bone formation at the suture margins during intramembranous bone growth, with these forces occurring in conjunction with increasing brain volume. Sutural strain magnitude in the cranial vault was shown to be small and decreased during the first 4 years of life, along with a decreasing bone deposition rate, consistent with a tensile strain in sutures influencing sutural osteoblast activity in a dose-dependent manner [Henderson et al., 2004]. Although these researchers note that the strains measured may be too small to influence bone deposition rates, there is little that is known about the least amount of tension required to stimulate osteoblast activity. Alternatively, sutures appear to be critical for modulating the biomechanical environment of the craniofacial complex during chewing, and these intermittent but high strains may be sufficient to activate bone formation at the margins of the suture.

Yen et al. [1989a] showed that applying a force across developing sutures rapidly increased and sustained COL III protein synthesis compared with unstressed sutures. This finding suggests that COL III may play a role in mediating forces across the suture, perhaps during sutural expansion, or during chewing when external forces are being applied across sutures by the masticatory muscles. In response to muscle contraction, cranial sutures have been found to experience vastly higher strains than their adjoining bones [Herring and Teng, 2000]. During mastication, both compression and tensional forces are exerted at the sutures [Rafferty and Herring, 1999]. Rafferty and Herring [1999] found that when sutures are examined histologically, sutures resisting compression are noted to be highly interdigitated, with collagen fibers arranged in a pattern that resists compression (fig. 3). In those sutures exposed to tensional forces, the fiber arrangement facilitated resistance to these forces during chewing. Interestingly, suture width increases when sutures are exposed to cyclic compressive forces, but not static loading [Kopher and Mao, 2003]. Furthermore, cyclic compressive forces increase bone deposition at the suture margins (fig. 4). Since chewing activity is cyclical, it will produce cyclical forces acting at the suture. It is interesting to speculate that the cyclical forces, along with the expanding brain and growing nasal capsular cartilages, may synergize to stimulate bone formation at the suture margins.

Sutures respond to tensional forces by upregulating ECM structural proteins like COL III and OPN [Yen et al., 1990; Morinobu et al., 2003], integrins [Takahashi et al., 2003], as well as MMPs [Green et al., 1990; Kopher and Mao, 2003; Collins et al., 2005], while expression of tissue inhibitors of metalloproteases is inhibited [Green et al., 1990]. The role of these factors in response to tension appears to be an increased remodeling of the ECM, although some factors will play specifically structural roles. For example, fibrillins are associated with elastic fibers required for resilience of tissues to tensional forces; mutations in fibrillin 1 are associated with Marfan syndrome [Nijbroek et al., 1995; Sood et al., 1996; Schaefer et al., 2004]. Similar resilience is conferred by OPN, which has been shown to increase the resistance of sutures to tension, with OPN-deficient sutures widening more rapidly than wildtype sutures [Morinobu et al., 2003]. OPN deficiency also results in reduced bone formation at the suture margins, so OPN may be responsible for modulating the increased bone formation at sutures in response to cyclical forces reported by Kopher and Mao [2003]. Tension at sutures also increases the production of secreted factors like BMPs [Ikegame et al., 2001]. The increased production of MMPs in response to tension would facilitate the release of bound latent factors like TGF-βs and FGFs from the ECM, and these factors would then contribute to the increased bone formation seen at the suture margins.

In conclusion, the suture ECM is a dynamic environment comprised of structural and signaling molecules highly attuned to the biomechanical forces exerted from their surroundings. The ECM is responsible for both resisting biomechanical forces and responding to these forces by modulating the presence of signaling molecules responsible for regulating bone formation at the suture margins. This modulation will occur both by the sequestering and release of growth factors from the ECM, and by the ECM signaling to the cells directly via integrins. In turn, cells within the suture can respond by synthesizing and secreting factors, or by upregulating other cell-related activities such as proliferation and apoptosis.

References

Adab, K., J.R. Sayne, D.S. Carlson, L.A. Opperman (2003) Nasal capsular cartilage is required for rat transpalatal suture morphogenesis. Differentiation *71:* 496–505.

Alberius, P., O. Johnell (1990) Immunohistochemical assessment of cranial suture development in rats. J Anat *173:* 61–68.

Ameye, L., M.F. Young (2002) Mice deficient in small leucine-rich proteoglycans: novel in vivo models for osteoporosis, osteoarthritis, Ehlers-Danlos syndrome, muscular dystrophy, and corneal diseases. Glycobiology *12:* 107–116.

Baer, M.J. (1954) Patterns of growth of the skull as revealed by vital staining. Hum Biol *26:* 80–126.

Bellus, G.A., K. Gaudenz, E.H. Zackai, L.A. Clarke, J. Szabo, C.A. Francomano, M. Muenke (1996) Identical mutations in three different fibroblast growth factor receptor genes in autosomal dominant craniosynostosis syndromes. Nat Genet *14:* 174–176.

Bradley, J.P., J.P. Levine, C. Blewett, T. Krummel, J.G. McCarthy, M.T. Longaker (1996) Studies in cranial suture biology: in vitro cranial suture fusion. Cleft Palate Craniofac J *33:* 150–156.

Burg, M.A., E. Tillet, R. Timpl, W.B. Stallcup (1996) Binding of the NG2 proteoglycan to type VI collagen and other extracellular matrix molecules. J Biol Chem *271:* 26110–26116.

Carter, D.H., P. Sloan, J.E. Aaron (1991) Immunolocalization of collagen types I and III, tenascin, and fibronectin in intramembranous bone. J Histochem Cytochem *39:* 599–606.

Clasper, S., S. Vekemans, M. Fiore, M. Plebanski, P. Wordsworth, G. David, D.G. Jackson (1999) Inducible expression of the cell surface heparan sulfate proteoglycan syndecan-2 (fibroglycan) on human activated macrophages can regulate fibroblast growth factor action. J Biol Chem *274:* 24113–24123.

Cohen, M.M., Jr. (2000) Craniosynostosis, Diagnosis, Evaluation and Management, ed 2. New York, Oxford University Press.

Cohen, M.M., Jr., S. Kreiborg (1996) Suture formation, premature sutural fusion, and suture default zones in Apert syndrome. Am J Med Genet *62:* 339–344.

Collins, J.M., K. Ramamoorthy, A.D. Silveira, P. Patston, J.J. Mao (2005) Expression of matrix metalloproteinase genes in the rat intramembranous bone during postnatal growth and upon mechanical stresses. J Biomech *38:* 485–492.

Corsi, A., T. Xu, X.D. Chen, A. Boyde, J. Liang, M. Mankani, B. Sommer, R.V. Iozzo, I. Eichstetter, P.G. Robey, P. Bianco, M.F. Young (2002) Phenotypic effects of biglycan deficiency are linked to collagen fibril abnormalities, are synergized by decorin deficiency, and mimic Ehlers-Danlos-like changes in bone and other connective tissues. J Bone Min Res *17:* 1180–1189.

Dallas, S.L., D.R. Keene, S.P. Bruder, J. Saharinen, L.Y. Sakai, G.R. Mundy, L.F. Bonewald (2000) Role of the latent transforming growth factor beta binding protein 1 in fibrillin-containing microfibrils in bone cells in vitro and in vivo. J Bone Min Res *15:* 68–81.

Dallas, S.L., J.L. Rosser, G.R. Mundy, L.F. Bonewald (2002) Proteolysis of latent transforming growth factor-beta (TGF-beta)-binding protein-1 by osteoclasts. A cellular mechanism for release of TGF-beta from bone matrix. J Biol Chem *277:* 21352–21360.

Danielson, K.G., H. Baribault, D.F. Holmes, H. Graham, K.E. Kadler, R.V. Iozzo (1997) Targeted disruption of decorin leads to abnormal collagen fibril morphology and skin fragility. J Cell Biol *136:* 729–743.

Drake, D.B., J.A. Persing, D.E. Berman, R.C. Ogle (1993) Calvarial deformity regeneration following subtotal craniectomy for craniosynostosis: a case report and theoretical implications. J Craniofac Surg *4:* 85–89.

Dunker, N., K. Krieglstein (2000) Targeted mutations of transforming growth factor-beta genes reveal important roles in mouse development and adult homeostasis. Eur J Biochem *267:* 6982–6988.

el Ghouzzi, V., M. Le Merrer, F. Perrin-Schmitt, E. Lajeunie, P. Benit, D. Renier, P. Bourgeois, A.L. Bolcato-Bellemin, A. Munnich, J. Bonaventure (1997) Mutations of the TWIST gene in the Saethre-Chotzen syndrome. Nat Genet *15:* 42–46.

Foley, W.J., V.G. Kokich (1980) The effects of mechanical immobilization on sutural development in the growing rabbit. J Neurosurg *53:* 794–801.

Fukushi, J., M. Inatani, Y. Yamaguchi, W.B. Stallcup (2003) Expression of NG2 proteoglycan during endochondral and intramembranous ossification. Dev Dynam *228:* 143–148.

Goretzki, L., M.A. Burg, K.A. Grako, W.B. Stallcup (1999) High-affinity binding of basic fibroblast growth factor and platelet-derived growth factor-AA to the core protein of the NG2 proteoglycan. J Biol Chem *274:* 16831–16837.

Grako, K.A., W.B. Stallcup (1995) Participation of the NG2 proteoglycan in rat aortic smooth muscle cell responses to platelet-derived growth factor. Exp Cell Res *221:* 231–240.

Green, D.D., R.M. Hembry, S.J. Atkinson, J.J. Reynolds, M.C. Meikle (1990) Immunolocalization of collagenase and tissue inhibitor of metalloproteinases (TIMP) in mechanically deformed fibrous joints. Am J Orthodont Dentofac Orthop *97:* 281–288.

Hall, B.K. (1987) Earliest evidence of cartilage and bone development in embryonic life. Clin Orthop Rel Res *225:* 255–272.

Hall, B.K. (1991) Cellular interactions during cartilage and bone development. J Craniofac Genet Dev Biol *11:* 238–250.

Hall, B.K., T. Miyake (1992) The membranous skeleton: the role of cell condensations in vertebrate skeletogenesis. Anat Embryol *186:* 107–124.

Hall, B.K., T. Miyake (1995) Divide, accumulate, differentiate: cell condensation in skeletal development revisited. Int J Dev Biol *39:* 881–893.

Hall, B.K., T. Miyake (2000) All for one and one for all: condensations and the initiation of skeletal development. Bioessays *22:* 138–147.

Hall, B.K., R.J. Van Exan (1982) Induction of bone by epithelial cell products. J Embryol Exp Morph *69:* 37–46.

Henderson, J.H., M.T. Longaker, D.R. Carter (2004) Sutural bone deposition rate and strain magnitude during cranial development. Bone *34:* 271–280.

Herring S.W., S. Teng (2000) Strain in the braincase and its sutures during function. Am J Phys Anthropol *112:* 575–593.

Hildebrand, A., M. Romaris, L.M. Rasmussen, D. Heinegard, D.R. Twardzik, W.A. Border, E. Ruoslahti (1994) Interaction of the small interstitial proteoglycans biglycan, decorin and fibromodulin with transforming growth factor beta. Biochem J *302:* 527–534.

Howard, T.D., W.A. Paznekas, E.D. Green, L.C. Chiang, N. Ma, R.I. Ortiz de Luna, C. Garcia Delgado, M. Gonzalez-Ramos, A.D. Kline, E.W. Jabs (1997) Mutations in TWIST, a basic helix-loop-helix transcription factor, in Saethre-Chotzen syndrome. Nat Genet *15:* 36–41.

Ignelzi, M.A., Jr., W. Wang, A.T. Young, F. Carinci, M. Bodo, L. Tosi, F. Francioso, R. Evangelisti, F. Pezzetti, L. Scapoli, M. Martinelli, T. Baroni, G. Stabellini, P. Carinci, C. Bellucci, C. Lilli, S. Volinia (2003) Fibroblast growth factors lead to increased Msx2 expression and fusion in calvarial sutures: expression profiles of craniosynostosis-derived fibroblasts. J Bone Min Res *18:* 751–759.

Ikegame, M., O. Ishibashi, T. Yoshizawa, J. Shimomura, T. Komori, H. Ozawa, H. Kawashima (2001) Tensile stress induces bone morphogenetic protein 4 in preosteoblastic and fibroblastic cells, which later differentiate into osteoblasts leading to osteogenesis in the mouse calvariae in organ culture. J Bone Min Res *16:* 24–32.

Izumi, T., S.P. Scully, A. Heydemann, M.E. Bolander (1992) Transforming growth factor beta 1 stimulates type II collagen expression in cultured periosteum-derived cells. J Bone Min Res *7:* 115–121.

Jabs, E.W., X. Li, A.F. Scott, G. Meyers, W. Chen, M. Eccles, J.I. Mao, L.R. Charnas, C.E. Jackson, M. Jaye (1994) Jackson-Weiss and Crouzon syndromes are allelic with mutations in fibroblast growth factor receptor 2. Nat Genet *8:* 275–279.

Jabs, E.W., U. Muller, X. Li, L. Ma, W. Luo, I.S. Haworth, I. Klisak, R. Sparkes, M.L. Warman, J.B. Mulliken, et al. (1993) A mutation in the homeodomain of the human MSX2 gene in a family affected with autosomal dominant craniosynostosis. Cell *75:* 443–450.

Janssens, K., P. ten Dijke, S.H. Ralston, C. Bergmann, W. Van Hul (2003) Transforming growth factor-beta 1 mutations in Camurati-Engelmann disease lead to increased signaling by altering either activation or secretion of the mutant protein. J Biol Chem *278:* 7718–7724.

Kan, M., X. Wu, F. Wang, W.L. McKeehan (1999) Specificity for fibroblast growth factors determined by heparan sulfate in a binary complex with the receptor kinase. J Biol Chem *274:* 15947–15952.

Kim, H.J., D.P. Rice, P.J. Kettunen, I. Thesleff (1998) FGF-, BMP- and Shh-mediated signalling pathways in the regulation of cranial suture morphogenesis and calvarial bone development. Development *125:* 1241–1251.

Kopher, R.A., J.J. Mao (2003) Suture growth modulated by the oscillatory component of micromechanical strain. J Bone Min Res *18:* 521–528.

Larsen, P.H., J.E. Wells, W.B. Stallcup, G. Opdenakker, V.W. Yong (2003) Matrix metalloproteinase-9 facilitates remyelination in part by processing the inhibitory NG2 proteoglycan. J Neurosci *23:* 11127–11135.

Levine, J.P., J.P. Bradley, D.A. Roth, J.G. McCarthy, M.T. Longaker (1998) Studies in cranial suture biology: regional dura mater determines overlying suture biology. Plast Reconstr Surg *101:* 1441–1447.

Liu, Y.H., R. Kundu, L. Wu, W. Luo, M.A. Ignelzi, Jr., M.L. Snead, R.E. Maxson, Jr. (1995) Premature suture closure and ectopic cranial bone in mice expressing Msx2 transgenes in the developing skull. Proc Nat Acad Sci USA *92:* 6137–6141.

Liu, Y.H., L. Ma, L.Y. Wu, W. Luo, R. Kundu, F. Sangiorgi, M.L. Snead, R. Maxson (1994) Regulation of the Msx2 homeobox gene during mouse embryogenesis: a transgene with 439 bp of 5′ flanking sequence is expressed exclusively in the apical ectodermal ridge of the developing limb. Mech Dev *48:* 187–197.

Loeys, B.L., J. Chen, E.R. Neptune, D.P. Judge, M. Podowski, T. Holm, J. Meyers, C.C. Leitch, N. Katsanis, N. Sharifi, F.L. Xu, L.A. Myers, P.J. Spevak, D.E. Cameron, J. De Backer, J. Hellemans, Y. Chen, E.C. Davis, C.L. Webb, W. Kress, P. Coucke, D.B. Rifkin, A.M. De Paepe, H.C. Dietz (2005) A syndrome of altered cardiovascular, craniofacial, neurocognitive and skeletal development caused by mutations in TGFBR1 or TGFBR2. Nat Genet *37:* 275–281.

Mabbutt, L.W., V.G. Kokich (1979) Calvarial and sutural re-development following craniectomy in the neonatal rabbit. J Anat *129:* 413–422.

Mabbutt, L.W., V.G. Kokich, B.C. Moffett, J.D. Loeser (1979) Subtotal neonatal calvariectomy. A radiographic and histological evaluation of calvarial and sutural redevelopment in rabbits. J Neurosurg *51:* 691–696.

Mackie, E.J., L.A. Abraham, S.L. Taylor, R.P. Tucker, L.I. Murphy (1998) Regulation of tenascin-C expression in bone cells by transforming growth factor-beta. Bone *22:* 301–307.

Mackie, E.J., S. Ramsey (1996) Modulation of osteoblast behaviour by tenascin. J Cell Sci *109:* 1597–1604.

Marie, P.J., F. Debiais, E. Hay (2002) Regulation of human cranial osteoblast phenotype by FGF-2, FGFR-2 and BMP-2 signaling. Histol Histopathol *17:* 877–885.

Marks, S.C., Jr., C. Lundmark, T. Wurtz, P.R. Odgren, C.A. MacKay, A. Mason-Savas, S.N. Popoff (1999) Facial development and type III collagen RNA expression: concurrent repression in the osteopetrotic (toothless, tl) rat and rescue after treatment with colony-stimulating factor-1. Dev Dynam *215:* 117–125.

Massague, J., S.W. Blain, R.S. Lo (2000) TGFbeta signaling in growth control, cancer and heritable disorders. Cell *103:* 295–309.

Mooney, M.P., A.M. Burrows, T.D. Smith, H.W. Losken, L.A. Opperman, J. Dechant, A.M. Kreithen, R. Kapuchu, G.M. Cooper, R.C. Ogle, M.I. Siegel (2000) Correction of coronal suture synostosis using suture and dura mater allografts in rabbits with familial craniosynostosis. Cleft Palate Craniofac J *38:* 72–91.

Mooney, M.P., A.M. Moursi, L.A. Opperman, M.I. Siegel (2004) Cytokine therapy for craniosynostosis. Expert Opin Biol Ther *4:* 279–299.

Mooney, M.P., M.I. Siegel (2002) Understanding Craniofacial Anomalies. The Etiopathogenesis of Craniosynostoses and Facial Clefting. New York, Wiley-Liss.

Morinobu, M., M. Ishijima, S.R. Rittling, K. Tsuji, H. Yamamoto, A. Nifuji, D.T. Denhardt, M. Noda (2003) Osteopontin expression in osteoblasts and osteocytes during bone formation under mechanical stress in the calvarial suture in vivo. J Bone Miner Res *18:* 1706–1715.
Moss, M.L. (1954) Growth of the calvaria in the rat. The determination of osseous morphology. Am J Anat *94:* 333–362.
Moss, M.L. (1960) The functional matrix; in Kraus, B.S., R.A. Riedel (eds): Vistas in Orthodontics. Philadelphia, Lea and Febiger, p 279.
Muenke, M., P.A. Beachy (2000) Genetics of ventral forebrain development and holoprosencephaly. Curr Opin Genet Dev *10:* 262–269.
Muenke, M., U. Schell, A. Hehr, N.H. Robin, H.W. Losken, A. Schinzel, L.J. Pulleyn, P. Rutland, W. Reardon, S. Malcolm, et al. (1994) A common mutation in the fibroblast growth factor receptor 1 gene in Pfeiffer syndrome. Nat Genet *8:* 269–274.
Nappen, D.L., V.G. Kokich (1983) Experimental craniosynostosis in growing rabbits. The role of the periosteum. J Neurosurg *58:* 101–108.
Nijbroek, G., S. Sood, I. McIntosh, C.A. Francomano, E. Bull, L. Pereira, F. Ramirez, R.E. Pyeritz, H.C. Dietz (1995) Fifteen novel FBN1 mutations causing Marfan syndrome detected by heteroduplex analysis of genomic amplicons. Am J Hum Genet *57:* 8–21.
Nishiyama, A., X.H. Lin, N. Giese, C.H. Heldin, W.B. Stallcup (1996) Co-localization of NG2 proteoglycan and PDGF alpha-receptor on O2A progenitor cells in the developing rat brain. J Neurosci Res *43:* 299–314.
Opperman, L.A. (2000) Cranial sutures as intramembranous bone growth sites. Dev Dyn *219:* 472–485.
Opperman, L.A., A. Chhabra, R.W. Cho, R.C. Ogle (1999) Cranial suture obliteration is induced by removal of transforming growth factor (TGF)-beta 3 activity and prevented by removal of TGF-beta 2 activity from fetal rat calvaria in vitro. J Craniofac Genet Dev Biol *19:* 164–173.
Opperman, L.A., R.W. Passarelli, E.P. Morgan, M. Reintjes, R.C. Ogle (1995) Cranial sutures require tissue interactions with dura mater to resist osseous obliteration in vitro. J Bone Miner Res *10:* 1978–1987.
Opperman, L.A., R.W. Passarelli, A.A. Nolen, T.J. Gampper, K.Y. Lin, R.C. Ogle (1996) Dura mater secretes soluble heparin-binding factors required for cranial suture morphogenesis. In Vitro Cell Dev Biol *32:* 627–632.
Opperman, L.A., J.A. Persing, R. Sheen, R.C. Ogle (1994) In the absence of periosteum, transplanted fetal and neonatal rat coronal sutures resist osseous obliteration. J Craniofac Surg *5:* 327–332.
Opperman, L.A., T.M. Sweeney, Redmon J., J.A. Persing, R.C. Ogle (1993) Tissue interactions with underlying dura mater inhibit osseous obliteration of developing cranial sutures. Dev Dyn *198:* 312–322.
Paine-Saunders, S., B.L. Viviano, A.N. Economides, S. Saunders (2002) Heparan sulfate proteoglycans retain Noggin at the cell surface: a potential mechanism for shaping bone morphogenetic protein gradients. J Biol Chem *277:* 2089–2096.
Persson, M. (1973) Mandibular asymmetry of hereditary origin. Am J Orthod *63:* 1–11.
Rafferty, K.L., S.W. Herring (1999) Craniofacial sutures: morphology, growth, and in vivo masticatory strains. J Morphol *242:* 167–179.
Richardson, T.P., V. Trinkaus-Randall, M.A. Nugent (1999) Regulation of basic fibroblast growth factor binding and activity by cell density and heparan sulfate. J Biol Chem *274:* 13534–13540.
Roth, D.A., J.P. Bradley, J.P. Levine, H.F. McMullen, J.G. McCarthy, M.T. Longaker (1996) Studies in cranial suture biology. 2. Role of the dura in cranial suture fusion. Plast Reconstr Surg *97:* 693–699.
Ruoslahti, E., Y. Yamaguchi, A. Hildebrand, W.A. Border (1992) Extracellular matrix/growth factor interactions. Cold Spring Harbor Symp Quant Biol *57:* 309–315.
Sandberg, M., H. Autio-Harmainen, E. Vuorio (1988) Localization of the expression of types I, III, and IV collagen, TGF-beta 1 and c-fos genes in developing human calvarial bones. Dev Biol *130:* 324–334.
Schaefer, L., D. Mihalik, A. Babelova, M. Krzyzankova, H.J. Grone, R.V. Iozzo, M.F. Young, D.G. Seidler, G. Lin, D.P. Reinhardt, R.M. Schaefer (2004) Regulation of fibrillin-1 by biglycan and decorin is important for tissue preservation in the kidney during pressure-induced injury. Am J Pathol *165:* 383–396.
Shibazaki, R., P.C. Dechow, K. Maki, L.A. Opperman (2006) Biomechanical strain and morphological changes with age in rat calvarial bones and sutures. Plast Reconstr Surg, in press.
Sood, S., Z.A. Eldadah, W.L. Krause, I. McIntosh, H.C. Dietz (1996) Mutation in fibrillin-1 and the Marfanoid-craniosynostosis (Shprintzen-Goldberg) syndrome. Nat Genet *12:* 209–211.
Sperber, G.H. (2001) Craniofacial Development. London, B.C. Decker.
Takahashi, I., K. Onodera, Y. Sasano, I. Mizoguchi, J.W. Bae, H. Mitani, M. Kagayama (2003) Effect of stretching on gene expression of beta1 integrin and focal adhesion kinase and on chondrogenesis through cell-extracellular matrix interactions. Eur J Cell Biol *82:* 182–192.
Tucker, R.P., J.A. Hammarback, D.A. Jenrath, E.J. Mackie, Y. Xu (1993) Tenascin expression in the mouse: in situ localization and induction in vitro by bFGF. J Cell Sci *104:* 69–76.
Van Wesenbeeck, L., P.R. Odgren, C.A. MacKay, M. D'Angelo, F.F. Safadi, S.N. Popoff, W. Van Hul, S.C. Marks, Jr. (2002) The osteopetrotic mutation toothless (tl) is a loss-of-function frameshift mutation in the rat Csf1 gene: evidence of a crucial role for CSF-1 in osteoclastogenesis and endochondral ossification. Proc Nat Acad Sci USA *99:* 14303–14308.
Viviano, B.L., S. Paine-Saunders, N. Gasiunas, J. Gallagher, S. Saunders (2004) Domain-specific modification of heparan sulfate by Qsulf1 modulates the binding of the bone morphogenetic protein antagonist Noggin. J Biol Chem *279:* 5604–5611.
Viviano, B.L., L. Silverstein, C. Pflederer, S. Paine-Saunders, K. Mills, S. Saunders (2005) Altered hematopoiesis in glypican-3-deficient mice results in decreased osteoclast differentiation and a delay in endochondral ossification. Dev Biol *282:* 152–162.
Wang, F., W. Lu, K. McKeehan, K. Mohamedali, J.L. Gabriel, M. Kan, W.L. McKeehan (1999) Common and specific determinants for fibroblast growth factors in the ectodomain of the receptor kinase complex. Biochemistry *38:* 160–171.
Warren, S.M., L.J. Brunet, R.M. Harland, A.N. Economides, M.T. Longaker (2003) The BMP antagonist noggin regulates cranial suture fusion. Nature *422:* 625–629.
Wilkie, A.O. (1997) Craniosynostosis: genes and mechanisms. Hum Molec Genet *6:* 1647–1656.
Wilkie, A.O., S.F. Slaney, M. Oldridge, M.D. Poole, G.J. Ashworth, A.D. Hockley, R.D. Hayward, D.J. David, L.J. Pulleyn, P. Rutland, et al. (1995) Apert syndrome results from localized mutations of FGFR2 and is allelic with Crouzon syndrome. Nat Genet *9:* 165–172.
Xu, T., P. Bianco, L.W. Fisher, G. Longenecker, E. Smith, S. Goldstein, J. Bonadio, A. Boskey, A.M. Heegaard, B. Sommer, K. Satomura, P. Dominguez, C. Zhao, A.B. Kulkarni, P.G. Robey, M.F. Young (1998) Targeted disruption of the biglycan gene leads to an osteoporosis-like phenotype in mice. Nat Genet *20:* 78–82.
Yen, E.H., D.J. Pollit, W.A. Whyte, D.M. Suga (1990) Continuous stressing of mouse interparietal suture fibroblasts in vitro. J Dent Res *69:* 26–30.
Yen, E.H., C.S. Yue, D.M. Suga (1989a) Effect of force level on synthesis of type III and type I collagen in mouse interparietal suture. J Dent Res *68:* 1746–1751.
Yen, E.H., C.S. Yue, D.M. Suga (1989b) The effect of sutural growth rate on collagen phenotype synthesis. J Dent Res *68:* 1058–1063.
Yu, J.C., J.S. McClintock, F. Gannon, X.X. Gao, J.P. Mobasser, M. Sharawy (1997) Regional differences of dura osteoinduction: squamous dura induces osteogenesis, sutural dura induces chondrogenesis and osteogenesis. Plast Reconstr Surg *100:* 23–31.
Zhou, G., Y. Chen, L. Zhou, K. Thirunavukkarasu, J. Hecht, D. Chitayat, B.D. Gelb, S. Pirinen, S.A. Berry, C.R. Greenberg, G. Karsenty, B. Lee (1999) CBFA1 mutation analysis and functional correlation with phenotypic variability in cleidocranial dysplasia. Hum Mol Genet *8:* 2311–2316.

Cells Tissues Organs

Cells Tissues Organs 2005;181:136–143
DOI: 10.1159/000091375

Mice Deficient in Biglycan and Fibromodulin as a Model for Temporomandibular Joint Osteoarthritis

Sunil Wadhwa[a, b] Mildred Embree[a] Laurent Ameye[c] Marian F. Young[a]

[a]Craniofacial and Skeletal Diseases Branch, National Institutes of Dental and Craniofacial Research, National Institutes of Health, Bethesda, Md., and [b]Department of Orthodontics, School of Dental Medicine, University of Connecticut Health Center, Farmington, Conn., USA; [c]Nestle Research Center, Department of Nutrition, Lausanne, Switzerland

Key Words

Proteoglycans · Biglycan · Fibromodulin · Temporomandibular joint · Osteoarthritis

Abstract

The temporomandibular joint (TMJ) within the craniofacial complex is unique. In humans, the TMJ can become diseased resulting in severe and disabling pain. There are no cures for TMJ disease at this time. Animal models of TMJ disease are scarce, but some exist, and they are described in this paper. We present in greater detail one animal model that is deficient in two extracellular matrix (ECM) proteoglycans, biglycan (BGN) and fibromodulin (FMOD). Doubly deficient BGN/FMOD mice develop premature TMJ osteoarthritis (OA). In order to explore the mechanistic basis of TMJ-OA, tissues from the condyle of mutant mice were examined for their relative capacity to differentiate and undergo apoptosis. Our data show that there is a redistribution of the critical ECM protein, type II collagen, in mutant mice compared with controls. Mutant mice also have increased apoptosis of the chondrocytes embedded in the articular cartilage. We speculate that the overall imbalance in apoptosis may be the cellular basis for the abnormal production of structural ECM proteins. The abnormal production of the ECM could, in turn, lead to premature erosion and degradation of the articular surface resulting in TMJ-OA. These data underscore the importance of the ECM in controlling the structural integrity of the TMJ.

S.W. and M.E. have joint first authorship.

Introduction

It is estimated that 10–40% of the population aged between 18 and 45 years has symptoms or signs of temporomandibular joint (TMJ) disease. Approximately 10% have osteoarthritis (OA) of the TMJ. However, the diagnosis of TMJ-OA is usually made only in later stages of

Abbreviations used in this paper

BGN	biglycan
ECM	extracellular matrix
FMOD	fibromodulin
TGF-β	transforming growth factor-β
TMJ	temporomandibular joint
OA	osteoarthritis
SLRP	small leucine-rich proteoglycan

KARGER
Fax +41 61 306 12 34
E-Mail karger@karger.ch
www.karger.com

Accessible online at:
www.karger.com/cto

Sunil Wadhwa, DDS, PhD
Division of Orthodontics, School of Dental Medicine
University of Connecticut Health Center
Farmington, CT 06030 (USA)
Tel. +1 860 679 4899, Fax +1 860 679 1920, E-Mail wadhwa@uchc.edu

the disease, and therefore, the number of people who have OA of the TMJ may be higher.

TMJ-OA seems to affect two different age groups and may have two different etiologies. The older patient population is estimated to have a 20–40% occurrence of TMJ-OA [Nannmark et al., 1990; Widmalm et al., 1994; Sato et al., 1996] and is very unlikely to seek treatment [Carlsson, 1999; Anastassaki and Magnusson, 2004]. On the other hand, patients under the age of 30 are more likely to seek treatment for TMJ disorders, and it has been estimated that 10–66% of those who seek treatment have OA of their TMJs [Ogus, 1979; Stewart and Standish, 1983; Wiberg and Wanman, 1998]. Currently, there are no biomarkers or effective treatments for TMJ-OA. Imaging techniques can be used to diagnose TMJ-OA but only after the joint has been subjected to irreversible damage, and by this point, treatment of TMJ-OA merely involves palliative relief of the symptoms. Due to the limited capacity of joints to regenerate, it would be beneficial to detect OA of the TMJ at an early stage in order to prevent permanent joint damage. Furthermore, because the biopsying of human pre-osteoarthritic TMJ samples is virtually impossible, generation of TMJ-OA animal models that undergo the entire disease process is necessary.

There are two types of animal models for TMJ-OA: one is induced by trauma, while the other is occurs naturally. Traumatic induction of TMJ-OA typically involves surgical manipulation [Tominaga et al., 2002], forced mouth opening [Fujisawa et al., 2003], or the administration of inflammatory mediators within the joint [Harper et al., 2001; Tominaga et al., 2002]. Unlike traumatic models of TMJ-OA, naturally occurring models cover the whole disease process, particularly the earlier stages. Because both genetic and environmental factors may be precisely defined and controlled, naturally occurring models hold the potential to reveal the molecular pathways that influence the degeneration of the TMJ.

Currently, there are four reported naturally occurring mouse models of TMJ-OA. The first model was described by Silbermann and Livne [1979] in a strain of mice in the Institute of Cancer Research. Male mice of this strain developed osteoarthritic lesions in their TMJs progressing with age [Silbermann and Livne, 1979]. Evidence of TMJ-OA first appeared at 6 months and consisted of fibrillations along the articular surface and in deeper tissue regions, a marked loss of tissue cellularity, and a reduction in safranin-0 staining. The authors concluded that the degenerative changes of mandibular condylar cartilage started at the more superficial regions and then proceeded towards the inferior regions [Livne and Silbermann, 1986]. The same group later hypothesized that the combination of reduced sulfated glycosaminoglycan and the decreased number of cells in the superficial articular layer of the mandibular condylar cartilage resulted in tissue with an architecture that is less suited to withstanding stress and thus more prone to the development of osteoarthritic lesions [Livne, 1994].

The second published naturally occurring mouse model of TMJ-OA was found in Del1 mice. Del1 transgenic mice produce a mutated form of the human type II collagen gene *(Col2A1)* driven by the human collagen type II promoter, which induces mutant protein expression solely in cartilage. At 3 months, the Del1 transgenic mice developed subchondral cysts in the mandibular condyle and occasional clefting. The osteoarthritic lesions became progressively worse until finally, at 15 months of age, the mandibular condylar cartilage was almost completely resorbed [Rintala et al., 1997]. Interestingly, the presence of the mutated type II collagen did not affect the growth of the mandibular condyle cartilage. The hypertrophic zone of the mandibular condylar cartilage appeared normal or even enhanced in Del1 transgenic mice compared with wildtype controls. After the growth period, the mandibular condylar cartilage starts to function as an articular cartilage. The authors hypothesized that it is at this time that an intact network of type II collagen molecules is needed to provide structural strength to the condylar cartilage. The fact that the osteoarthritic lesions started after the active growth period supports this concept.

The third naturally occurring TMJ-OA mouse model has a loss-of-function mutation in the gene encoding the α_1-chain of type XI collagen (Cho mice). Heterozygote Cho mice show evidence of TMJ-OA by 3 months of age consisting of changes in proteoglycan staining in the superficial articular layer of the mandibular condylar cartilage. By 9 months of age, fibrillations extending across the entire surface of the mandibular articular cartilage become evident [Xu et al., 2003]. Changes in collagen fibril diameter and matrix metalloproteinase 3 production were observed in the knee joint of these mice; however, it is not known if similar changes occur in the TMJ.

In this paper, we describe in detail a mouse model unable to produce the two extracellular matrix (ECM) proteoglycans, biglycan (BGN) and fibromodulin (FMOD). We have previously shown that mice doubly deficient in BGN and FMOD develop OA of the knee [Ameye et al., 2002] and their TMJs [Wadhwa et al., 2005]. In the TMJ, osteoarthritic lesions first start to develop at 6 months and worsen progressively. When the doubly deficient mice are 18 months old, there is almost complete destruction of their TMJs. Our model is similar to the other naturally occurring mouse models of TMJ OA: (1) the osteoarthritic lesions do not develop until after the active growth period, and (2) the destruction of the TMJ complex progresses with age.

Naturally occurring mouse models of TMJ-OA are similar to the human form of the disease in that it usually occurs after the growth period; however, the progression may be different. Researchers have postulated that human TMJ-OA follows three stages. In the first stage, there is clicking of the joint and periodic locking, which are also common signs in other TMJ disorders. In the second stage, the TMJ becomes painful both at rest and during function. In the third stage, there is a reduction in clinical symptoms and normalization of function; however, radiographically, there is an increase in TMJ deformation [Zarb and Carlsson, 1999]. Since the evaluation of the signs and symptoms of TMJ-OA has not been assessed and is extremely difficult to perform in the naturally occurring mouse models, we do not know if the progression of TMJ-OA is similar to the human form of the disease.

BGN and FMOD are members of the small leucine repeat proteoglycan family (SLRP). Members of this family are characterized by having a small protein core, which consists predominantly of leucine-rich repeats. There are 13 known members that are divided into three classes (I, II and III) depending on their genomic organization and the similarity of their amino acid sequences. BGN belongs to the class I type and FMOD to the class II type of SLRP. Both proteoglycans are ubiquitously found in skeletal and connective tissues [Iozzo, 1997, 1999; Hocking et al., 1998; Ameye and Young, 2002; Wadhwa et al., 2004]. In this paper, we show that several cellular events were changed during the progression of TMJ-OA. They included altered expression of type II collagen and increased levels of apoptosis. These data reveal some of the molecular events occurring in the ECM that may regulate TMJ integrity and function.

Material and Methods

Generation of BGN and FMOD Single- and Double-Deficient Mice

All experiments were performed under an institutionally approved protocol for the use of animals in research (NIDCR-DIR-98-058 and 01-151). Mice deficient in BGN or FMOD were generated as described previously [Ameye et al., 2002]. Heterozygous BGN/FMOD-deficient mice were produced by breeding a homozygous BGN-deficient female *(bgn–/–/fmod+/+)* with a FMOD-deficient male *(bgn+/0/fmod–/–)*; BGN males are designed as *bgn–/0* since the *bgn* gene is located on the X chromosome and absent from the Y chromosome. F2 BGN/FMOD double-deficient (male *bgn–/0/fmod–/–*) mice were obtained by interbreeding F1 heterozygous BGN/FMOD mice.

Genotyping

All mice were genotyped for *bgn* and *fmod* alleles by polymerase chain reaction analysis as described previously [Ameye et al., 2002]. Polymerase chain reaction products were resolved by electrophoresis through 1.8% agarose gels, yielding bands of 212 bp for the wildtype *bgn* allele, 310 bp for the disrupted *bgn* allele, 280 bp for the wildtype *fmod* allele, and 603 bp for the disrupted *fmod* allele.

Histology

Wildtype and mutant mice were collected for histology at 3, 6, and 18 months. Whole mouse heads were sectioned into two halves and fixed in 10% formalin for 2 weeks at room temperature. The samples were washed with tap water for 5 min and decalcified in formic acid bone decalcifier solution (Immunocal, Decal Corporation, Tallman, N.Y., USA) for 4 weeks. Following decalcification, the heads were washed in tap water for 5 min and fixed for an additional 3 days in buffered zinc formalin (Z-fix, Anatech Ltd., Battle Creek, Mich., USA). Subsequently, the samples were processed for standard paraffin embedding and cut in sagittal sections.

Immunohistochemistry

Tissue sections were deparaffinized, rehydrated in graded ethanol series, and treated with 3% peroxide in methanol. The sections were digested for 1 h with 0.015 U/ml chondroitinase ABC (cat No. KE01502, Seikagaku Corp., Tokyo, Japan), rinsed in phosphate-buffered saline, and subsequently digested for 10 min with pepsin (Pepsin reagent^{TM} for unmasking; Abcam). Immunohistochemistry staining was performed using the mouse broad-spectrum AEC kit (Histomouse Max, Zymed Laboratories Inc.) following the procedure recommended by the manufacturer. The expression for collagen type II was studied using primary antibody raised against mouse collagen type II antigen (1:100 in 10% goat serum; Chemicon, clone No. 8887). In order to evaluate for non-specific binding, substitution of the primary antibody with mouse immunoglobulin G was performed.

Labeling and Evaluation of Apoptotic Condylar Chondrocytes

Tissue sections from 3 wildtype mice and 3 mutant mice were deparaffinized and rehydrated in graded ethanol series. Condylar chondrocytes undergoing apoptosis were labeled using the Klenow FragEL DNA Fragmentation Kit (cat No. QIA21-1EA; Calbiochem) following the procedure recommended by the manufacturer. Images from the labeled tissue sections were captured using an AxioCam MR camera (Zeiss). Within a fixed area, the number of positively labeled condylar chondrocytes was counted and divided by the total number of cells. For each tissue section, three portions were analyzed, corresponding to anterior, center and posterior parts of the mandibular condylar cartilage.

Results

Type II Collagen Abnormal Expression in Normal Double Knockout Mice

At 3 months, in both wildtype and double-deficient mice, collagen type II expression was restricted to the inferior portions of the mandibular condylar cartilage and absent in the superficial layers (fig. 1). At 6 months of age, when the double-deficient mice first started to show histological evidence of TMJ-OA, we found that collagen type II expression lost its restricted localization and was expressed in the superficial layer of the condylar cartilage. On the other hand, at 6 months of age, collagen type II expression remained unchanged in the wildtype mice. This loss of the restriction of collagen type II expression did not become apparent until 18 months of age in the wildtype mice. Interestingly, at this age, wildtype mice also began to show histological evidence of TMJ-OA. Therefore, the loss of the restriction of collagen type II expression in both wildtype and double-deficient mice appears to be a biomarker of osteoarthritic degeneration of the condylar cartilage.

Apoptosis Levels in the Condyle of the Normal and Mutant Mice

FragEL labeling of cells undergoing programmed cell death (apoptosis) revealed an increase in the number of apoptotic positive cells from the double-deficient mice compared with the wildtype mice (fig. 2a, b). Examination of FragEL immunostaining in 10 sections from 2 different 3-month-old double knockout mice and 10 sections from 2 different 3-month-old wildtype mice revealed a 2-fold increase in the percentage of apoptotic cells in the mandibular condylar cartilage from the mutant mice compared with the wildtype mice (fig. 2d).

Discussion

Changes in the expression and localization of collagen type II in the mandibular condylar cartilage during OA could be due to a number of different mechanisms. One possible mechanism is that during the development of TMJ-OA, there is an increase in apoptosis of cells of the mandibular condylar cartilage that do not express collagen type II, as well as an increase in proliferation of chondroblastic cells on the surface that do express collagen type II. The fact that we have shown that there is an increase in apoptosis in the mandibular condylar cartilage from 3-month-old BGN/FMOD double-deficient mice compared with age-matched wildtype mice (fig. 2) and that there is an increase in proliferation in the mandibular condylar cartilage at 6 months in the doubly deficient mice [Wadhwa et al., 2005] supports this concept. Another possible mechanism which could be causing the expression of collagen type II in the articular layer of the mandibular condylar cartilage during TMJ-OA is total erosion of the superficial articular layer. We do not think this is likely, because at 3 months, there was no histological evidence of erosion in the mandibular condylar cartilage from double-deficient mice [Wadhwa et al., 2005]. Furthermore, at 6 months, when we started to see the uncharacteristic expression of collagen type II in the mandibular condylar cartilage from the double-deficient mice, there were only small vertical clefts, which did not extend to more than one quarter of the total thickness of the mandibular condylar cartilage.

Differences in the Progression of OA in the Knee and TMJ in the BGN/FMOD Double Knockout Mice

In this paper, we have shown that mice deficient in the ECM proteins BGN and FMOD develop TMJ-OA at 6 months, and by 18 months of age, there was almost complete destruction of the joint. Interestingly, in the knees of the same double-deficient mice, we found that OA first appeared as early as 1–3 months, and by 6 months, there was almost complete destruction of the joint [Ameye et al., 2002].

We propose that the differences between the progression of OA in these two tissues may be due to the differences in the anatomy and structure of the joints.

Unlike the articular cartilage of the knee, the cartilage of the mandibular condyle is considered a secondary cartilage in structure, function and development [Symons, 1965; Shen and Darendeliler, 2005]. Furthermore, the mandibular condylar cartilage is composed of fibrocartilage rather than hyaline cartilage [for a review, see Benjamin and Ralphs, 2004]. One of the unique properties of fibrocartilage is that it contains both type I and type II collagen compared with articular hyaline cartilage, which only contains type II collagen [Mizoguchi et al., 1992].

Additionally, unlike the articular cartilage of the knee, the mandibular condylar cartilage contains a growth plate during the active growth period. The growth plate is unique compared with other growth plates because it does not have linear columns of daughter cells (fig. 3). This nonlinear arrangement of daughter cells allows the mandibular condylar cartilage to have a multidirectional proliferative capacity. Therefore, unlike the growth plate of long bones, which can only expand unidirectionally, the random arrangement of daughter cells in mandibular

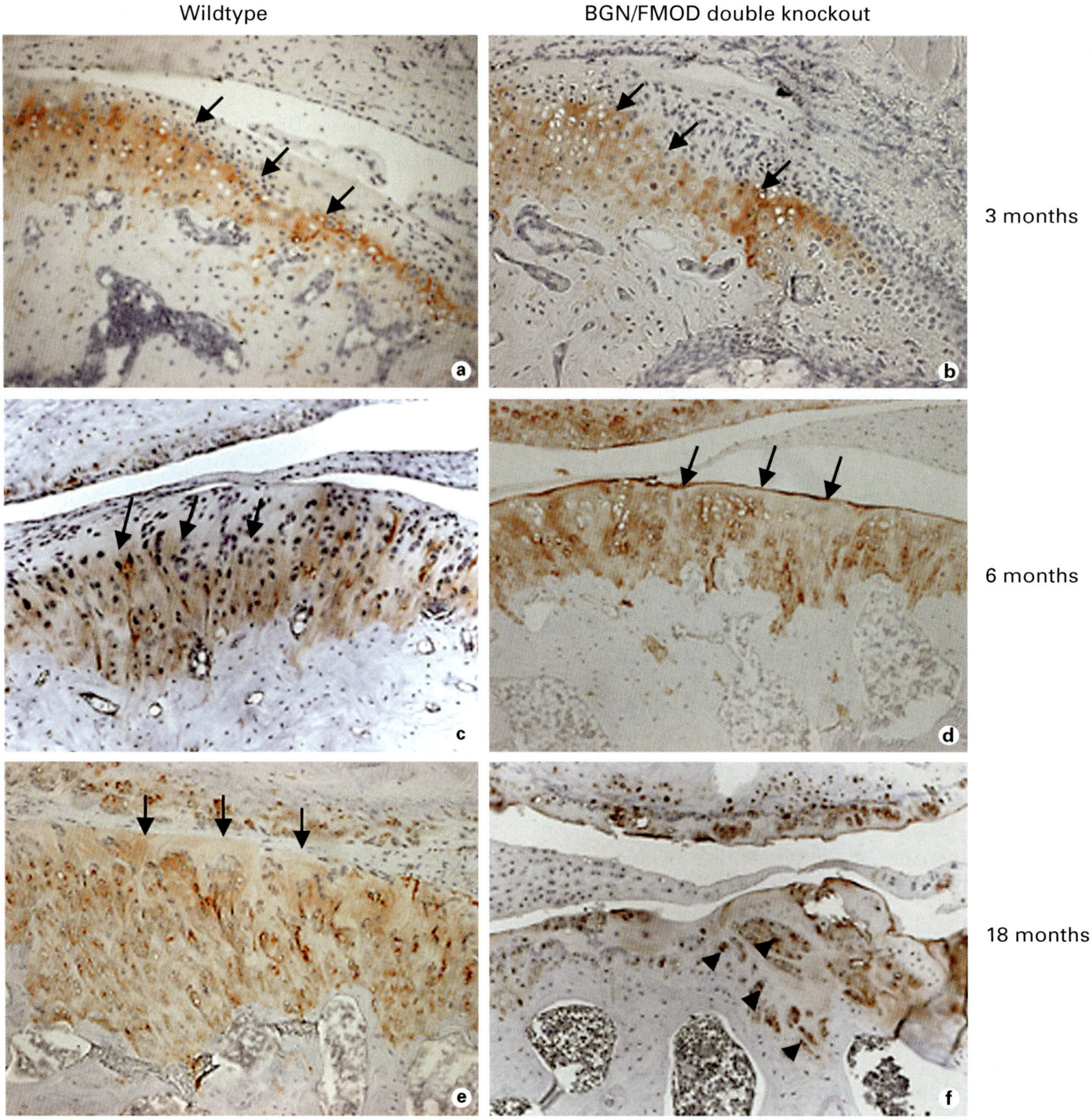

Fig. 1. Type II collagen immunohistochemistry (red) of wildtype (**a**, **c**, **e**) and BGN/FMOD double-deficient (**b**, **d**, **f**) mouse TMJ at 3, 6 and 18 months of age. Type II collagen localization is restricted to the inferior portions of the condylar cartilage in both wildtype (**a**) and BGN/FMOD double-deficient (**b**) mice at 3 months. At 6 months, type II collagen localization remains unchanged in wildtype mice (**c**), but becomes apparent in the superficial portion of the condylar cartilage in the BGN/FMOD double-deficient mice (**d**). Type II collagen expression does not become localized in the superficial portion of the condylar cartilage until 18 months in the wildtype mice (**e**). At this age, type II collagen expression increases in the BGN/FMOD double-deficient mice (**f**). Arrows indicate type II collagen immunostaining; arrowheads indicate intracellular type II collagen immunostaining.

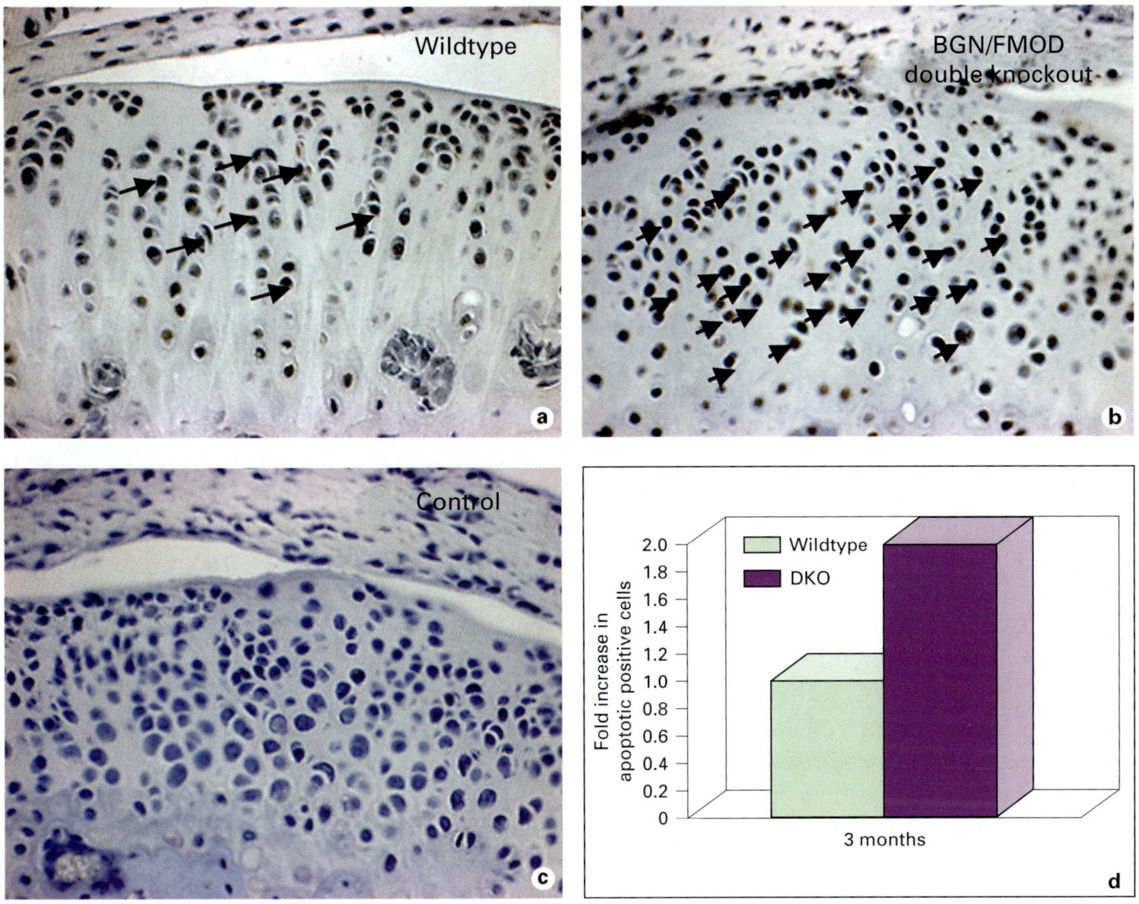

2

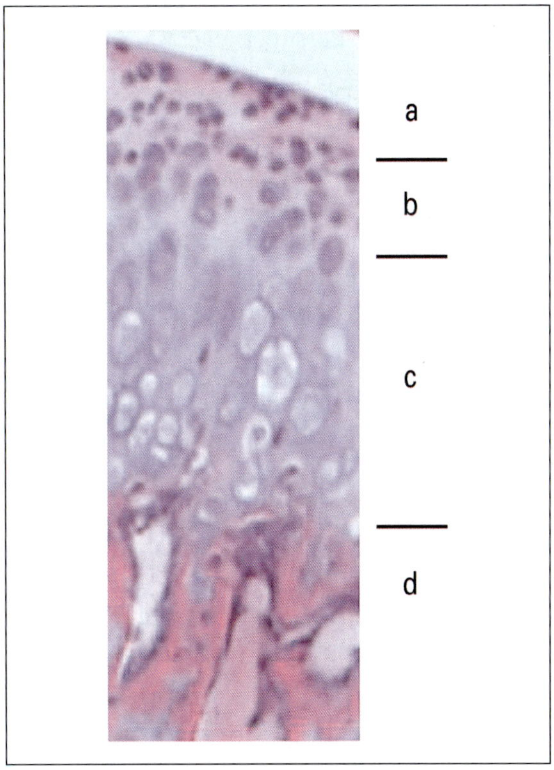

3

Fig. 2. FragEL labeling (arrows) of cells in the mandibular condylar cartilage undergoing apoptosis in 3-month-old wildtype (**a**) and BGN/FMOD double-deficient (**b**) mice. Tissue sections treated with mouse immunoglobulin G served as a negative control (**c**). Apoptosis measured by FragEL labeling of condylar chondrocytes in wildtype and BGN/FMOD double-deficient mice. There was a 2-fold increase in cells undergoing apoptosis in the BGN/FMOD double-deficient mice compared with wildtype mice (**d**).

Fig. 3. Hematoxylin and eosin staining of a 49-day-old mandibular condylar cartilage. The mandibular condylar cartilage can be divided into four layers. **a** Superficial articular layer; **b** middle chondroblastic layer; **c** inferior hypertrophic layer; **d** subchondral bone. Note the non-linear arrangement of cells in the middle layer.

condylar cartilage allows growth in a multitude of directions [Enlow and Hans, 1996].

Because the TMJ and the knee are different, we suggest that the molecular basis for the development of disease may also be different. More specifically, it is possible that similar molecular pathways that are activated during OA cause a different outcome in the TMJ compared with the knee. For example, in both OA of the TMJ and OA of other joints, it has been reported that there is an increase in apoptosis [Aigner et al., 2004; Meng et al., 2005]. However, in the healthy mandibular condylar cartilage, there is a percentage of cells that normally undergo apoptosis [Huang et al., 2004]. In contrast, in healthy articular cartilage, there is almost a complete absence of cells undergoing apoptosis [Drissi et al., 2005]. In addition, the adult mandibular condylar cartilage has the ability to respond to growth factors by an increase in matrix synthesis and proliferation [Sviri et al., 2000], while the adult articular hyaline cartilage is believed to be unresponsive to growth factors. Therefore, we predict that an increase in apoptosis during OA in the knee would cause a more marked decrease in the cellularity of the articular cartilage compared with the fibrocartilage of the TMJ.

It has been reported that during development of OA in the knee, there is an increase in collagen type II expression [Salminen et al., 2001], and we have shown that there is also an increase in collagen type II expression during TMJ-OA. However, in contrast to the articular cartilage of other joints, the superficial layer of the mandibular condylar cartilage does not normally express type II collagen. The functional significance of the absence of collagen type II in the superficial layer of the mandibular cartilage is unknown, but we predict that the uncharacteristic expression of collagen type II in this layer during OA causes structural changes in the fibrocartilage of the TMJ, which differ from the increase in expression of collagen type II in hyaline articular cartilage.

Possible Role of BGN and FMOD

The exact cause by which the absence of BGN and FMOD accelerates the development of TMJ-OA is unknown. One possible explanation is that the absence of BGN and FMOD causes changes in the extracellular collagen network making the joint structures less suited to withstand physiologic mechanical loading. In support of this, we have found that in the knee of BGN/FMOD double-deficient mice, there were changes in the collagen fibril diameters compared with age-matched wildtype mice and mechanically compromised tendons. These changes were present before OA started to develop. In addition, increased mechanical loading by forced treadmill running caused an increased severity of OA in the knee [Ameye et al., 2002]. A similar mechanism could be taking place in the TMJ complex of double-deficient mice. A second possible explanation is that OA arises indirectly from changes in the underlying bone [Hayami et al., 2004]. Male mice who are deficient in BGN have been shown to have age-dependent osteoporosis [Xu et al., 1998]. However, whether there are changes in the bone of BGN/FMOD double-deficient mice is unknown. A third possible explanation is that changes in the TMJ fibrocartilage arise from the ability of BGN and FMOD to modulate members of the transforming growth factor (TGF)-β superfamily, which has been shown previously [Hildebrand et al., 1994]. The binding of BGN and FMOD to members of the TGF-β family may regulate their activity by sequestering them into the ECM, thereby preventing their binding with the cellular receptors. Support of this hypothesis comes from the examination of another SLRP-deficient mouse. In the bone marrow stromal cells from BGN/decorin double-deficient mice, we found that there is an increase in TGF-β activity [Bi et al., 2005]. Interestingly, a recent report has identified an increase in the susceptibility to OA in individuals with polymorphisms in asporin (an SLRP family member). Thus, the authors speculate that the identified polymorphisms cause changes in TGF-β activity [Kizawa et al., 2005].

Conclusion

In summary, we present new information about a mouse model of TMJ-OA and provide details of how it compares with other genetic and acquired models of this disease. Our data specifically show that mice deficient in the ECM proteoglycans, BGN and FMOD, acquired TMJ-OA earlier and to a greater extent compared with wildtype controls. The cell and molecular basis appears to be a combination of increased apoptosis of affected tissue leading to abnormal expression of a key structural component, type II collagen. The difference in the development of OA in the condyle compared with the knee is attributed to the differences in anatomy and suggests that each tissue must be studied separately to understand the basis of OA.

Acknowledgement

This research was supported by the Division of Intramural Research/National Institute of Dental and Craniofacial Research of the NIH.

References

Aigner, T., H.A. Kim, H.I. Roach (2004) Apoptosis in osteoarthritis. Rheum Dis Clin North Am *30:* 639–653, xi.

Ameye, L., D. Aria, K. Jepsen, A. Oldberg, T. Xu, M.F. Young (2002) Abnormal collagen fibrils in tendons of biglycan/fibromodulin-deficient mice lead to gait impairment, ectopic ossification, and osteoarthritis. FASEB J *16:* 673–680.

Ameye, L., M.F. Young (2002) Mice deficient in small leucine-rich proteoglycans: novel in vivo models for osteoporosis, osteoarthritis, Ehlers-Danlos syndrome, muscular dystrophy, and corneal diseases. Glycobiology *12:* 107R–116R.

Anastassaki, A., T. Magnusson (2004) Patients referred to a specialist clinic because of suspected temporomandibular disorders: a survey of 3194 patients in respect of diagnoses, treatments, and treatment outcome. Acta Odontol Scand *62:* 183–192.

Benjamin, M., J.R. Ralphs (2004) Biology of fibrocartilage cells. Int Rev Cytol *233:* 1–45.

Bi, Y., C.H. Stuelten, T. Kilts, S. Wadhwa, R.V. Iozzo, P.G. Robey, X.D. Chen, M.F. Young (2005) Extracellular matrix proteoglycans control the fate of bone marrow stromal cells. J Biol Chem *280:* 30481–30489.

Carlsson, G.E. (1999) Epidemiology and treatment need for temporomandibular disorders. J Orofac Pain *13:* 232–237.

Drissi, H., M. Zuscik, R. Rosier, R. O'Keefe (2005) Transcriptional regulation of chondrocyte maturation: potential involvement of transcription factors in OA pathogenesis. Mol Aspects Med *26:* 169–179.

Enlow, D., M.G. Hans (1996) Essential of Facial Growth. Philadelphia, WB Saunders.

Fujisawa, T., T. Kuboki, T. Kasai, W. Sonoyama, S. Kojima, J. Uehara, C. Komori, H. Yatani, T. Hattori, M. Takigawa (2003) A repetitive, steady mouth opening induced an osteoarthritis-like lesion in the rabbit temporomandibular joint. J Dent Res *82:* 731–735.

Harper, R.P., C.A. Kerins, J.E. McIntosh, R. Spears, L.L. Bellinger (2001) Modulation of the inflammatory response in the rat TMJ with increasing doses of complete Freund's adjuvant. Osteoarthritis Cartilage *9:* 619–624.

Hayami, T., M. Pickarski, G.A. Wesolowski, J. McLane, A. Bone, J. Destefano, G.A. Rodan, T. le Duong (2004) The role of subchondral bone remodeling in osteoarthritis: reduction of cartilage degeneration and prevention of osteophyte formation by alendronate in the rat anterior cruciate ligament transection model. Arthritis Rheum *50:* 1193–1206.

Hildebrand, A., M. Romaris, L.M. Rasmussen, D. Heinegard, D.R. Twardzik, W.A. Border, E. Ruoslahti (1994) Interaction of the small interstitial proteoglycans biglycan, decorin and fibromodulin with transforming growth factor beta. Biochem J *302:* 527–534.

Hocking, A.M., T. Shinomura, D.J. McQuillan (1998) Leucine-rich repeat glycoproteins of the extracellular matrix. Matrix Biol *17:* 1–19.

Huang, Q., B. Singh, M. Sharawy (2004) Immunohistochemical analysis of Bcl-2 and Bax oncoproteins in rabbit craniomandibular joint. Arch Oral Biol *49:* 143–148.

Iozzo, R.V. (1997) The family of the small leucine-rich proteoglycans: key regulators of matrix assembly and cellular growth. Crit Rev Biochem Mol Biol *32:* 141–174.

Iozzo, R.V. (1999) The biology of the small leucine-rich proteoglycans. Functional network of interactive proteins. J Biol Chem *274:* 18843–18846.

Kizawa, H., I. Kou, A. Iida, A. Sudo, Y. Miyamoto, A. Fukuda, A. Mabuchi, A. Kotani, A. Kawakami, S. Yamamoto, A. Uchida, K. Nakamura, K. Notoya, Y. Nakamura, S. Ikegawa (2005) An aspartic acid repeat polymorphism in asporin inhibits chondrogenesis and increases susceptibility to osteoarthritis. Nat Genet *37:* 138–144.

Livne, E. (1994) Matrix synthesis in mandibular condylar cartilage of aging mice. Osteoarthritis Cartilage *2:* 187–197.

Livne, E., M. Silbermann (1986) Further characterization of spontaneous arthritic changes in murine squamo-mandibular joint: histopathological aspects. Histol Histopathol *1:* 161–170.

Meng, J., X. Ma, D. Ma, C. Xu (2005) Microarray analysis of differential gene expression in temporomandibular joint condylar cartilage after experimentally induced osteoarthritis. Osteoarthritis Cartilage *13:* 1115–1125.

Mizoguchi, I., M. Nakamura, I. Takahashi, M. Kagayama, H. Mitani (1992) A comparison of the immunohistochemical localization of type I and type II collagens in craniofacial cartilages of the rat. Acta Anat (Basel) *144:* 59–64.

Nannmark, U., L. Sennerby, T. Haraldson (1990) Macroscopic, microscopic and radiologic assessment of the condylar part of the TMJ in elderly subjects. An autopsy study. Swed Dent J *14:* 163–169.

Ogus, H. (1979) Degenerative disease of the temporomandibular joint in young persons. Br J Oral Surg *17:* 17–26.

Rintala, M., M. Metsaranta, A.M. Saamanen, E. Vuorio, O. Ronning (1997) Abnormal craniofacial growth and early mandibular osteoarthritis in mice harbouring a mutant type II collagen transgene. J Anat *190:* 201–208.

Salminen, H., E. Vuorio, A.M. Saamanen (2001) Expression of Sox9 and type IIA procollagen during attempted repair of articular cartilage damage in a transgenic mouse model of osteoarthritis. Arthritis Rheum *44:* 947–955.

Sato, H., T. Osterberg, M. Ahlqwist, G.E. Carlsson, H.G. Grondahl, B. Rubinstein (1996) Association between radiographic findings in the mandibular condyle and temporomandibular dysfunction in an elderly population. Acta Odontol Scand *54:* 384–390.

Shen, G., M.A. Darendeliler (2005) The adaptive remodeling of condylar cartilage – a transition from chondrogenesis to osteogenesis. J Dent Res *84:* 691–699.

Silbermann, M., E. Livne (1979) Age-related degenerative changes in the mouse mandibular joint. J Anat *129:* 507–520.

Stewart, C.L., S.M. Standish (1983) Osteoarthritis of the TMJ in teenaged females: report of cases. J Am Dent Assoc *106:* 638–640.

Sviri, G.E., I.I. Blumenfeld, E. Livne (2000) Differential metabolic responses to local administration of TGF-beta and IGF-1 in temporomandibular joint cartilage of aged mice. Arch Gerontol Geriatr *31:* 159–176.

Symons, N.B. (1965) A histochemical study of the secondary cartilage of the mandibular condyle in the rat. Arch Oral Biol *10:* 579–584.

Tominaga, K., S. Hirashima, J. Fukuda (2002) An experimental model of osteoarthrosis of the temporomandibular joint in monkeys. Br J Oral Maxillofac Surg *40:* 232–237.

Wadhwa, S., M.C. Embree, Y. Bi, M.F. Young (2004) Regulation, regulatory activities, and function of biglycan. Crit Rev Eukaryot Gene Expr *14:* 301–315.

Wadhwa, S., M.C. Embree, T. Kilts, M.F. Young, L.G. Ameye (2005) Accelerated osteoarthritis in the temporomandibular joint of biglycan/fibromodulin double-deficient mice. Osteoarthritis Cartilage *13:* 817–827.

Wiberg, B., A. Wanman (1998) Signs of osteoarthrosis of the temporomandibular joints in young patients: a clinical and radiographic study. Oral Surg Oral Med Oral Pathol Oral Radiol Endod *86:* 158–164.

Widmalm, S.E., P.L. Westesson, I.K. Kim, F.J. Pereira, Jr., H. Lundh, M.M. Tasaki (1994) Temporomandibular joint pathosis related to sex, age, and dentition in autopsy material. Oral Surg Oral Med Oral Pathol *78:* 416–425.

Xu, L., C.M. Flahiff, B.A. Waldman, D. Wu, B.R. Olsen, L.A. Setton, Y. Li (2003) Osteoarthritis-like changes and decreased mechanical function of articular cartilage in the joints of mice with the chondrodysplasia gene (cho). Arthritis Rheum *48:* 2509–2518.

Xu, T., P. Bianco, L.W. Fisher, G. Longenecker, E. Smith, S. Goldstein, J. Bonadio, A. Boskey, A.M. Heegaard, B. Sommer, K. Satomura, P. Dominguez, C. Zhao, A.B. Kulkarni, P.G. Robey, M.F. Young (1998) Targeted disruption of the biglycan gene leads to an osteoporosis-like phenotype in mice. Nat Genet *20:* 78–82.

Zarb, G.A., G.E. Carlsson (1999) Temporomandibular disorders: osteoarthritis. J Orofac Pain *13:* 295–306.

Cells Tissues Organs

Cells Tissues Organs 2005;181:144–153
DOI: 10.1159/000091376

Variation in Mineral Properties in Normal and Mutant Bones and Teeth

Adele L. Boskey[a] Marian F. Young[b] Tina Kilts[b] Kostas Verdelis[a]

[a]Mineralized Tissue Research Laboratory, Musculoskeletal Integrity Program, Hospital for Special Surgery, New York, N.Y., and [b]National Institute of Dental and Craniofacial Research, National Institutes of Health, Bethesda, Md., USA

Key Words

Hydroxyapatite · Mineralization · Micro-computed tomography · Fourier transform infrared microspectroscopy · Biglycan-knockout mice

Abstract

Hydroxyapatite mineral is deposited in an organized fashion in the matrices of bones and teeth. The amount of mineral present, the composition of the mineral, and the size of the mineral crystals varies with both tissue and animal age, diet, health status, and the tissue being examined. Here, we review methods for measuring these differences in mineral properties and provide some illustrations from bones and teeth of animals in which the small leucine-rich proteoglycans (biglycan and decorin) were ablated. Differences in mineral properties between biglycan-deficient bones and teeth are related to the functions of this small proteoglycan in these tissues.

Introduction

The mineral in physiologically calcified tissues is an analogue of the geologic mineral, hydroxyapatite [HA; $Ca_{10}(PO_4)_6(OH)_2$]. Bone, dentin, and cementum crystals deposit upon a collagen template in an oriented fashion [Robey, 1996] and tend to be relatively small, having a large portion of their unit cells on their surface. This small size leads the crystals to have many adsorbed ions and imperfections [Posner and Beebe, 1975], causing the Ca/P ratio to vary significantly from the stoichiometric 10:6 ratio [Peru and Daculsi, 1994]. The crystals in enamel, not formed on a collagen matrix, are significantly larger and have fewer impurities than those in bone, dentin, and cementum [Bonar et al., 1991].

There are a number of physical and chemical techniques that have been used to characterize the mineral in these tissues. The nature of the phase present and the av-

Abbreviations used in this paper

BGN	biglycan
DCN	decorin
DMP-1	dentin matrix protein 1
FTIR	Fourier transform infrared spectroscopy
FTIRI	Fourier transform infrared imaging spectroscopy
HA	hydroxyapatite
KO	knockout
NIDCR	National Institute of Dental and Craniofacial Research
PCR	polymerase chain reaction
PMMA	polymethylmethacrylate
SLRP	small leucine-rich proteoglycan
WT	wildtype

KARGER

Fax +41 61 306 12 34
E-Mail karger@karger.ch
www.karger.com

Accessible online at:
www.karger.com/cto

Adele L. Boskey, PhD
Mineralized Tissue Research Laboratory
Musculoskeletal Integrity Program, Hospital for Special Surgery
535 E 70th St., New York, NY 10021 (USA)
Tel. +1 212 606 1453, Fax +1 212 472 5331, E-Mail boskeya@hss.edu

erage size/perfection of the crystals is usually determined by wide-angle X-ray or electron diffraction [Boskey, 2001]. Such analyses require either the presence of single crystals (not feasible with these tissues) or homogenization of the tissue prior to analysis. The sizes, shapes, and orientation of the crystals with respect to the underlying matrix can be determined by electron microscopic techniques including scanning, transmission, and atomic force microscopy [Landis et al., 1984; Kirkham et al., 1998; Tong et al., 2003], and the ionic composition can be determined by chemical analyses or electron microprobe analyses [Akesson et al., 1994]. The distribution of the mineral within the tissue can be determined by backscatter electron imaging [Roschger et al., 1995], microcomputed tomography (CT) [Genant et al., 2000], or radiographic techniques using appropriate standards. Unique information about the spatial distribution of both mineral and matrix can be obtained by vibrational spectroscopic techniques such as infrared and Raman spectroscopy and spectroscopic imaging [Boskey and Mendelsohn, 2005].

The nature, properties, and distribution of these properties of the mineral in calcified tissues affect the ability of the tissue to be remodeled and, more significantly, the mechanical strength of the tissue [Boskey, 2003]. The nature of the matrix upon which the crystals are deposited, along with physicochemical factors, determines these properties. Analyses of changes in mineral (and matrix properties) in healthy and diseased tissues as well as in the mineralized tissues of genetically modified animals provide insights into the functions of specific matrix components on the properties of the tissues. For example, mice with the gene for osteocalcin ablated, while initially reported to have thickened bones [Ducy et al., 1996] suggesting osteocalcin was regulating bone formation, were later shown to have smaller crystals that did not remodel based on infrared microspectroscopy [Boskey et al., 1998], indicating the importance of osteocalcin in bone remodeling. Similarly, analysis of the bones of the osteopontin knockout (KO) mouse demonstrated the importance of osteopontin for the regulation of crystal size – crystals were larger and more perfect than in the wildtype (WT) controls – as well as its role in osteoclast recruitment [Boskey et al., 2002]. Mice lacking dentin matrix protein 1 (DMP-1), a protein produced abundantly by hypertrophic chondrocytes and osteoblasts [Feng et al., 2003], had decreased bone density and osteomalacia with decreased mineral content and increased crystal size [Ling et al., 2005], showing that DMP-1 (or some fragment thereof) was acting as a mineral nucleator. In this paper, we illustrate the use of vibrational spectroscopy and micro-CT for the study of teeth as well as bones of mice lacking one of the small leucine-rich proteoglycans (SLRPs), decorin (DCN) or biglycan (BGN). The properties of the bones of the BGN-KO mice have been described previously [Xu et al., 1998], but in less detail than in this review. The bones of BGN-KO mice, while normal at birth, appeared osteopenic with advancing age, developing thin widely spaced trabeculae, a decreased mineral content, and increased crystal size at bone-forming sites.

The SLRPs belong to the leucine-rich repeat superfamily of proteins [Hocking et al., 1998] which, as reviewed elsewhere [Ameye and Young, 2002], is characterized by domains of disulfide bond-forming cysteine-rich clusters, flanking the central leucine-rich repeats. The SLRPs are small in relation to the large proteoglycans such as aggrecan and versican [Iozzo, 1998]. DCN, BGN and some other SLRPs bind to collagen and transforming growth factor-β, and through these interactions, are not only involved in the regulation of collagen fibril size but also appear to be involved in cell proliferation and differentiation [Ameye and Young, 2002]. BGN deficiency tends to result in increased collagen fibril diameter in bone [Corsi et al., 2002] and in decreased diameter during dentin development [Goldberg et al., 2003].

Part of the effect of BGN deficiency on bone development is related to changes in cell proliferation. In vitro, the number of bone marrow stromal cells decreases more rapidly in BGN-KO than in WT mice [Chen et al., 2002]. These cells, which are osteoblast precursors, also produce less type I collagen in culture, suggesting that the matrix in the BGN-KO animals may be abnormal. BGN in solution is a HA nucleator [Boskey et al., 1997] which, in combination with the abnormal matrix that forms in the absence of BGN, may explain why there is a lower mineral content in the bones of the BGN-KO mice. In the jaw, a day after birth, the BGN-KO first molar shows altered dentin mineralization [Goldberg et al., 2003], and structural defects are also observed in forming enamel, with increasing thickness.

DCN-KO mice [Danielson, 1997] show abnormal collagen fibrillogenesis in skin and tendon. In contrast to the BGN-KO mice, the DCN-deficient animals were not reported to show alterations in bone mass, or any other major phenotypic changes in bone at the histological or macroscopic level [Corsi et al., 2002]. In this review, we illustrate how micro-CT and Fourier transform infrared imaging (FTIR) microspectroscopy provide new insight into the mineral and matrix properties of the BGN- and DCN-deficient teeth and the BGN-deficient bones.

Materials and Methods

Animals

WT, BGN-KO, and DCN-KO mice were generated at the National Institute of Dental and Craniofacial Research (NIDCR) under an institutionally approved protocol for the use of animals in research (NIDCR 98-058 and 03-280). The mice used in this experiment were generated by backcrossing the original BGN-KO and DCN-KO strain (129B6/C57 mixture), i.e. strains were maintained separately, for over ten generations. In some experiments, the 129 B6/C57 BGN-KO and DCN-KO mice were backcrossed with the C3H/HeNHsd strain to a purity greater than 95% (in this study, indicated as C3H strain). Approximately 2 mm of the tip of the tail was removed from animals just after weaning (approximately 21 days) and DNA extracted using the commercial purification kit Highpure (Invitrogen). Purified DNA (10 μl) was used for a polymerase chain reaction (PCR)-based genotype assay consisting of 1 × PCR buffer with $MgCl_2$ (Invitrogen), 0.2 m*M* dNTP, and 2 ng of the following two primers: BGN exon 2, 5 prime end (forward) 5′caggaacattgaccatg3′, and BGN exon 2, 3 prime end (reverse) 5′gaaaggacacatggcactgaag3′. These primers detected the WT allele yielding a PCR band of 212 bp. A PGK1 primer (backward) 5′tggatgtggaatgtgtgcgagg3′ was used with the BGN exon 2, 5′ primer to detect the BGN-KO allele that was 310 bp. The overall genotype strategy to detect the DCN-KO allele was similar to that used to detect the BGN-KO alleles except that DCN exon 2, 5 prime end (forward) 5′ccttctggcacaagtctcttgg3′, and DCN exon 2, 3 prime end (backward) 5′tcgaagatgacactggcatcgg3′ primers were used to detect the WT DCN allele of 161 bp. The DCN-KO allele was detected as a 238-bp product when the DCN exon 2, 5 prime primer and PGK1 primer (see above) were used in combination. The PCR reactions were carried out by heating them at 95°C for 5 min prior to the addition of 0.5 μl AmpliTaq Gold Polymerase (Invitrogen). The PCR reaction was carried out with 35 cycles of a three-tiered program consisting of 95°C for 1 min, 57°C for 20 s, and 72°C for 30 s. The reaction was terminated by incubating the mixture at 72°C for 7 min. The resulting PCR products were separated by electrophoresis and visualized by staining with ethidium bromide. After analysis of each genotyping reaction, WT (+/0) and BGN-KO (–/0) males and WT (+/+) and BGN-KO (–/–) females, or WT (+/+) or DCN-KO (–/–) males or females were identified and housed separately until the time of tissue harvest. Mice of the desired age were euthanized by CO_2 inhalation and dissected using aseptic procedures. After decapitation, the skin was carefully removed from the head and the remaining experimental material placed in sterile gauze soaked in phosphate-buffered saline. The dissected tissue was immediately placed on dry ice and stored at –80°C until further analysis.

Tissue Samples

Mice for all the studies were provided by one of the authors from the collection at NIDCR. Mice for the teeth (jaw) studies were derived from the C3H background, and mice for the bone studies from the 129B6/C57 background. The jaws from BGN-deficient mice and their WT controls and from DCN-deficient mice and their WT controls used in the FTIR imaging (FTIRI) studies came from 3-month-old male mice. Extracted first and second molars from 6- to 7-month-old male and female BGN-deficient and WT animals were used in the micro-CT analysis. The mice for the BGN-deficient bone study (all males, 129B6/C57) were derived by gene targeting in embryonic stem cells [Xu et al., 1998], and the genotype was verified by PCR.

For FTIRI, the posterior parts of mouse hemi-jaws were dissected, cleaned of soft tissue, fixed in 90% ethanol, dehydrated through a series of solvents, and embedded in polymethylmethacrylate (PMMA). PMMA blocks were sectioned at 2–3 μm using a sliding microtome (Leica SM 2500, Leica, Germany), and sections were placed on BaF_2 windows for analysis.

Infrared Analyses of Teeth of WT and Mutant Animals

Semi-thin (2–3 μm) sections of the 3-month-old BGN- and DCN-deficient mouse molars and WT control molars were examined by FTIRI to acquire spectral images using the Perkin Elmer Spotlight Imaging system (Perkin Elmer Instruments, Shelton, Conn., USA). The spectral resolution was 8 cm^{-1} and the entire tooth section was scanned in each image, with 2–3 replicates per tooth. The spatial resolution was approximately 7 μm. Spectra were transferred to yield images corresponding to infrared band areas, peak height ratios and integrated area ratios by a combination of instrument software and ISYS chemical imaging software (version 2.1, Spectral Dimensions Inc., Olney, Md., USA) [Boskey and Mendelsohn, 2005]. Background spectra were collected under identical conditions from the same BaF_2 windows. After acquisition, spectra were truncated to allow analysis of the spectral data of interest, baseline was corrected, and the spectral contribution of the PMMA-embedding media was subtracted using ISYS software.

The spectroscopic parameters calculated were: mineral-to-matrix ratio, carbonate-to-matrix ratio, crystallinity, and collagen cross-link ratio. The mineral-to-matrix ratio – v1, v3 PO4 band (900–1,200 cm^{-1})/amide I band (1,590–1,720 cm^{-1}) integrated areas ratio – is linearly related to ash weight. Mineral crystallinity corresponds to the crystallite size and perfection as determined by X-ray diffraction and was calculated from the intensity ratios of subbands at 1,030 (stoichiometric apatite) and 1,020 cm^{-1} (nonstoichiometric apatite). The cross-link ratio is a parameter reflecting the maturity of the collagen, expressed as the absorbance ratio at two specific wave numbers (1,660 and 1,690 cm^{-1}). In the spectral images, pixels devoid of tissue (no mineral and/or matrix spectral signature) were set equal to zero and excluded from calculations. The spectroscopic results were expressed as histograms describing the pixel distribution of the parameters, mean values and standard deviations of the pixel distribution, and corresponding color-coded images were generated at the same time by ISYS.

Micro-CT

Mineral density of dentin and total volume of the crown of the BGN-deficient, DCN-deficient, and WT molars were calculated by quantitative micro-CT (Enhanced Vision Systems Model MS-8 in vitro micro-CT scanner, GE Healthcare, London, Ont., Canada). First and second molars from WT and KO animals were extracted from the mouse jaws using dental micro-spoon excavators, and their roots were cleaned of alveolar bone remains through careful use of a periodontal curette. Molars from 3 male and 4 female hemi-jaws were analyzed in both WT and KO groups (n_{total} = 28). The extracted molars were then positioned in a 70% alcohol-filled plastic container and fixed, while a calibration phantom was fixed in the same container. Two-dimensional projections of all the molars at the same time were collected by Evolver software (GE Healthcare) in three consecutive scans; the isotropic voxel size was 12 × 12 × 12 μm. The hardware of the Enhanced Visions System micro-

CT scanner employs filtering of the low-energy portion of the X-ray spectrum with aluminum, acrylic, and a saline bath to minimize beam hardening associated with polychromatic X-ray and to ensure uniformity of the beam at the detector array. To minimize noise, a large number of views (400), increased frame averaging, and increased shutter exposure time (3,000 ms) were utilized resulting in 4-hour scans. Each scan of the phantom containing air, saline and a bone reference material (1.18 g/cm^3) gave calibration in Hounsfield units to mineral density in grams per cubic centimeter. Scanner linearity was previously established by the manufacturer with a phantom containing nine densities of similar calibration material (Gammex RMI, Middleton, Wisc., USA). Reconstruction of projections into CT volume data was accomplished by Beam software (GE Healthcare) with a modified Parker algorithm [Tommasini et al., 2005]. A sub-volume was selected in Microview software (GE Healthcare) to segregate each molar for reconstruction.

The crowns were reoriented so that the cervical circumference lay, as much as possible, on the final x-plane, at which point all the mineralized structure that was above the x-plane was defined as the anatomical crown, and the part of the sample that was below the x-plane was defined as the root. The smallest parallelepiped subvolumes into which the entire crown or roots could fit were positioned around each of these, respectively. Attenuation histograms of the volumes of interest were generated and Hounsfield units versus frequency values exported to Microsoft Excel for further processing. Individual thresholds were selected based on mineral density distribution for each molar, due to the fact that the transition between mineralized tissue and background soft tissue is very clear in our samples under the conditions used (fig. 3, histogram). An additional threshold was selected between dentin and enamel density distribution curves in crowns. Dentin mineral density for crowns and roots was computed based on density distribution between the two thresholds and the total volume crown, based on the total number of voxels with a density above the background-mineralized tissue threshold. Values for each of the three parameters (mineral dentin density in crown, in root, and crown volume) in every molar from all three scans were averaged, in order to reduce experimental error associated with factors such as X-ray scattering by very dense enamel, or operator bias (e.g., precise positioning of the crown cervix) in data processing.

Results

Infrared Microspectroscopy of BGN-KO and WT Bones

We have previously reported that there was increased crystallinity and a decreased mineral content in the bones of the male BGN-KO mice [Xu et al., 1998], although the data were not shown in that publication. We also reported that by 6 months of age, there were fewer trabeculae detectable in the KO than in the WT mice. Properties of the cortical bone, displayed as a function of location in the cortical bone, are summarized in figure 1a–c. In WT mice, as the animal ages, there is an initial increase in mineral content (fig. 1a) at all tissue sites, but at 6 months,

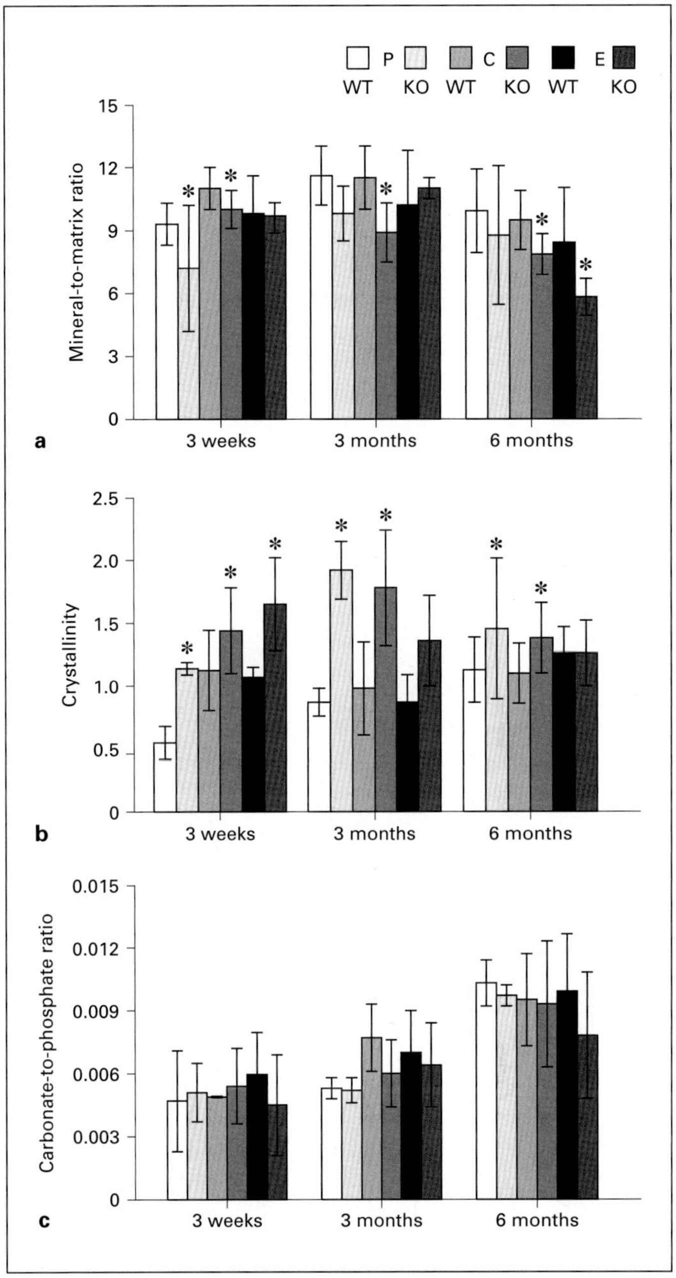

Fig. 1. FTIR microspectroscopic analysis of the bones of male BGN-KO and age- and sex-matched WT mice. Mean values from multiple (5–12) spectra obtained mid-shaft in each of three regions are shown. The mineral-to-matrix ratio (**a**) is decreased at all tissue sites except in the endosteum at all 3 ages, although statistical significance (* $p < 0.05$) was not found at 6 months in the periosteal region. Crystallinity (**b**) was significantly increased in KO in relation to WT mice in all but the endosteal regions at all time points. The carbonate-to-phosphate ratio (**c**) did not vary significantly between KO and WT mice at any time point, although values did increase significantly with time in each group, and the KO values tended to be decreased in older tissues at later time points. P = Bone adjacent to the periosteal surface; C = bone in the center of the cortex; E = bone adjacent to the endosteum.

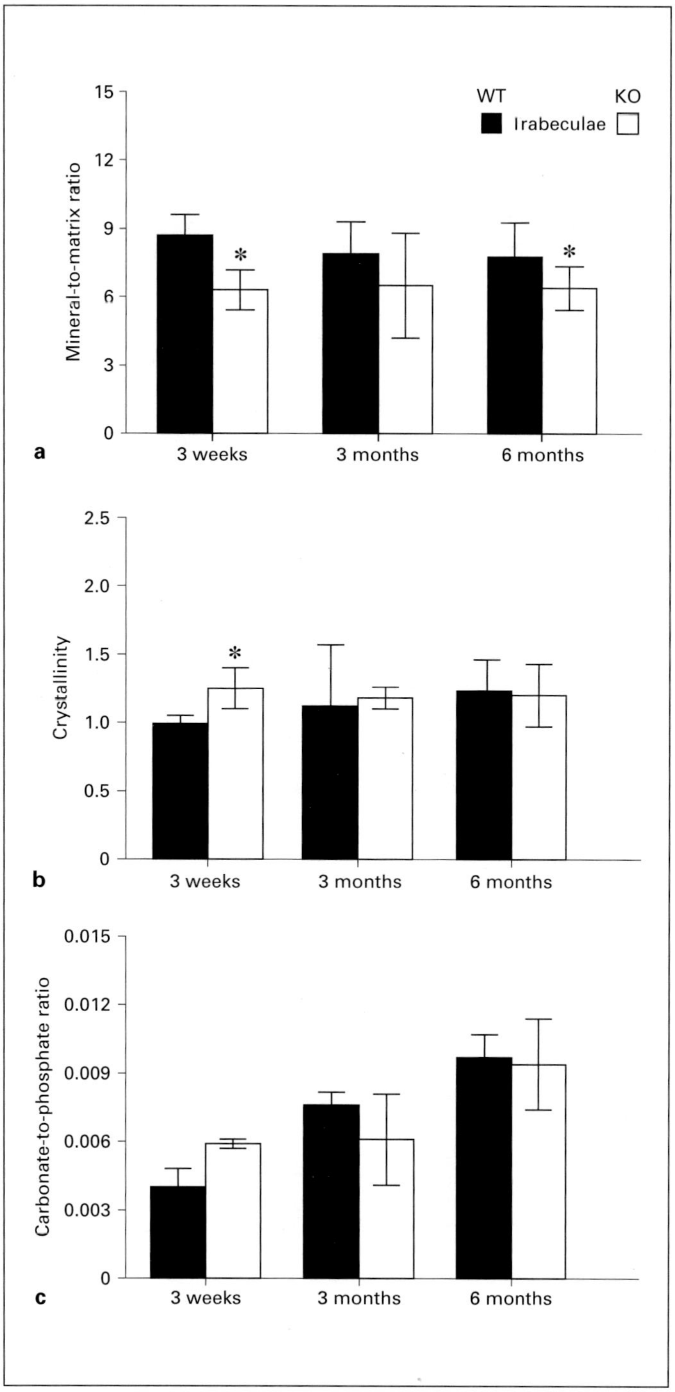

Fig. 2. FTIR microspectroscopic analysis of the trabecular bone of male BGN-KO and age- and sex-matched WT mice. Mean values from multiple (5–12) spectra obtained at sites below the epiphysis are shown. The mineral-to-matrix ratio (**a**) was decreased in KO compared with WT trabeculae at all ages, with statistical significance (* $p < 0.05$) in the youngest and oldest bones. Crystallinity (**b**) was significantly increased in the 3-week bones, but was equivalent to WT mice in the older bones. The carbonate-to-phosphate ratio (**c**) did not vary significantly between KO and WT trabeculae, but did increase with age in all bones.

the mineral content decreased slightly. In contrast, in the KO mice, the mineral content at all sites other than the mineral adjacent to the endosteum was decreased in relation to age-matched controls. At 6 months, there was a significant decrease in the mineral content of the endosteum. The crystallinity, an indication of crystal size and perfection, increased with animal age at all tissue sites in the WT mice, and was significantly higher at all sites and ages in the KO mice (fig. 1b). In the endosteal region, crystallinity was comparable with WT mice at 6 months. The carbonate-to-phosphate ratio increased with animal and tissue age (where periosteal bone is younger than bone in the central cortex, and younger than the endosteal bone) in the WT mice, and was not significantly different in the KO mice when similar sites and animal ages were compared (fig. 1c).

Examining the same parameters in the trabecular bone, again, there is a decreased mineral content in the BGN-KO bone compared with the control (fig. 2a), but in contrast to the cortical bone, the mineral content remained constant as a function of age in both the WT and the KO trabeculae. Crystallinity was again increased in the BGN-KO mice (fig. 2b), but the difference between WT and KO mice was only significant in the youngest animals. The carbonate-to-phosphate ratio in the trabecular bone (fig. 2c) also tended ($p = 0.06$) to be higher in the youngest BGN-KO mice, but was equivalent at all other time points.

Micro-CT of BGN-KO Teeth

Micro-CT was used to measure the properties of the BGN-deficient animals in relation to age- and sex-matched controls at 3 months. The tooth crown as defined by the area of interest is shown in 3-dimensional rendering of a first WT molar (fig. 3a). Both crown and root mineral dentin densities were not significantly different between WT molars in male or female animals and their KO counterparts (data not shown). Although the interface between dentin and enamel voxels (fig. 3b, arrows) is not very steep, as it is likely that some enamel voxels have mineral density values which are very similar to high-mineral-density dentin voxels, distribution of mineral density in dentin was reproducible between scans. Figure 3c shows the measurement of the total crown volume (dentin and enamel) for male and female BGN-KO and WT control first molars (7 each, total specimens = 28). While there is essentially no difference between male WT and KO animals, crowns of first molars in female BGN-KO animals were significantly smaller (approximately 10%) than in their WT counterparts.

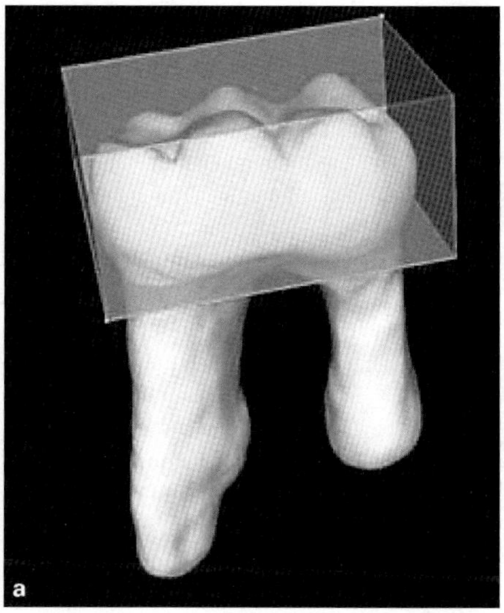

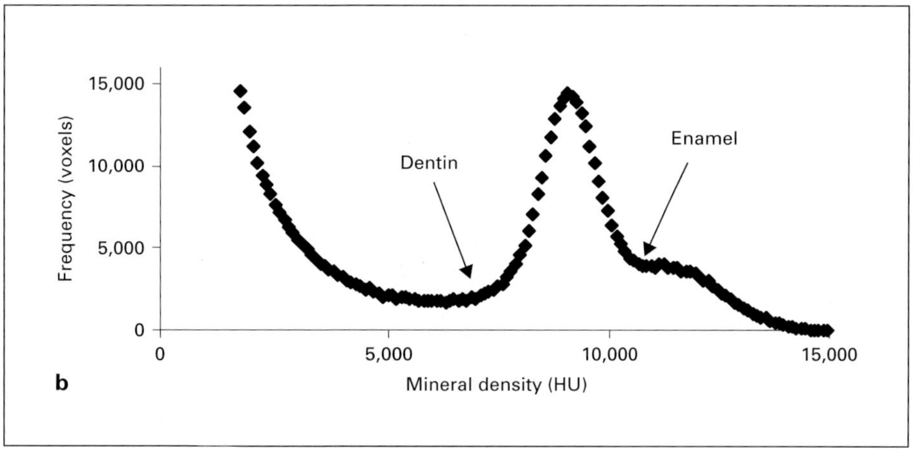

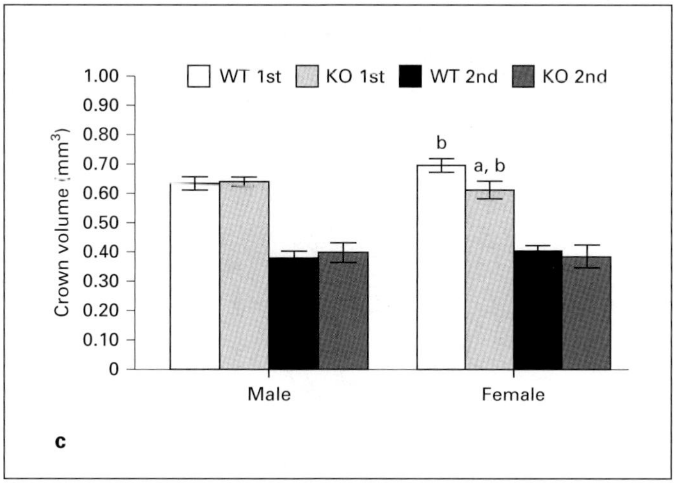

Fig. 3. Micro-CT analysis of mouse molar crowns. **a** Typical 3-dimensional reconstruction of a BGN-KO and age- and sex-matched WT first molar crown at 3 months. **b** Histogram of 3-dimensional density allows easy separation of enamel and dentin contributions in the BGN-KO and WT teeth. HU = Hounsfield unit. **c** Mean and standard deviation for crown volumes of first and second molars in male and female BGN-KO and WT animals. [a] $p < 0.05$ compared with the same tooth in WT mice; [b] $p < 0.05$ compared with the same tooth, the same genotype in males.

FTIRI of BGN- and DCN-KO Teeth

Typical spatial variation in mineral and matrix properties of first molars of 3-month-old male BGN- (n = 4) and DCN-deficient (n = 3) animals were compared (fig. 4a–d) with those of sex- and background-matched controls (n = 3). The mineral-to-matrix ratio (fig. 4a) visually appeared slightly higher in the BGN-KO teeth, compared with the WT and DCN-KO teeth. Crystallinity, measured as the 1030 cm^{-1}/1020 cm^{-1} intensity ratio (fig. 4b), appeared to have a comparable distribution in all three genotypes. In contrast, the carbonate-to-amide I peak area ratio visually appeared appreciably higher in all BGN-deficient first molars in relation to the other genotypes. The 1660 cm^{-1}/1690 cm^{-1} intensity ratio, indicative of collagen maturity, also appeared higher in the BGN-deficient teeth. Figure 5 compares the average for each of the above-mentioned parameters observed for each image in the 10 teeth analyzed. There was no statistically significant difference in the mineral-to-matrix ratio, although there was a sharper distribution in the BGN-deficient animals as seen in the pixel histograms (data not shown). There was no significant difference in the crystallinity parameter, although it was slightly increased in both BGN- and DCN-deficient molars in relation to WT molars. The carbonate-to-amide I ratio was significantly decreased in the BGN-KO molars and significantly increased in the DCN-KO molars compared with controls, while the 1660 cm^{-1}/1690 cm^{-1} ratio was slightly increased in the BGN-KO molars, but had a broader distribution. The pixel distribution showed a greater population of low and high values in the molars of BGN-KO mice (data not shown).

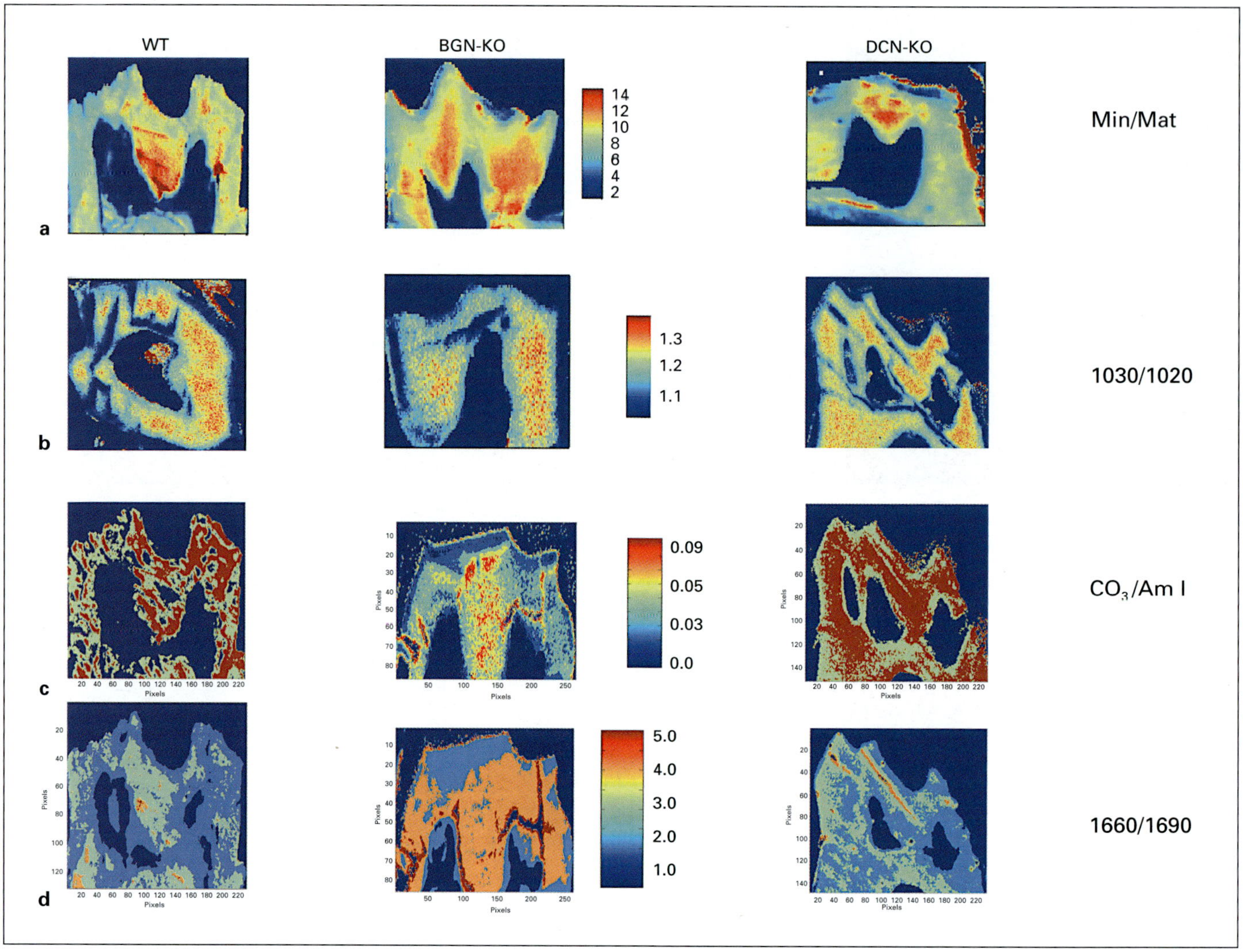

Fig. 4. Infrared imaging of first molars from several different 3-month-old male BGN-KO, DCN-KO, and age- and sex-matched WT teeth. Typical images of mineral-to-matrix (Min/Mat) ratio (**a**), crystallinity (1030 cm^{-1}/1020 cm^{-1} intensity ratio) (**b**), carbonate-to-amide I (CO_3/Am I) (**c**), and collagen (1660 cm^{-1}/1690 cm^{-1} intensity ratio) (**d**) maturity. Color scales for each category of images are identical. Each image is approximately 750 × 850 μm^2.

Discussion

This report highlights the use of micro-CT and FTIR microscopy and microscopic imaging to obtain new information, not derivable from light or electron microscopy, about the mineral and matrix composition of bones and teeth. We have extensively used the FTIR technique in the analysis of bones of mutant animals [Boskey and Mendelsohn, 2005], but this report is the first to document the use of infrared imaging to characterize changes in rodent teeth. Differences between bone and tooth properties in the BGN-KO mouse provide additional insights into the effects of this protein.

BGN-KO Bones and Teeth Show Different Patterns of Mineral Alterations

The BGN-deficient bones at all ages analyzed were thinner, mechanically weaker, and had distinct material properties compared with WT animals [Xu et al., 1998]. The detailed material analysis of the bones based on infrared microspectroscopy showed that the more recently formed bone adjacent to the periosteum and in the center

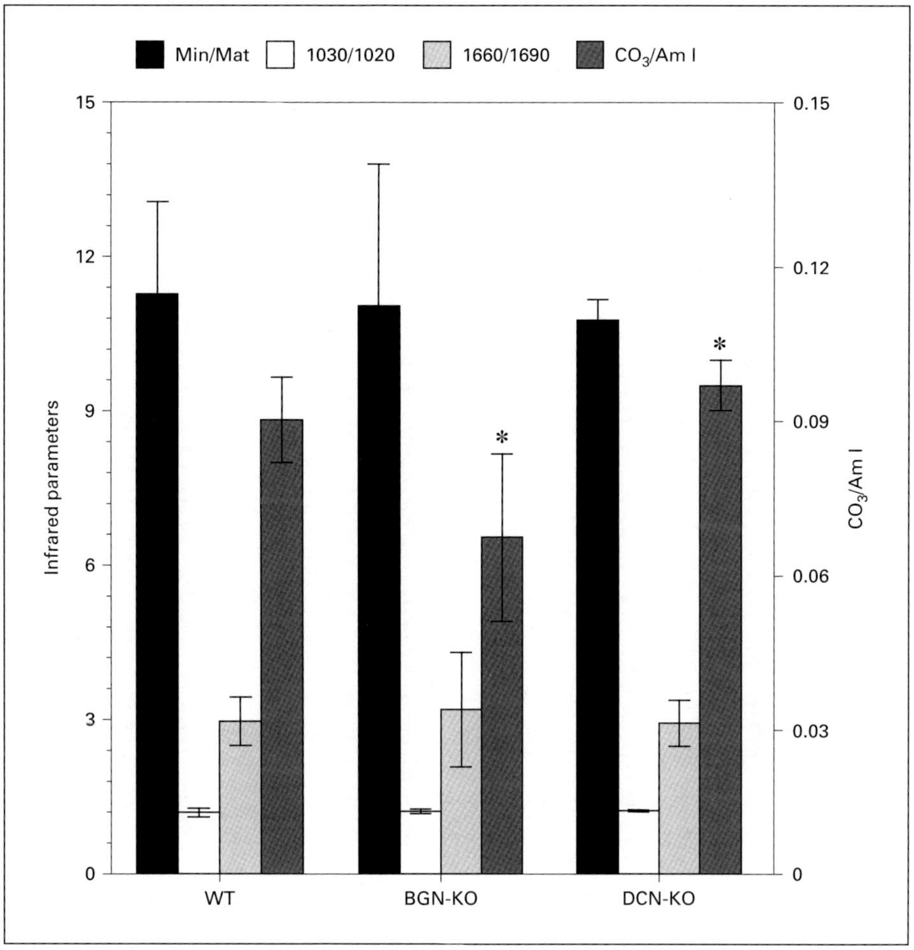

Fig. 5. Variation in FTIR parameters in 3-month-old male BGN-KO, DCN-KO, and age-, background- (C3H), and sex-matched WT teeth; mean and standard deviations from 3–5 images of each first molar. * $p < 0.05$. Min/Mat = Mineral-to-matrix ratio; 1030/1020 = 1030 cm^{-1}/1020 cm^{-1} intensity ratio; 1660/1690 = 1660 cm^{-1}/1690 cm^{-1} intensity ratio; CO_3/Am I = carbonate-to-amide I ratio.

of the cortex showed the most difference from WT controls, suggesting an effect of BGN on mineral formation rather than remodeling, as was seen in the bone adjacent to the endosteal surface in the osteocalcin [Boskey et al., 1998] and osteopontin [Boskey et al., 2002] KO mice. The BGN-KO bone contained a lower mineral-to-matrix ratio, but had larger (more perfect) crystals. Since the collagen fibrils within the BGN-KO bone tend to be larger [Corsi et al., 2002], this could be due to a lack of appropriate sites for new mineral deposition within the collagen itself, since collagen forms the template upon which the mineral is deposited [Gokhale et al., 2001]. Thus, the observed changes in material properties might be an indirect effect of the modification of the collagen fibrils. BGN regulates the collagen fibril diameter, both in vitro and in the tissues of KO animals [Goldberg et al., 2003]. On the other hand, an initial study showed that cartilage BGN and a mixture of SLRPs isolated from bone were HA nucleators [Boskey et al., 1997]. This would suggest that in the absence of BGN, there would be fewer nucleation sites, although bone has more than one matrix protein involved in nucleation. With fewer nucleation sites, and the same local calcium and phosphate concentrations, those nuclei that are present would tend to grow to a larger size, hence the observed increased crystallinity in the BGN-KO bones. It is important to note that the material properties of the DMP-1 KO bones are similar to those of the BGN-KO bones (lower mineral-to-matrix ratio and larger crystals) [Ling et al., 2005], and DMP-1 is also a HA nucleator [Tartaix et al., 2004].

The phenotype in the BGN-KO tooth was quite different from the bone. There was no significant reduction in mineral content in the teeth; in contrast, there was no difference in mineral content (mineral-to-matrix ratio) in relation to WT controls. Crystal size was not significantly altered, but the relative carbonate content, which in both bone [Tarnowski et al., 2002] and dentin increases with tissue age [Coklica et al., 1969], was decreased in the

BGN-KO teeth. Additionally, while the BGN-KO bone has thicker collagen fibrils, the BGN-deficient tooth has thinner ones [Goldberg et al., 2002]. The presence of thinner collagen fibrils in the dentin might suggest that there would be more sites for initiation of mineralization, although earlier electron microscopic studies of primary mineralization in calvaria reported that DCN disappears and fibrils fuse prior to mineral deposition [Hoshi et al., 1999]. Similar data are not available for BGN. Even in the absence of one of the potential HA nucleators, the number of sites on collagen might be closer to normal in the tooth, thus there would be a lesser difference in mineral content in the tooth, and hence, a lesser change in crystallinity. The decreased carbonate content in the BGN-deficient molar suggests impaired or delayed mineralization, but this is difficult to reconcile in the absence of data from younger animals. The increased carbonate content in the DCN-deficient teeth, in the absence of other changes in material properties, suggests that the mineral is older, but again, additional studies on younger animals are needed.

It should be noted that the BGN-deficient bone and dentin studies were done in mice from different backgrounds; however, based on preliminary analyses of the bones of the C3H BGN-KO mice, we do not think that this is a major contributor to the difference. It is much more likely that the different material properties observed are tissue specific, rather than background specific. Since bones in the DCN-deficient mice like those in the BGN-deficient mice have smaller fibril diameters [Corsi et al., 2002], it will be interesting to characterize the bones in the DCN-deficient mice.

Sex-Dependent Differences in WT and BGN-Deficient Teeth

The BGN gene is located on human [McBride et al., 1990] and mouse [Chatterjee et al., 1993] X chromosomes, and thus, in males, has no second allele (on Y). In females, normally, one allele is inactivated so that men and women have equal amounts of BGN expression. Initial analyses were performed only on the bones of males lacking BGN. Yet the female mice, like female children with Turner syndrome who lack BGN [Heegard et al., 1997] and may fail to express another factor that controls BGN expression, showed greater differences in tooth volume than male mice. In that respect, it is interesting to note that human males with Klinefelter syndrome (XXY), who may express extra BGN, have larger permanent tooth crowns than normal males and females [Alvesalo et al., 1991]. There are no consistent reports of sexual dimorphism in crown size in humans and primates, although several studies have addressed this question [Dempsey et al., 1999; Koppe and Swindler, 2004; Anderson, 2005; Harris and Lease, 2005]. This report is the first to note sexual dimorphism in crown size in mice.

Conclusions

Variations in mineral properties in bones and teeth contribute to the mechanical performance of these tissues. Genetically derived mutant animals lacking one or more extracellular matrix component are being studied to provide insight not only into the mechanical strength and geometry of these tissues, but also, as described in this review, into the functions of the proteins that are ablated. Combing these data with histology, gene expression data, mechanical testing, and cell culture studies will certainly facilitate the understanding of more than one of the functions of these proteins.

Acknowledgments

This study was supported in part by NIH DE04141 (A.L.B.), NIH DE K08 467 (K.V.) and by the Intramural Research Program of the NIH, NIDCR (M.Y.).

References

Akesson, K., M.D. Grynpas, R.G. Hancock, R. Odselius, K.J. Obrant (1994) Energy-dispersive X-ray microanalysis of the bone mineral content in human trabecular bone: a comparison with ICPES and neutron activation analysis. Calcif Tissue Int *55:* 236–239.

Alvesalo, L., E. Tammisalo, G. Townsend (1991) Upper central incisor and canine tooth crown size in 47,XXY males. J Dent Res *70:* 1057–1060.

Ameye, L., M.F. Young (2002) Mice deficient in small leucine-rich proteoglycans: novel in vivo models for osteoporosis, osteoarthritis, Ehlers-Danlos syndrome, muscular dystrophy, and corneal diseases. Glycobiology *12:* 107R–116R.

Anderson, A.A. (2005) Dentition and occlusion development in African American children: mesiodistal crown diameters and tooth-size ratios of primary teeth. Pediatr Dent *27:* 121–128.

Bonar, L.C., M. Shimizu, J.E. Roberts, R.G. Griffin, M.J. Glimcher (1991) Structural and composition studies on the mineral of newly formed dental enamel: a chemical, X-ray diffraction, and 31P and proton nuclear magnetic resonance study. J Bone Miner Res *6:* 1167–1176.

Boskey, A.L. (2001) Bone mineralization; in Cowin, S.C. (ed): Bone Biomechanics, ed 3. Boca Raton, CRC Press, pp 5.1–5.34.

Boskey, A.L. (2003) Bone mineral crystal size. Osteoporos Int *14(suppl 5):* 16–21.
Boskey, A.L., S. Gadaleta, C. Gundberg, S.B. Doty, P. Ducy, G. Karsenty (1998) Fourier transform infrared microspectroscopic analysis of bones of osteocalcin-deficient mice provides insight into the function of osteocalcin. Bone *23:* 187–96.
Boskey, A.L., R. Mendelsohn (2005) Infrared spectroscopic characterization of mineralized tissues. Vibrational Spectroscopy *38:* 107–114.
Boskey, A.L., L. Spevak, S.B. Doty, L. Rosenberg (1997) Effects of bone CS-proteoglycans, DS-decorin, and DS-biglycan on hydroxyapatite formation in a gelatin gel. Calcif Tissue Int *61:* 298–305.
Boskey, A.L., L. Spevak, E. Paschalis, S.B. Doty, M.D. McKee (2002) Osteopontin deficiency increases mineral content and mineral crystallinity in mouse bone. Calcif Tissue Int *71:* 145–154.
Chatterjee, A., C.J. Faust, G.E. Herman (1993) Genetic and physical mapping of the biglycan gene on the mouse X chromosome. Mamm Genome *4:* 33–36.
Chen, X.D., S. Shi, T. Xu, P.G. Robey, M.F. Young (2002) Age-related osteoporosis in biglycan-deficient mice is related to defects in bone marrow stromal cells. J Bone Miner Res *17:* 331–340.
Coklica, V., F. Brudevold, B.H. Amdur (1969) The distribution and composition of density fractions from human crown dentine. Arch Oral Biol *14:* 451–460.
Corsi, A., T. Xu, X.D. Chen, A. Boyde, J. Liang, M. Mankani, B. Sommer, R.V. Iozzo, I. Eichstetter, P.G. Robey, P. Bianco, M.F. Young (2002) Phenotypic effects of biglycan deficiency are linked to collagen fibril abnormalities, are synergized by decorin deficiency, and mimic Ehlers-Danlos-like changes in bone and other connective tissues. J Bone Miner Res *17:* 1180–1189.
Danielson, K., H. Baribault, D. Holmes, H. Graham, K. Kadler, R. Iozzo (1997) Targeted disruption of decorin leads to abnormal collagen fibril morphology and skin fragility. J Cell Biol *136:* 729–749.
Dempsey, P.J., G.C. Townsend, L.C. Richards (1999) Increased tooth crown size in females with twin brothers: evidence for hormonal diffusion between human twins in utero. Am J Hum Biol *11:* 577–586.
Ducy, P., C. Desbois, B. Boyce, G. Pinero, B. Story, C. Dunstan, E. Smith, J. Bonadio, S. Goldstein, C. Gundberg, A. Bradley, G. Karsenty (1996) Increased bone formation in osteocalcin-deficient mice. Nature *382:* 448–452.
Feng, J.Q., H. Huang, Y. Lu, L. Ye, Y. Xie, T.W. Tsutsui, T. Kunieda, T. Castranio, G. Scott, L.B. Bonewald, Y. Mishina (2003) The dentin matrix protein 1 (Dmp1) is specifically expressed in mineralized, but not soft, tissues during development. J Dent Res *82:* 776–780.
Genant, H.K., C. Gordon, Y. Jiang, T.M. Link, D. Hans, S. Majumdar, T.F. Lang (2000) Advanced imaging of the macrostructure and microstructure of bone. Horm Res *54(suppl 1):* 24–30.
Gokhale, J., P.G. Robey, A.L. Boskey (2001) The biochemistry of bone; in Marcus, R., D. Feldman, J. Kelsey (eds): Osteoporosis, ed 2. San Diego, Academic Press, vol 1, pp 107–189.
Goldberg, M. (2002) Biglycan is a repressor of amelogenin expression and enamel formation: an emerging hypothesis. J Dent Res *81:* 520–524.
Goldberg, M., O. Rapoport, D. Septier, K. Palmier, R. Hall, G. Embery, M. Young, L. Ameye (2003) Proteoglycans in predentin: the last 15 micrometers before mineralization. Connect Tissue Res *44(suppl 1):* 184–188.
Harris, E.F., L.R. Lease (2005) Mesiodistal tooth crown dimensions of the primary dentition: a worldwide survey. Am J Phys Anthropol *128:* 593–607.
Heegaard, A.M., P. Gehron Robey, W. Vogel, W. Just, R.L. Widom, J. Scholler, L.W. Fisher, M.F. Young (1997) Functional characterization of the human biglycan 5′-flanking DNA and binding of the transcription factor c-Krox. J Bone Miner Res *12:* 2050–2060.
Hocking, A.M., T. Shinomura, D.J. McQuillan (1998) Leucine-rich repeat glycoproteins of the extracellular matrix. Matrix Biol *17:* 1–19.
Hoshi, K., S. Kemmotsu, Y. Takeuchi, N. Amizuka, H. Ozawa (1999) The primary calcification in bones follows removal of decorin and fusion of collagen fibrils. J Bone Miner Res *14:* 273–280.
Iozzo, R.V. (1998) Matrix proteoglycans: from molecular design to cellular function. Annu Rev Biochem *67:* 609–652.
Kirkham, J., S.J. Brookes, R.C. Shore, W.A. Bonass, D.A. Smith, M.L. Wallwork, C. Robinson (1998) Atomic force microscopy studies of crystal surface topology during enamel development. Connect Tissue Res *38:* 91–100.
Koppe, T., D.R. Swindler (2004) Metric sexual dimorphism in the deciduous teeth of Old World monkeys. Ann Anat *186:* 367–374.
Landis, W.J., M. Navarro, J.R. Neuringer, K. Kurz (1984) Single bovine enamel particles examined by electron optics. J Dent Res *63:* 629–634.
Ling, Y., H.F. Rios, E.R. Myers, Y. Lu, J.Q. Feng, A.L. Boskey (2005) DMP1 depletion decreases bone mineralization in vivo: an FTIR imaging analysis. J Bone Miner Res *20:* 2169–2177.
McBride, O.W., L.W. Fisher, M.F. Young (1990) Localization of PGI (biglycan, BGN) and PGII (decorin, DCN, PG-40) genes on human chromosomes Xq13-qter and 12q, respectively. Genomics *6:* 219–225.
Otsu, N. (1979) A threshold selection method from gray-level histograms. IEEE Trans Syst Man Cybern *9:* 62–66.
Peru, L., G. Daculsi (1994) Synthetic calcium phosphates: models for biological crystals? Clin Mater *15:* 267–272.
Posner, A.S., R.A. Beebe (1975) The surface chemistry of bone mineral and related calcium phosphates. Semin Arthritis Rheum *4:* 267–291.
Robey, P.G. (1996) Vertebrate mineralized matrix proteins: structure and function. Connect Tissue Res *35:* 131–136.
Roschger, P., H. Plenk, Jr., K. Klaushofer, J. Eschberger (1995) A new scanning electron microscopy approach to the quantification of bone mineral distribution: backscattered electron image grey-levels correlated to calcium K alpha-line intensities. Scanning Microsc *9:* 75–86.
Tarnowski, C.P., M.A. Ignelzi, Jr., M.D. Morris (2002) Mineralization of developing mouse calvaria as revealed by Raman microspectroscopy. J Bone Miner Res *17:* 1118–1126.
Tartaix, P.H., M. Doulaverakis, A. George, L.W. Fisher, W.T. Butler, C. Qin, E. Salih, M. Tan, Y. Fujimoto, L. Spevak, A.L. Boskey (2004) In vitro effects of dentin matrix protein-1 on hydroxyapatite formation provide insights into in vivo functions. J Biol Chem *279:* 18115–18120.
Tommasini, S.M., T.G. Morgan, M.C.H. van der Meulen, K.J. Jepsen (2005) Genetic variation in structure-function relationships for the inbred mouse lumbar vertebral body. J Bone Miner Res *20:* 817–827.
Tong, W., M.J. Glimcher, J.L. Katz, L. Kuhn, S.J. Eppell (2003) Size and shape of mineralites in young bovine bone measured by atomic force microscopy. Calcif Tissue Int *72:* 592–598.
Xu, T., P. Bianco, L.W. Fisher, G. Longenecker, E. Smith, S. Goldstein, J. Bonadio, A. Boskey, A.M. Heegaard, B. Sommer, K. Satomura, P. Dominguez, C. Zhao, A.B. Kulkarni, P.G. Robey, M.F. Young (1998) Targeted disruption of the biglycan gene leads to an osteoporosis-like phenotype in mice. Nat Genet *20:* 78–82.

Cells Tissues Organs

Cells Tissues Organs 2005;181:154–165
DOI: 10.1159/000091377

Collagenase in Cranial Morphogenesis

Kenn Holmbeck

Craniofacial and Skeletal Diseases Branch, Matrix Metalloproteinase Unit, National Institute of Dental and Craniofacial Research, National Institutes of Health, Bethesda, Md., USA

Key Words
Membrane type 1 matrix metalloproteinase · Cartilage remodeling · Collagenase · Craniofacial morphogenesis

Abstract
Collagen is the most abundant extracellular matrix protein in connective tissues of higher animals. The growth of connective tissues is intimately linked to the ability to model and remodel the collagen-rich matrices of the organism at critical points during development and growth to allow expansion and adaptation of tissue interfaces. The mammalian cranium is one such place where collagen remodeling is required for proper growth, and this review explores the consequences of abrogated collagen remodeling as they materialize in a mouse model deficient for the membrane type 1 matrix metalloproteinase.

Introduction

From an architectural perspective, growth is a major challenge in morphogenesis of the mammalian cranium. The task of developing and growing a rigid casing without total demolition of the structure during its expansion appears at first glance to be an impossible feat. Yet, to overcome this challenge, nature has cleverly devised a strategy in which growth is coordinated between multiple individual smaller components that in unison form an organ. The evolution of the structural properties of the cranium is principally driven by a need to protect the brain and house sensory organs, while at the same time comprising the mastication apparatus refined further by the addition of teeth. The adaptation of the cranial subentities to growth and shape change in the process of development not only means that the bony and cartilaginous structures must undergo some degree of remodeling themselves, but equally important, the interfaces between these objects have to undergo remodeling as well in order for the cranium as an organ to achieve harmonious growth (fig. 1).

Fibrillar collagen, principally type I and to a lesser extent type II, is by far the most abundant extracellular matrix component in the organism (fig. 2A). Type I collagen is a heterotrimeric molecule made up of two α1(I) and one α2(I) polypetide chains.

Following maturation of procollagen, which involves processing by the proteinases ADAMTS-2 and bone mor-

Abbreviations used in this paper

BMP	bone morphogenetic protein
MMP	matrix metalloproteinase
MT1	membrane type 1
TRAP	tartrate resistant acid phosphatase

Kenn Holmbeck, PhD
National Institute of Dental and Craniofacial Research, Craniofacial and Skeletal Diseases Branch, Matrix Metalloproteinase Unit, 30 Convent Drive Building 30/Room 125
MSC 4380, National Institutes of Health, Bethesda, MD 20892 (USA)
Tel. +1 301 496 3922, Fax +1 301 594 1253, E-Mail kenn.holmbeck@nih.gov

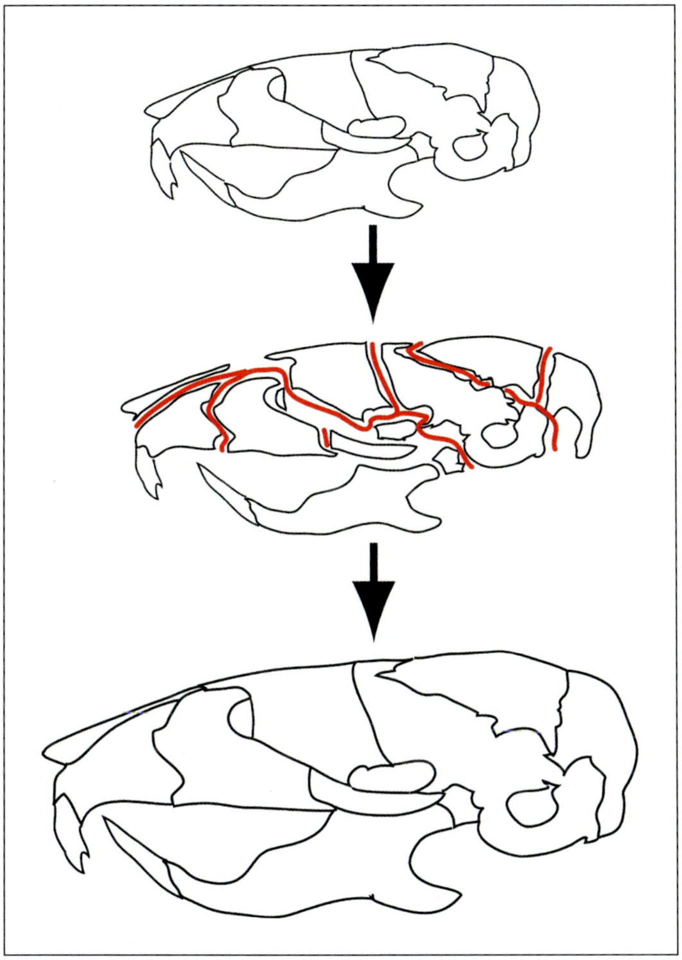

Fig. 1. Cranium substructure facilitates growth and functionality. Model diagram of a rodent cranium demonstrating the subdivision into smaller bony entities. This architecture facilitates the growth of the entire cranium as a case-like structure without the need to tear down the head as it grows. Each individual bony entity grows on its own, but is synchronized with the other bony entities, to facilitate proper morphogenesis. The bones are connected by sutures (red) which themselves are sites of extensive remodeling to allow apposition of bone and dispersal of physical stress induced by the growth process. The net function of this architecture is a rigid structure which is able to grow in size while retaining all its functional properties despite constant change.

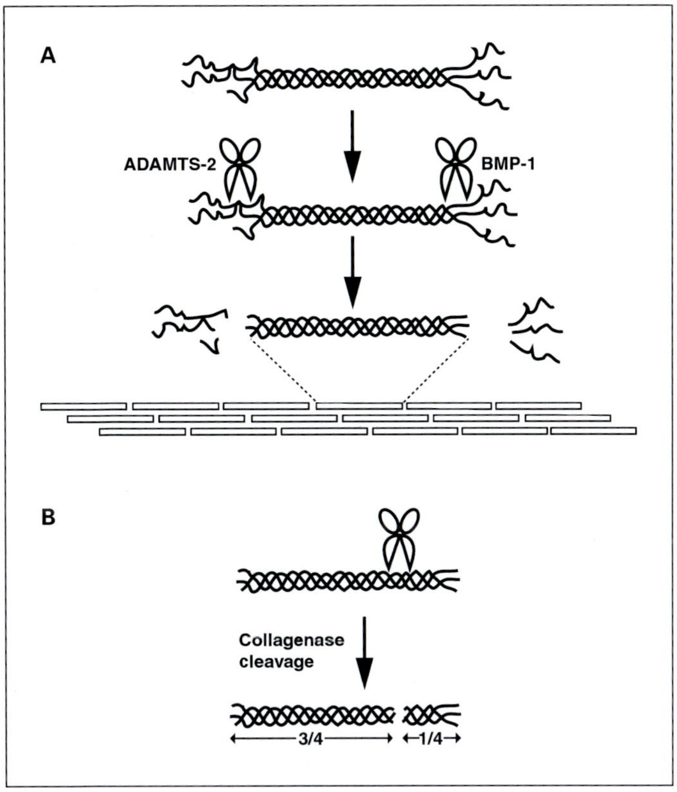

Fig. 2. Collagen maturation, fibril assembly and collagenase cleavage. **A** The collagen molecule is assembled from three individual polypeptide chains. In type I collagen, most molecules have the composition $\alpha 1(I)_2\alpha 2(I)_1$. The three chains make up the triple helical molecule – procollagen which is further processed on the N and C termini by ADAMTS-2 and bone morphogenetic protein 1 (BMP-1), respectively – to generate mature collagen. These monomers will self-assemble into fibrils of great tensile strength and resistance to enzymatic degradation. **B** Classical MMP collagenases cleave collagen into a 3/4 N-terminal residue sometimes referred to as TcA. The resulting 1/4 C-terminal residue is referred to as TcB. The actual cleavage site is situated between glycin 775 and isoleucin 776 in the $\alpha 1(I)$ and $\alpha 2(I)$ chains of type I collagen [Gross et al., 1980].

phogenetic protein 1, the helical collagen monomer assembles into fibrils with impressive mechanical strength. The cranium is a site particularly abundant in these macromolecules that make up the bulk of the organic substances in bone, cartilage, teeth and associated connective tissues. Hence, for proper growth to progress, timely dissolution of collagen is an obligate requirement in craniofacial development.

Collagen – A Tough Substrate for Matrix Metalloproteinases

The structural properties of collagen restrict the remodeling of this abundant matrix molecule to a selective group of enzymes. The resistance of collagen to chemical and enzymatic attack is unique, and until the 1960s, collagen was only known to be susceptible to bacterial enzymes. However, the notion that a proteolytic activity in higher organisms could cleave collagen was considered a prerequisite for proper development.

Fig. 3. The MMP family of zinc endopeptidases. The MMP family is divided into several subgroups based on primary structure homology. All enzymes in this group feature a signal peptide, which is subject to processing during the polypeptide maturation (S). This domain is followed by a prodomain (PRO), responsible for maintaining latency of the zymogen through the PRCG(V/N)PD cysteine residue which interacts with the catalytic site zinc ion. Some family members feature a furin or furin-like proprotein convertase-sensitive region (F), essential for activation of the zymogen. The catalytic region (CAT) of the proteins harbors the active site HEXXHXXGXXH signature sequence responsible for coordinating the zinc ion. Additionally, some family members feature a hemopexin-like domain (PEX), conferring substrate specificity on the enzyme. The gelatinases MMP-2 and MMP-9 are unique among MMPs by containing fibronectin type II repeat-like sequences in the catalytic domain (FN). Moreover, MMP-9 has a sequence homologous to collagen (CL). The nonsecreted forms of MMPs fall into three main groups, including the true type I transmembrane proteins containing a transmembrane domain (TM), and proteins tethered through a glycosylphosphatidylinositol anchor (GPI). MMP-23 is special in several ways, but foremost, it is a type II transmembrane protein and harbors a cysteine array (CA), in addition to an immunoglobulin-like sequence (Ig). Notably absent from this figure are MMP-18 and MMP-21 which are both frog proteins. PMN = Polymorphonuclear leukocyte; CA-MMP = cysteine array MMP.

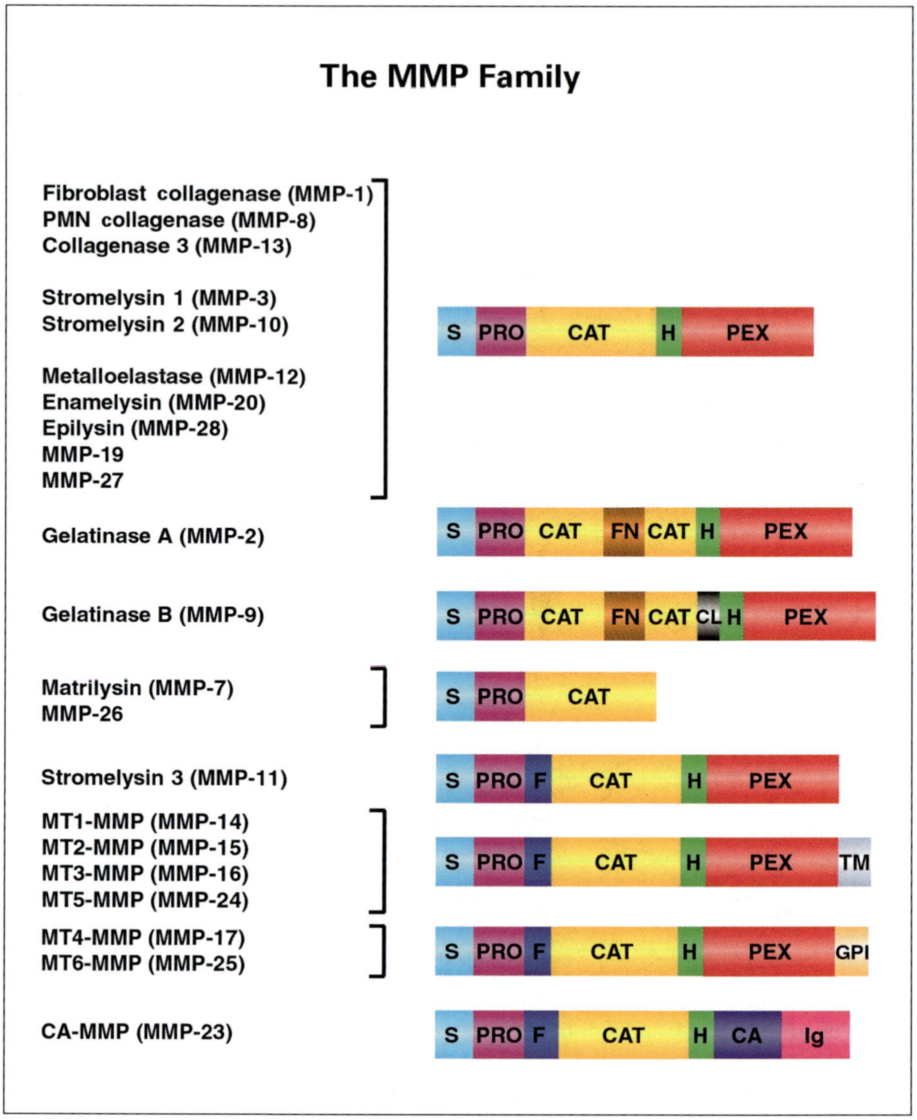

In the early 1960s, Jerome Gross and Charles Lapiere demonstrated that such an activity indeed existed in the tadpole tail, which is completely dissolved as the juvenile metamorphoses into a frog [Gross and Lapiere, 1962]. It was later demonstrated that the cleavage of the substrate occurred in a highly reproducible pattern generating a 3/4 and 1/4 part of the triple helical molecule following digestion (fig. 2B) [Gross and Nagai, 1965]. A similar activity was identified in human rheumatoid synovium by Evanson et al. [1967], and following years of additional discoveries, a group of structurally related enzymes was defined and now counts more than 25 in number [Evanson et al., 1967]. These proteinases are commonly known as matrix metalloproteinases (MMPs) and comprise soluble as well as membrane-bound zinc endopeptidases with a classical latency domain, a catalytic domain, and a hemopexin-like domain responsible for substrate specificity (fig. 3). The cell-associated MMPs are found as both true transmembrane forms and as glycosylphosphatidyl inositol-anchored proteins [Itoh et al., 1999; Kojima et al., 2000]. The proteolytic activity of MMPs is tightly regulated by the tissue inhibitors of metalloproteinases of which four are known [Brinckerhoff and Matrisian 2002; Egeblad and Werb, 2002; Murphy et al., 2003; Nagase and Brew, 2003].

While many of the MMPs display potent collagenolytic activity in vitro, the application of mouse genetics has demonstrated that the substrates are more diverse in nature and also suggests that very few of these enzymes are principally collagen-cleaving enzymes, but rather target other substrates in the extracellular matrix [Shipley et al., 1996; Itoh et al., 1997; Wilson et al., 1997; Masson et al., 1998; Mudgett et al., 1998; Vu et al., 1998; Holmbeck et al., 1999; Caterina et al., 2002; Balbin et al., 2003; Inada et al., 2004; Komori et al., 2004; Pendas et al., 2004; Stickens et al., 2004]. In addition, mouse genetics studies have demonstrated the important point that the tissue or organ context in which a matrix component exists determines which enzymes the given substrate is susceptible to. This is illustrated, for instance, in mice deficient for the soluble metalloproteinase MMP-13 [Inada et al., 2004; Stickens et al., 2004]. Ordinarily, this enzyme is thought of as a potent in vitro collagenase, yet deficiency for this MMP is associated with a specific delay of primary ossification and removal of mineralized cartilage matrix rather than a systemic remodeling of all collagenous substrates as implied by the in vitro substrate specificity.

Given these results, it appears that collagen as a substrate within the context of hard tissues is defined as much by its association with mineral (as in bone or calcified cartilage) as by the primary molecular structure [Holmbeck et al., 1999, 2003; Inada et al., 2004; Stickens et al., 2004; Kennedy et al., 2005].

Soft collagen or collagen not associated with mineral is cleaved in a membrane type 1 (MT1)-MMP-dependent manner, and the enzyme is an obligate requirement for collagen dissolution in the mouse [Holmbeck et al., 1999; Zhou et al., 2000]. This observation in itself is rather surprising given the huge body of literature documenting its role as an activator of the soluble MMP, MMP-2, or the 72-kDa type VI collagenase [Strongin et al., 1993; Sato et al., 1994]. It is beyond doubt that MT1-MMP can work in the activator capacity, but elegant work has recently demonstrated that deficiency for MT1-MMP in conjunction with deficiency for MMP-2 is perinatally lethal and distinct in nature from the phenotype of MT1-MMP alone or MMP-2 alone [Oh et al., 2004]. Consequently, the principal function of MT1-MMP is not solely that of MMP-2 activation, but it has a separate function tied to collagen dissolution. Indeed, cells deficient in MT1-MMP fail to degrade dense reconstituted fibrillar collagen in vitro, while cells sufficient for the protein harbor a protease activity capable of dissolving collagen [Holmbeck et al., 1999]. These results do not by themselves prove that MT1-MMP is the collagenase; however, following ablation, none of the proteins purported to be downstream targets of MT1-MMP in a proteolytic cascade (MMP-2, MMP-9 and MMP-13) replicate the collagen indigestion phenotype observed in MT1-MMP-deficient mice [Itoh et al., 1997; Vu et al., 1998; Inada et al., 2004; Stickens et al., 2004]. Moreover, cells otherwise unable to degrade collagen readily degrade it upon forced expression of MT1-MMP, while this property cannot be achieved by expressing either of the potential downstream targets of MT1-MMP, MMP-2 or MMP-13 in their activated form [Knauper et al., 1996; Cowell et al., 1998; Hotary et al., 2003].

MT1-MMP Deficiency and the Cranium

In the cranium, the need for collagen metabolism in the process of development and growth is vividly illustrated in particular by the loss of MT1-MMP following targeted disruption of the gene in the mouse [Holmbeck et al., 1999]. Moreover, the phenotype associated with MT1-MMP deficiency has revealed a separate and previously undescribed mode of tissue remodeling, which represents a paradigm for skeletal and connective tissue remodeling in its own right [Holmbeck et al., 2003]. MT1-MMP deficiency is manifested by a severe, progressive skeletal phenotype, which has its root in impaired growth and remodeling of the interfacial connective tissues associated with the skeleton [Holmbeck et al., 1999]. It is noteworthy that the tissues affected by deficiency of MT1-MMP are 'soft' in nature despite being in intimate contact with the hard, mineralized skeleton. The disease materializes as a severe cranial dysmorphism and diminished longitudinal bone growth (fig. 4) [Holmbeck et al., 1999].

The most surprising finding in the cranium is the presence of cartilage rudiments on the inner aspect of the cranial vault [Holmbeck et al., 1999]. Bone in this location was thought to ossify via intramembranous ossification and be devoid of any cartilage templates (fig. 5). However, a closer inspection does reveal that the cranial vault is the site of conspicuous embryonic cartilages visible in most of the ordinary alizarin red alcian blue stains [Kaufman, 1995; Chen et al., 1998]. The fate of this cartilage, documented by sectioning of skulls from mice of progressive ages, reveals a gradual dissolution and regression of the cartilage and a replacement with the overlying bone.

This MT1-MMP-dependent process leads to the complete removal of the cartilage around 10 days after birth where the overlying bone is now well developed [Holmbeck et al., 2003].

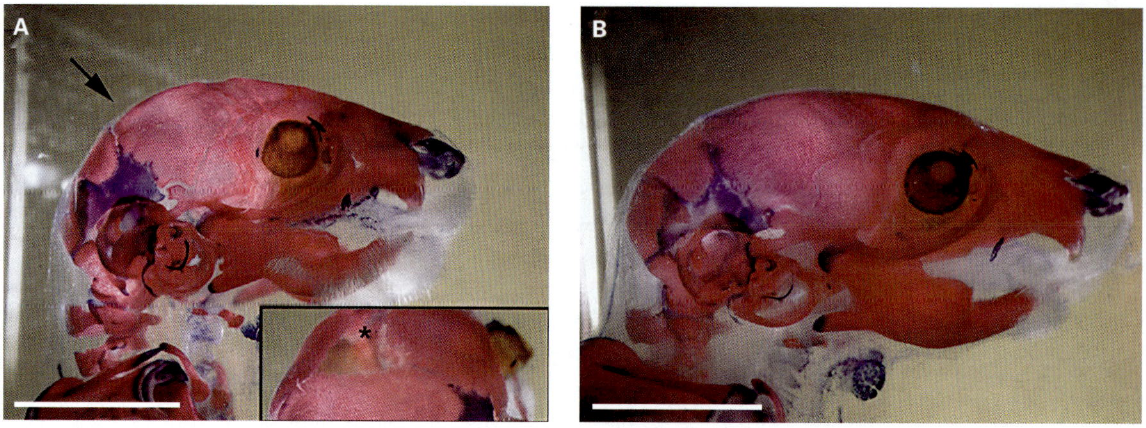

4

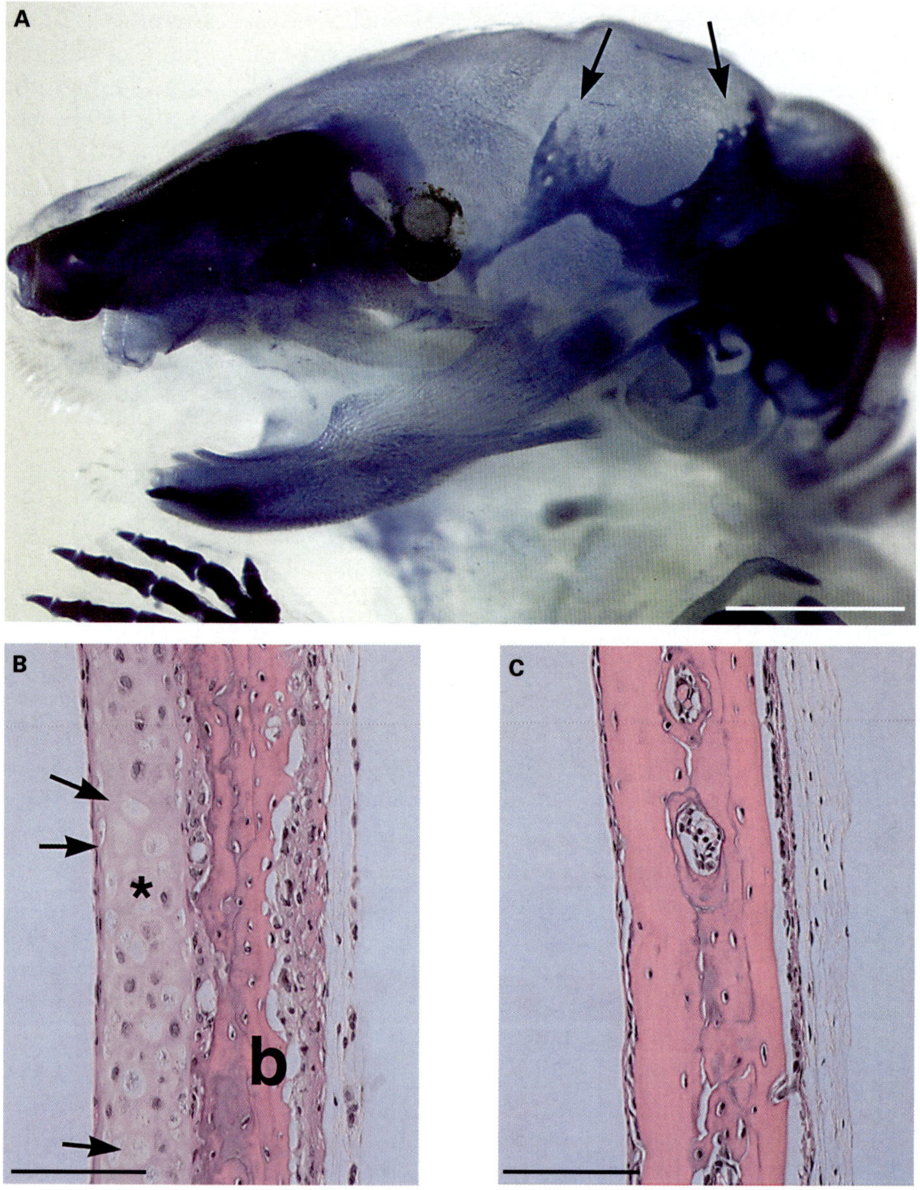

5

Fig. 4. Craniofacial dysmorphism in MT1-MMP-deficient mice. Eight-day-old mice stained with alizarin red for bone and alcian blue for cartilage. The dramatic difference in head shape is already evident at this stage. Note the domed shape of the cranial vault of the mutant mouse (**A**) compared with the more elongated and flat features of the wildtype littermate (**B**). The loss of MT1-MMP is associated with patent sutures (arrow) due to diminished bone formation and excessive osteoclastic resorption of the bone edges at the sutures (**A**, inset with asterisk). Scale bars = 0.5 cm.

Fig. 5. Cranial vault formation required removal of unmineralized cartilages. The formation of the calvarium or vault of the cranium requires the dissolution of cartilages developed in embryogenesis. **A** Alcian blue stain of a 17.5 post coitum mouse embryo demonstrates the extensive cartilages of the neurocranium (arrows). These are remodeled away during early postnatal life by an MT1-MMP-dependent mechanism of collagen dissolution. Scale bar = 100 μm. **B** In the MT1-MMP mutant mice at 33 days, this remodeling is disrupted and the mice retain a proteoglycan-depleted vestige of the cartilage lining the bone (b) (asterisk), with multiple empty lacunae of former chondrocytes (arrows). **C** The cranial bone of a wildtype littermate. Scale bars (**B**, **C**) = 25 μm.

Two Distinct Pathways for Cartilage Dissolution

Strikingly, the cellular and molecular basis for the removal of this cartilage is distinct from what can be observed during remodeling of calcified cartilage in endochondral ossification, which has been thoroughly dissected in both cellular and molecular aspects [Wagner and Karsenty, 2001; Karsenty and Wagner, 2002; Ortega et al., 2004]. In the process of endochondral ossification, a condensed mesenchyme develops successively to form a cartilage anlage, which in time undergoes maturation and ultimately shifts from synthesis of collagen type II, XI, IX and cartilage-enriched proteoglycans to the expression of type X collagen [Chan and Jacenko, 1998; Ortega et al., 2004]. The cartilage will subsequently undergo hypertrophy, a process in which most of the pericellular matrix around the chondrocytes is degraded and the remaining residue ultimately mineralizes and becomes a substratum for osteoclasts [Teitelbaum, 2000; Vaananen et al., 2000].

These multinucleated cells of the hemapoietic lineage are brought into the mineralized cartilage matrix by vessel in-growth, a crucial step in the subsequent resorption process, which is responsible for the removal of the calcified cartilage and the apoptotic demise of the chondrocytes [Gerber et al., 1999; Cancedda et al., 2000; Karsenty and Wagner, 2002].

Notably, the cartilage retains its proteoglycan content throughout this maturation process and readily stains with proteoglycan-specific stains such as alcian blue [Holmbeck et al., 2003]. The osteoclast resorption and the coordinated cell death leave behind a scaffold of chondrocyte-depleted cartilage cores on which bone-forming osteoblasts now deposit bone matrix. Elegant work has demonstrated that the vascular invasion in this process is dependent upon the release of vascular endothelial growth factor from the cartilage matrix by a process shown to rely on proteolysis [Gerber et al., 1999]. Vascular endothelial growth factor in turn guides blood vessels to the cartilage anlage and facilitates the marshalling of osteoclasts to the appropriate location [Gerber et al., 1999]. The hallmark of this ossification process is that bone is deposited within the calcified cartilage after the majority of the matrix has been degraded by osteoclasts to make way for the bone. This has earned the process the name endochondral ossification or bone formation, while it actually describes both the processes, by which calcified cartilage is removed and the subsequent deposition of the bone, which replaces the resorbed cartilage matrix.

Intramembranous ossification, in contrast to endochondral ossification, is considered to be a process independent of a preexisting cartilage [Cohen, 2000]. Instead, bone matrix is deposited directly into a soft connective tissue between osteogenic cells residing there.

However, closer analysis revealed that almost all bones of intramembranous origin are to some extent associated with cartilage anlagen, but the developing bone and the associated cartilages are physically separated, thus making the process distinct from endochondral ossification [Riminucci et al., 1998]. In the cranium, the most conspicuous cartilages of this type are located in the prospective cranial vault in late stages of embryogenesis and in early post-natal life (fig. 5) [Kaufman, 1995; Chen et al., 1998; Holmbeck et al., 1999, 2003]. Here, intramembranous bone, for instance the parietal bone, is in close association with the embryonic cartilage, called the parietal cartilage, but physically separated from this entity by a connective tissue [Chen et al., 1998]. Moreover, the cartilage displays cellular and molecular characteristics as it is remodeled, which are quite separate from those found in a cartilage undergoing resorption in the context of endochondral ossification [Holmbeck et al., 2003]. Initially, the parietal cartilage displays the same molecular expression profile with respect to collagen type II and proteoglycans as found in cartilages undergoing resorption in endochondral ossification. However, as the cartilage matures, the ensuing bone formation process is accompanied by a halt in the expression of type II collagen and the proteoglycan content of the cartilage is lost. Notably, collagen type X is not expressed in the cartilage nor does the cartilage undergo hypertrophy or mineralization, but remains a hyaline, unmineralized cartilage [Holmbeck et al., 2003]. At this stage, the chondrocytes in the parietal cartilage commence expression of MT1-MMP at levels that far exceed the expression level found in any other tissues expressing MT1-MMP. The expression of this metalloproteinase follows the loss of the proteoglycan from the cartilage matrix and facilitates the complete dissolution of the remaining collagenous scaffold surrounding the resident chondrocytes.

Simultaneous with the loss of matrix, the chondrocytes undergo programmed cell death, readily detectable by the presence of apoptotic bodies and transferase-mediated dUTP nick-end labeling-positive cells.

Notably, no osteoclasts are seen in this dissolution process nor is bone matrix deposited within this cartilage. Collectively, these steps constitute a non-endochondral cartilage dissolution mechanism, which is separate and distinct from endochondral ossification and necessary for formation of bone and other tissues in very particular sites (fig. 5) [Holmbeck et al., 2003].

In the absence of MT1-MMP, this matrix-remodeling program is disrupted. The cellular program leading to the cessation of type II collagen and the ensuing depletion of proteoglycan is unperturbed. However, the following step of dissolution of the collagen scaffold matrix is completely abrogated. This leads to the persistence of a tissue, which over time becomes increasingly depleted of cells. The significance of this process for the proper formation of the cranial vault is abundantly clear from the dysmorphism associated with the loss of MT1-MMP expression. The calvarium of MT1-MMP-deficient mice, in addition to the undissolved cartilage vestiges, also display a pronounced lack of bone deposition in the location occupied by the devitalized cartilage (fig. 5B). In some locations of the cranial vault, this in effect prevents the formation of the inner plate of the calvarium and the bone appears to have half the thickness of bone in wildtype mice. In addition, the cartilage vestige left in the cranium physically obstructs expansion of the cranium, thereby severely inhibiting growth [Holmbeck et al., 2003].

Non-Endochondral Cartilage Remodeling Is a General Paradigm

A close analysis of the mouse cranium reveals that the cartilage dissolution process responsible for the remodeling of the parietal cartilage is not confined to this one location, but also governs the remodeling of part of Meckel's cartilage. This is of particular significance in the context of tissue remodeling given the complex fate of Meckel's cartilage [Muhlhauser, 1986]. The anterior part of Meckel's cartilage ossifies endochondrally, while the middle part is remodeled and bone of intramenbranous origin is deposited in its place. The posterior part is remodeled into the sphenomandibular ligament and the malleus and the incus. Hence, the cartilage as such is remodeled into bone of two different types, endochondral and intramembranous, as well as into ligament. Analysis of the middle and posterior part of Meckel's cartilage reveals that the process responsible for remodeling of the cartilage directly into bone and ligament is that mediated in part by MT1-MMP. A closer histological survey of serial sections reveals that a molecular fingerprint identical to that described in the remodeling of the parietal cartilage can be found. The fact that cartilage is remodeled into ligament prompts the question of whether or not this process is general in nature. A survey of ligaments in other joints reveals that this is indeed the case. This remodeling process is also specifically localized to the interface between articular cartilage and ligament. Here, the cartilage remodeling mechanism suggests that MT1-MMP-dependent matrix dissolution is a general paradigm for direct remodeling of one tissue into another.

In other developmental contexts, this is routinely considered to be metamorphosis, and as such, the mechanism can be considered the mammalian version of metamorphosis equivalent to that of lower species. The fact that this mechanism has attracted little attention is due in part to the speed with which it normally occurs. The swift removal of the various unmineralized cartilages only becomes evident in the MT1-MMP-deficient mouse model. The mutant mouse provides a retrograde image of the cartilage dissolution mechanism by abrogating the most substantial part of it – namely the removal of the cartilaginous collagen scaffold. This in turn leaves behind conspicuous evidence of a physiologically essential mechanism in the form of vestiges of unremodeled matrix [Holmbeck et al., 1999, 2003].

The availability of MT1-MMP-deficient animals enables a distinction between two separate paradigms for dissolution of cartilage (fig. 6), both of which are crucial to the formation of bone and associated connective tissues. One is restricted to cartilage matrices, which undergo hypertrophy and mineralize, after which osteoclasts are recruited and carry out the actual matrix dissolution. This occurs in a low pH environment within the ruffled border of osteoclasts aided by a suite of acidic proteinases, among which some cathepsins are major facilitators of matrix dissolution [Garnero et al., 1998; Roodman, 1999; Teitelbaum, 2000; Vaananen et al., 2000]. The other mode of cartilage remodeling is restricted to cartilages that do not hypertrophy and mineralize, but rather maintain their hyaline nature throughout their entire existence. In this remodeling mechanism, resident chondrocytes rather than recruited osteoclasts initiate the dissolution of their surrounding matrix by expression of MT1-MMP in a neutral, pericellular environment. This in turn leads to elimination of both cells and the surrounding collagenous matrix, enabling the replacement of the cartilage with a definitive tissue of bone or ligament [Holmbeck et al., 2003].

Differentiation or Death

A noteworthy observation associated with the persistent cartilage vestiges in MT1-MMP-deficient mice is that not all cells die over time. The cartilage also harbors

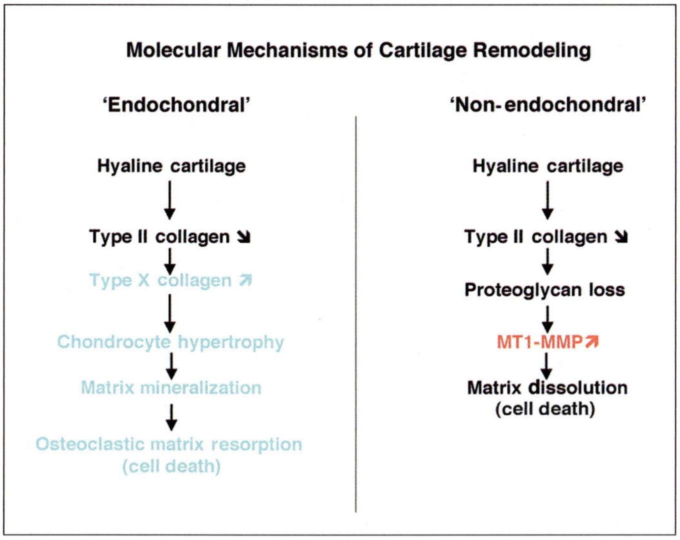

Fig. 6. Two schemes for cartilage remodeling. Cartilage is remodeled via two distinctly different mechanisms which both initiate with a hyaline cartilage. During endochondral ossification, the cartilage undergoes hypertrophy and mineralization in advance of osteoclast resorption, but retains its proteoglycan content throughout this process. In non-endochondral remodeling, the cartilage retains its hyaline nature, does not undergo mineralization, but loses its proteoglycan content in advance of dissolution via an MT1-MMP-mediated process. One mechanism requires the recruitment of non-resident cells (osteoclasts), whereas the other relies on resident chondrocytes to effectuate the matrix dissolution and commit suicide in the process.

some longlived cells which display mitotic figures and engage in DNA synthesis. When hybridized for cell markers of mesenchymal cell commitment, the cells display expression of type I collagen and, moreover, also express osteocalcin [Holmbeck et al., 2003]. These cells clearly reside deep within the cartilage remnant, in lacunae, and thus they have all the cytological characteristics of a chondrocyte proper. However, their expression pattern suggests that they are able to attain, at least in terms of their expression profile, the phenotype of mature bone cells. This suggests that cells in the embryonic unmineralized cartilages may retain the ability not only to commit to a chondrocytic phenotype and die as they engage in dissolution of their resident matrix. They may also have the capacity to differentiate and become bone cells and thus contribute to the generation of the tissue that is slated to replace the embryonic tissue where these cells originated. Therefore, these tissues may be repositories of mesenchymal progenitor cells, capable of undergoing differentiation from chondrocyte to bone cell. This suggestion is supported by the fact that the inner plate of the calvarium is missing in mice with cartilage vestiges – a condition which can be explained in part by the inability to recruit cells out of the dissolving tissues. The notion that this actually happens is substantiated by observations that chondrocytes in vascular canals are reported to survive matrix dissolution [Alvarez et al., 2005].

Problems in Soft Tissues Spell Doom for Hard Tissues

In the cranium, the interfaces of the bone plates, the sutures, are essential to the growth of the cranium and the head as a whole unit. The cranial sutures are the major sites in which the boundary of the individual subentities can undergo the physical enlargement required for the growth process [Yu et al., 2004]. The interaction with neighboring entities, as each individual bone grows separately but also in unison with its surroundings, requires a lot from the interfacing tissue. In essence, the suture has to provide an adaptive transitional zone between two hard mineralized plates, yet at the same time, it must possess a high degree of toughness and structural rigidity that affords the cranium and masticatory apparatus full function. To fulfill these requirements, the sutures are sites of intense matrix turnover and only cease this activity when growth is arrested in adulthood.

By definition, sutures are ligaments, as they facilitate articulation between two or more bone entities, and in line with ligaments in the rest of the mouse, sutures are remodeled as dictated by growth and aging of the tissue. To achieve functionality, sutures are highly collagenous structures with abundant fibers of collagen anchored in the bone and extending into the soft tissue between the bone plates of the skull. These characteristic Sharpey's fibers are found at all sites of ligament and tendon insertions into hard tissue, and molecular analysis reveals that the expression of MT1-MMP is abundant is such sites [Holmbeck et al., 2003]. In the absence of MT1-MMP, turnover of the suture tissue is significantly disrupted and the tissue displays marked signs of matrix accumulation, fibrosis and scarring. However, this dysfunction is not only restricted to the soft tissue of the suture itself. Because the suture, its maintenance and growth, is so intimately tied to bone growth, bone apposition at the bone edge is also arrested. This deficit in bone formation is in essence caused by a non-permissive extracellular matrix environment, which affects cell function. The bone-forming cells live in the collagenous environment of the periosteum, which is continuous with the suture and subject to the same fibrosis and scarring as the suture tissue. This in turn causes cells to be trapped in their own matrix and prevents migration to the bone surface where they ordinarily deposit bone matrix. The effect of the proteolytic deficiency is accumulative, such that bone formation gradually becomes affected, culminating in a condition where essentially no bone is formed [Holmbeck et al., 1999].

Because growth is the principal objective in the postnatal skull, the rescue mechanisms employed to counter conditions that impair growth are readily marshaled by the remodeling tissue. In the case of collagen indigestion, the rescue is unfortunately as adverse to growth as the growth inhibition itself. Matrix dissolution is shifted from the soft tissue which is unable to remodel due to MT1-MMP deficiency to a tissue that can still be remodeled, namely the bone, via osteoclast activity. Bone now becomes a target for aggressive osteoclast resorption, which severely depletes the existing bone matrix and induces an osteopenia that is compounded by the aforementioned lack of bone apposition due to osteoblast entrapment. The net effect is that growth of the bone is rapidly accompanied by an excessive osteclastic resorption at all interfaces in the skeleton where major soft tissue remodeling takes place as part of the growth process. The extent of bone resorption in MT1-MMP-deficient mice is vividly illustrated by the literal painting of cranial sutures with tartrate resistant acid phosphatase (TRAP)-positive cells, which in part explains the loss of bone in the cranial vault (fig. 7A).

MT1-MMP Deficiency Severely Affects Tooth Eruption

As in the cranial vault ligaments (sutures), other regions of the cranium are affected by the loss of the MT1-MMP-dependent collagenase activity. This is particularly evident in the periodontium, where collagen turnover is extraordinarily high. Consistent with this high state of metabolism, the consequences of MT1-MMP deficiency are grave in this tissue. Molar eruption and root formation are disturbed, and the molars never penetrate the gingiva despite resorption of the overlying bone. Instead, the molars present with stunted roots and remain covered by the oral mucosa as long as MT1-MMP-deficient mice live (fig. 8B). In addition, the rescue remodeling of hard tissue is also prominent in the alveolar bone where rampant resorption can be observed and bone is replaced by abundant fibrotic tissue, which is frequently associated with ectopic calcification.

Sharpey's fibers, which are especially abundant in the normal periodontal ligament, are absent and demonstrate that a high collagen turnover rate is required for the maintenance of these characteristic connective tissue structures that are required for anchorage of the teeth within the alveolar bone (fig. 8A).

The periodontal ligament of MT1-MMP-deficient mice offers another opportunity to observe the diversity of mechanisms that cells may employ when faced with adverse conditions, or when the load on remodeling pathways requires additional processing capacity. Mesenchymal cells, for the most part, turn over matrix in the pericellular environment, yet there is ample evidence for a phagocytic pathway of collagen metabolism which is thought to rout collagen fibrils to the phagosome and phagolysosomal compartment [Everts et al., 1996]. Indeed, cells in the periodontal ligament demonstrate coarse cross-banded fibrils in the intracellular vacuoles. In the absence of MT1-MMP, cells are noted for a significant increase in intracellular collagen uptake and accumulation in phagosomes, which can reach levels of 50-fold more than in wildtype mice [Beertsen et al., 2002]. This observation suggests that a defective pericellular processing pathway is compensated by routing of collagen into the phagocytic pathway. The phagolysosome is known to posses the most potent collagenolytic proteinase characterized in mammals to date – cathepsin K [Garnero et al., 1998]. Interestingly, this proteinase is abundant in osteoclasts, and loss of cathepsin K in humans causes pycnodysostosis – a condition leading to short stature and aberrant tooth eruption [Gelb et al., 1996]. Fibroblasts are known to employ a similar proteolytic strategy for intracellular collagen degradation, which complements the extracellular collagen degradation [Engelholm et al., 2003; Everts et al., 2003]. Even so, the load of matrix to be processed in the absence of MT1-MMP is so overwhelming that connective tissue cells are unable to properly degrade collagen by routing it into the cell. These observations suggest that fibroblasts or other non-osteclastic cells mainly rely on the extracellular digestion of collagen and mainly employ the phagocytic pathway when the load of matrix is so overwhelming that pericellular proteolysis is exhausted.

Lessons Learned from a Mouse

Collectively, the data obtained from analysis of MT1-MMP-dependent collagen degradation demonstrate how significant collagenase activity is for proper cranial morphogenesis and tooth eruption. While many aspects of

7

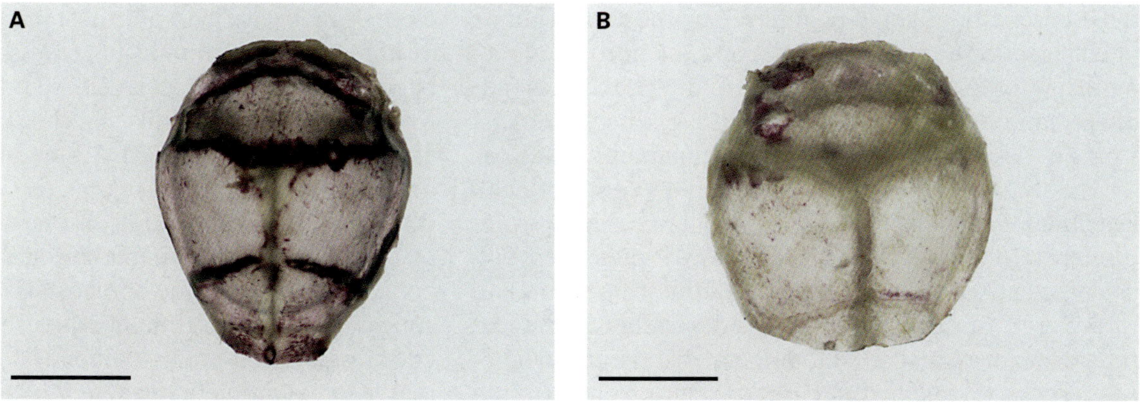

8

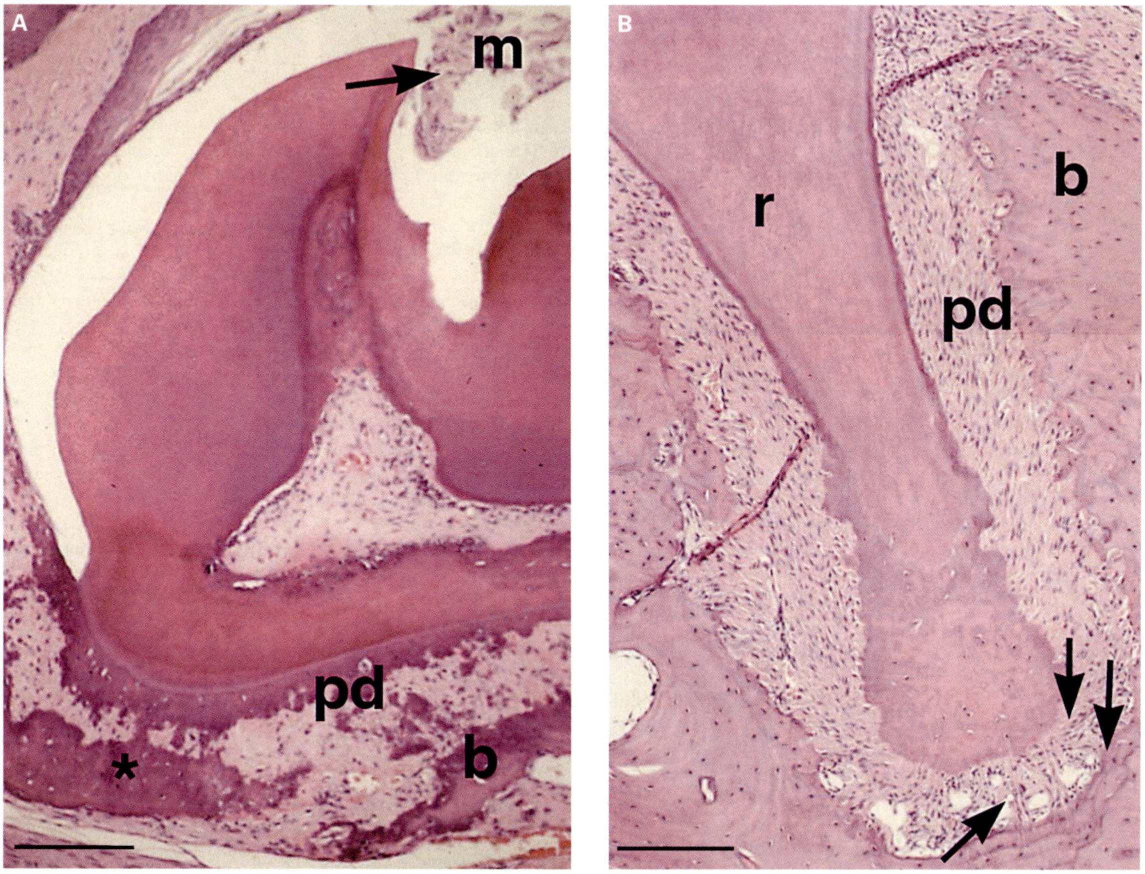

Fig. 7. MT1-MMP deficiency-induced osteoclasia. The loss of the ability to remodel soft connective tissue forces the organism to rescue the growth process in any way possible. The only recourse in the absence of soft tissue remodeling is to remodel the hard tissue, i.e. bone. This induces a wealth of osteoclasts at sites of remodeling such as cranial sutures. **A** The cranial sutures of a 67-day-old mutant mouse is 'painted' by TRAP-positive cells indicating rampant osteoclast activity. The effect of this is visible in the form of the fibrous membrane located where the sagittal suture should otherwise be. **B** Wildtype littermate displaying little or no TRAP activity in the calvarium. Scale bars = 0.5 cm.

Fig. 8. Tooth eruption and molar root development are collagenase dependent. Tooth eruption requires collagenase activity. **A** In the absence of MT1-MMP, the eruption of molars is disrupted due to a lack of collagen remodeling in the periodontal ligament (pd). Moreover, this deficiency inhibits root formation and prevents the upward movement of the tooth, which is covered by oral mucosa (m) (arrow). **B** The characteristic Sharpey's fibers in the wildtype mouse (arrows) which anchor the root (r) to the alveolar bone (b) are absent in the mutant mouse and replaced by a dense fibrotic tissue with conspicuous ectopic calcification (**A**, asterisk) and erosion of the neighboring alveolar bone. Scale bars = 25 μm.

these observations could be inferred by the sheer volume of collagen in the affected tissues and the need for its remodeling, one surprising and novel finding is the existence of a separate and distinct mode of cartilage dissolution that works in tissues that maintain an unmineralized state.

The second significant revelation in the context of collagen metabolism is that resorption of bone matrix is not directly affected by loss of the MT1-MMP-dependent collagenase activity. This demonstrates that resorption and turnover of mineralized matrix is dependent on a separate mechanism restricted to mineralized tissue – whether it is bone or calcified cartilage or dentin/cementum in teeth. Finally, and perhaps most important in the context of bone and cranial morphogenesis is the apparent link between the soft connective tissue of the skeleton, bone formation and homeostasis of the skeleton. The disease-associated loss of MT1-MMP-mediated collagen degradation highlights the fact that the skeleton, despite its diverse matrix components, is one entity comprised of a soft connective tissue that is contiguous with mineralized bone. Disruption of the homeostasis within a part of this continuous organ ultimately disturbs the balance of the entire organ and elicits compensatory rescue pathways that lead to complete organ destruction.

References

Alvarez, J., L. Costales, A. Lopez-Muniz, J.M. Lopez (2005) Chondrocytes are released as viable cells during cartilage resorption associated with the formation of intrachondral canals in the rat tibial epiphysis. Cell Tissue Res *320:* 501–507.

Balbin, M., A. Fueyo, A.M. Tester, A.M. Pendas, A.S. Pitiot, A. Astudillo, C.M. Overall, S.D. Shapiro, C. Lopez-Otin (2003) Loss of collagenase-2 confers increased skin tumor susceptibility to male mice. Nat Genet *35:* 252–257.

Beertsen, W., K. Holmbeck, A. Niehof, P. Bianco, K. Chrysovergis, H. Birkedal-Hansen, V. Everts (2002) On the role of MT1-MMP, a matrix metalloproteinase essential to collagen remodeling, in murine molar eruption and root growth. Eur J Oral Sci *110:* 445–451.

Brinckerhoff, C.E., L.M. Matrisian (2002) Matrix metalloproteinases: a tail of a frog that became a prince. Nat Rev Mol Cell Biol *3:* 207–214.

Cancedda, R., P. Castagnola, F.D. Cancedda, B. Dozin, R. Quarto (2000) Developmental control of chondrogenesis and osteogenesis. Int J Dev Biol *44:* 707–714.

Caterina, J.J., Z. Skobe, J. Shi, Y. Ding, J.P. Simmer, H. Birkedal-Hansen, J.D. Bartlett (2002) Enamelysin (matrix metalloproteinase 20)-deficient mice display an amelogenesis imperfecta phenotype. J Biol Chem *277:* 49598–49604.

Chan, D., O. Jacenko (1998) Phenotypic and biochemical consequences of collagen X mutations in mice and humans. Matrix Biol *17:* 169–184.

Chen, H., D. Ovchinnikov, C.L. Pressman, A. Aulehla, Y. Lun, R.L. Johnson (1998) Multiple calvarial defects in lmx1b mutant mice. Dev Genet *22:* 314–320.

Cohen, M.M., Jr. (2000) Merging the old skeletal biology with the new. 1. Intramembranous ossification, endochondral ossification, ectopic bone, secondary cartilage, and pathologic considerations. J Craniofac Genet Dev Biol *20:* 84–93.

Cowell, S., V. Knauper, M.L. Stewart, M.P. D'Ortho, H. Stanton, R.M. Hembry, C. Lopez-Otin, J.J. Reynolds, G. Murphy (1998) Induction of matrix metalloproteinase activation cascades based on membrane-type 1 matrix metalloproteinase: associated activation of gelatinase A, gelatinase B and collagenase 3. Biochem J *331:* 453–458.

Egeblad, M., Z. Werb (2002) New functions for the matrix metalloproteinases in cancer progression. Nat Rev Cancer *2:* 161–174.

Engelholm, L.H., K. List, S. Netzel-Arnett, E. Cukierman, D.J. Mitola, H. Aaronson, L. Kjoller, J.K. Larsen, K.M. Yamada, D.K. Strickland, K. Holmbeck, K. Dano, H. Birkedal-Hansen, N. Behrendt, T.H. Bugge (2003) uPARAP/Endo180 is essential for cellular uptake of collagen and promotes fibroblast collagen adhesion. J Cell Biol *160:* 1009–1015.

Evanson, J.M., J.J. Jeffrey, S.M. Krane (1967) Human collagenase: identification and characterization of an enzyme from rheumatoid synovium in culture. Science *158:* 499–502.

Everts, V., W.S. Hou, X. Rialland, W. Tigchelaar, P. Saftig, D. Bromme, B.D. Gelb, W. Beertsen (2003) Cathepsin K deficiency in pycnodysostosis results in accumulation of non-digested phagocytosed collagen in fibroblasts. Calcif Tissue Int *73:* 380–386.

Everts, V., E. van der Zee, L. Creemers, W. Beertsen (1996) Phagocytosis and intracellular digestion of collagen, its role in turnover and remodelling. Histochem J *28:* 229–245.

Garnero, P., O. Borel, I. Byrjalsen, M. Ferreras, F.H. Drake, M.S. McQueney, N.T. Foged, P.D. Delmas, J.M. Delaisse (1998) The collagenolytic activity of cathepsin K is unique among mammalian proteinases. J Biol Chem *273:* 32347–32352.

Gelb, B.D., G.P. Shi, H.A. Chapman, R.J. Desnick (1996) Pycnodysostosis, a lysosomal disease caused by cathepsin K deficiency. Science *273:* 1236–1238.

Gerber, H.P., T.H. Vu, A.M. Ryan, J. Kowalski, Z. Werb, N. Ferrara (1999) VEGF couples hypertrophic cartilage remodeling, ossification and angiogenesis during endochondral bone formation. Nat Med *5:* 623–628.

Gross, J., J.H. Highberger, B. Johnson-Wint, C. Biswas (1980) Mode of action and regulation of tissue collagenases; in Wolley, D.E., J.M. Evanson (eds): Collagenase in Normal and Pathological Connective Tissues. Manchester, Wiley and Sons, pp 11–35.

Gross, J., C.M. Lapiere (1962) Collagenolytic activity in amphibian tissues: a tissue culture assay. Proc Natl Acad Sci USA *48:* 1014–1022.

Gross, J., Y. Nagai (1965) Specific degradation of the collagen molecule by tadpole collagenolytic enzyme. Proc Natl Acad Sci USA *54:* 1197–1204.

Holmbeck, K., P. Bianco, J. Caterina, S. Yamada, M. Kromer, S.A. Kuznetsov, M. Mankani, P.G. Robey, A.R. Poole, I. Pidoux, J.M. Ward, H. Birkedal-Hansen (1999) MT1-MMP-deficient mice develop dwarfism, osteopenia, arthritis, and connective tissue disease due to inadequate collagen turnover. Cell *99:* 81–92.

Holmbeck, K., P. Bianco, K. Chrysovergis, S. Yamada, H. Birkedal-Hansen (2003) MT1-MMP-dependent, apoptotic remodeling of unmineralized cartilage: a critical process in skeletal growth. J Cell Biol *163:* 661–671.

Hotary, K.B., E.D. Allen, P.C. Brooks, N.S. Datta, M.W. Long, S.J. Weiss (2003) Membrane type I matrix metalloproteinase usurps tumor growth control imposed by the three-dimensional extracellular matrix. Cell *114:* 33–45.

Inada, M., Y. Wang, M.H. Byrne, M.U. Rahman, C. Miyaura, C. Lopez-Otin, S.M. Krane (2004) Critical roles for collagenase-3 (Mmp13) in development of growth plate cartilage and in endochondral ossification. Proc Natl Acad Sci USA *101:* 17192–17197.

Itoh, T., T. Ikeda, H. Gomi, S. Nakao, T. Suzuki, S. Itohara (1997) Unaltered secretion of beta-amyloid precursor protein in gelatinase A (matrix metalloproteinase 2)-deficient mice. J Biol Chem *272:* 22389–22392.

Itoh, Y., M. Kajita, H. Kinoh, H. Mori, A. Okada, M. Seiki (1999) Membrane type 4 matrix metalloproteinase (MT4-MMP, MMP-17) is a glycosylphosphatidylinositol-anchored proteinase. J Biol Chem *274:* 34260–34266.

Karsenty, G., E.F. Wagner (2002) Reaching a genetic and molecular understanding of skeletal development. Dev Cell *2:* 389–406.

Kaufman, M.H. (1995) The Atlas of Mouse Development, rev. ed. London, Academic Press.

Kennedy, A.M., M. Inada, S.M. Krane, P.T. Christie, B. Harding, C. Lopez-Otin, L.M. Sanchez, A.A. Pannett, A. Dearlove, C. Hartley, M.H. Byrne, A.A. Reed, M.A. Nesbit, M.P. Whyte, R.V. Thakker (2005) MMP13 mutation causes spondyloepimetaphyseal dysplasia, Missouri type (SEMD(MO)). J Clin Invest *115:* 2832–2842.

Knauper, V., H. Will, C. Lopez-Otin, B. Smith, S.J. Atkinson, H. Stanton, R.M. Hembry, G. Murphy (1996) Cellular mechanisms for human procollagenase-3 (MMP-13) activation. Evidence that MT1-MMP (MMP-14) and gelatinase a (MMP-2) are able to generate active enzyme. J Biol Chem *271:* 17124–17131.

Kojima, S., Y. Itoh, S. Matsumoto, Y. Masuho, M. Seiki (2000) Membrane-type 6 matrix metalloproteinase (MT6-MMP, MMP-25) is the second glycosylphosphatidyl inositol (GPI)-anchored MMP. FEBS Lett *480:* 142–146.

Komori, K., T. Nonaka, A. Okada, H. Kinoh, H. Hayashita-Kinoh, N. Yoshida, I. Yana, M. Seiki (2004) Absence of mechanical allodynia and Abeta-fiber sprouting after sciatic nerve injury in mice lacking membrane-type 5 matrix metalloproteinase. FEBS Lett *557:* 125–128.

Masson, R., O. Lefebvre, A. Noel, M.E. Fahime, M.P. Chenard, C. Wendling, F. Kebers, M. LeMeur, A. Dierich, J.M. Foidart, P. Basset, M.C. Rio (1998) In vivo evidence that the stromelysin-3 metalloproteinase contributes in a paracrine manner to epithelial cell malignancy. J Cell Biol *140:* 1535–1541.

Mudgett, J.S., N.I. Hutchinson, N.A. Chartrain, A.J. Forsyth, J. McDonnell, I.I. Singer, E.K. Bayne, J. Flanagan, D. Kawka, C.F. Shen, K. Stevens, H. Chen, M. Trumbauer, D.M. Visco (1998) Susceptibility of stromelysin 1-deficient mice to collagen-induced arthritis and cartilage destruction. Arthritis Rheum *41:* 110–121.

Muhlhauser, J. (1986) Resorption of the unmineralized proximal part of Meckel's cartilage in the rat. A light and electron microscopic study. J Submicrosc Cytol *18:* 717–724.

Murphy, G., V. Knauper, M.H. Lee, A. Amour, J.R. Worley, M. Hutton, S. Atkinson, M. Rapti, R. Williamson (2003) Role of TIMPs (tissue inhibitors of metalloproteinases) in pericellular proteolysis: the specificity is in the detail. Biochem Soc Symp *70:* 65–80.

Nagase, H., K. Brew (2003) Designing TIMP (tissue inhibitor of metalloproteinases) variants that are selective metalloproteinase inhibitors. Biochem Soc Symp *70:* 201–212.

Oh, J., R. Takahashi, E. Adachi, S. Kondo, S. Kuratomi, A. Noma, D.B. Alexander, H. Motoda, A. Okada, M. Seiki, T. Itoh, S. Itohara, C. Takahashi, M. Noda (2004) Mutations in two matrix metalloproteinase genes, MMP-2 and MT1-MMP, are synthetic lethal in mice. Oncogene *23:* 5041–5048.

Ortega, N., D.J. Behonick, Z. Werb (2004) Matrix remodeling during endochondral ossification. Trends Cell Biol *14:* 86–93.

Pendas, A.M., A.R. Folgueras, E. Llano, J. Caterina, F. Frerard, F. Rodriguez, A. Astudillo, A. Noel, H. Birkedal-Hansen, C. Lopez-Otin (2004) Diet-induced obesity and reduced skin cancer susceptibility in matrix metalloproteinase 19-deficient mice. Mol Cell Biol *24:* 5304–5313.

Riminucci, M., J.N. Bradbeer, A. Corsi, C. Gentili, F. Descalzi, R. Cancedda, P. Bianco (1998) Vis-a-vis cells and the priming of bone formation. J Bone Miner Res *13:* 1852–1861.

Roodman, G.D. (1999) Cell biology of the osteoclast. Exp Hematol *27:* 1229–1241.

Sato, H., T. Takino, Y. Okada, J. Cao, A. Shinagawa, E. Yamamoto, M. Seiki (1994) A matrix metalloproteinase expressed on the surface of invasive tumour cells. Nature *370:* 61–65.

Shipley, J.M., R.L. Wesselschmidt, D.K. Kobayashi, T.J. Ley, S.D. Shapiro (1996) Metalloelastase is required for macrophage-mediated proteolysis and matrix invasion in mice. Proc Natl Acad Sci USA *93:* 3942–3946.

Stickens, D., D.J. Behonick, N. Ortega, B. Heyer, B. Hartenstein, Y. Yu, A.J. Fosang, M. Schorpp-Kistner, P. Angel, Z. Werb (2004) Altered endochondral bone development in matrix metalloproteinase 13-deficient mice. Development *131:* 5883–5895.

Strongin, A.Y., B.L. Marmer, G.A. Grant, G.I. Goldberg (1993) Plasma membrane-dependent activation of the 72-kDa type IV collagenase is prevented by complex formation with TIMP-2. J Biol Chem *268:* 14033–14039.

Teitelbaum, S.L. (2000) Bone resorption by osteoclasts. Science *289:* 1504–1508.

Vaananen, H.K., H. Zhao, M. Mulari, J.M. Halleen (2000) The cell biology of osteoclast function. J Cell Sci *113:* 377–381.

Vu, T.H., J.M. Shipley, G. Bergers, J.E. Berger, J.A. Helms, D. Hanahan, S.D. Shapiro, R.M. Senior, Z. Werb (1998) MMP-9/gelatinase B is a key regulator of growth plate angiogenesis and apoptosis of hypertrophic chondrocytes. Cell *93:* 411–422.

Wagner, E.F., G. Karsenty (2001) Genetic control of skeletal development. Curr Opin Genet Dev *11:* 527–532.

Wilson, C.L., K.J. Heppner, P.A. Labosky, B.L. Hogan, L.M. Matrisian (1997) Intestinal tumorigenesis is suppressed in mice lacking the metalloproteinase matrilysin. Proc Natl Acad Sci USA *94:* 1402–1407.

Yu, J.C., J.L. Borke, G. Zhang (2004) Brief synopsis of cranial sutures: optimization by adaptation. Semin Pediatr Neurol *11:* 249–255.

Zhou, Z., S.S. Apte, R. Soininen, R. Cao, G.Y. Baaklini, R.W. Rauser, J. Wang, Y. Cao, K. Tryggvason (2000) Impaired endochondral ossification and angiogenesis in mice deficient in membrane-type matrix metalloproteinase I. Proc Natl Acad Sci USA *97:* 4052–4057.

Cells Tissues Organs

Cells Tissues Organs 2005;181:166–175
DOI: 10.1159/000091378

Role of Matrix Gla Protein in Parathyroid Hormone Inhibition of Osteoblast Mineralization

Rajaram Gopalakrishnan[a] Supaporn Suttamanatwong[a] Ann E. Carlson[a] Renny T. Franceschi[b]

[a]Department of Diagnostic and Biological Sciences, University of Minnesota School of Dentistry, Minneapolis, Minn., and [b]Department of Periodontics and Oral Medicine, University of Michigan School of Dentistry, Ann Arbor, Mich., USA

Key Words

Parathyroid hormone · Matrix Gla protein · Osteoblast · Mineralization · Osteopontin · Vascular calcification

Abstract

Parathyroid hormone (PTH) exerts biphasic effects on bone, dependent on the frequency and dose of administration. The catabolic actions of PTH on bone have been associated with continuous treatment, an increase in osteoblast-mediated resorption of bone via osteoclast activation, and inhibition of osteoblast activity and mineralization. Downregulation of differentiation markers and inhibition of mineralization by PTH have been reported in primary calvarial explants and osteoblast cell lines. Using MC3T3-E1 osteoblast-like cells, we have shown that matrix Gla protein (MGP) can be induced by PTH, and that this induction may explain the PTH-mediated inhibition of osteoblast biomineralization. MGP is a known inhibitor of mineralization, and mice deficient in *Mgp* show severe vascular calcification and premature bone mineralization. This review discusses the role of MGP in mineralization, comparing bone and vascular mineralization. In addition to MGP, the regulation and possible role of osteopontin, another known regulator of osteoblast mineralization, in PTH-mediated regulation of bone and vascular mineralization is discussed.

Parathyroid hormone (PTH), an 84-amino-acid circulating hormone secreted by the parathyroid gland, maintains extracellular calcium levels primarily by targeting bone and kidney [Hock et al., 2002]. In the kidney, PTH functions by increasing reabsorption, and reducing excretion, of calcium in the distal convoluted tubule [Bringhurst and Strewler, 2002]. The calcium homeostatic functions of PTH in bone are catabolic, leading to bone resorption mediated by activating osteoclasts, and thereby releasing calcium from bone [Bringhurst and Strewler, 2002]. The effect of PTH on osteoclasts is indirect and

Abbreviations used in this paper

AA	ascorbic acid
BSP	bone sialoprotein
cAMP	cyclic adenosine monophosphate
ECM	extracellular matrix
FGF2	fibroblast growth factor 2
Gla	γ-carboxyglutamic acid
MGP	matrix Gla protein
OCN	osteocalcin
OPG	osteoprotegerin
OPN	osteopontin
PTH	parathyroid hormone
RANK	receptor activator of nuclear factor-κB
RANKL	receptor activator of nuclear factor-κB ligand
RT-PCR	reverse transcription polymerase chain reaction

KARGER

Fax +41 61 306 12 34
E-Mail karger@karger.ch
www.karger.com

Accessible online at:
www.karger.com/cto

Rajaram Gopalakrishnan, BDS, PhD
Department of Diagnostic and Biological Sciences
University of Minnesota School of Dentistry, 16-108B Moos Tower
515 Delaware St SE, Minneapolis, MN 55455 (USA)
Tel. +1 612 624 0918, Fax +1 612 626 3076, E-Mail gopal007@umn.edu

occurs through the interaction of the receptor activator of nuclear factor-κB ligand (RANKL) on osteoblasts and its receptor RANK on osteoclast precursor cells. This leads to recruitment of osteoclast precursor cells, followed by differentiation and activation [Lee and Loenzo, 1999]. The interaction between RANK and RANKL is inhibited by a decoy receptor, osteoprotegerin (OPG), and the ratio of RANKL:OPG determines the level of osteoclast activation and differentiation [Lacey et al., 1998; Yasuda et al., 1998]. Recent studies have shown that PTH can alter the RANKL:OPG ratio, thereby regulating bone resorption [Ma et al., 2001]. In addition to its effect on osteoclasts, PTH also acts catabolically on bone by inhibiting osteoblast activity and mineralization [Bellows et al., 1990; Koh et al., 1999; Gopalakrishnan et al., 2001]. These effects of PTH on bone can be simulated by a continuous infusion of PTH. Interestingly, PTH also shows an anabolic effect on bone, observed as an increase in bone formation when PTH is intermittently administered [Tam et al., 1982; Hock and Gera, 1992; Burr et al., 2001; Qin et al., 2004]. This anabolic feature of PTH has generated an enormous recent interest in the treatment of osteoporosis [Kurland et al., 2000; Neer et al., 2001; Black et al., 2003; Brixen et al., 2004]. Forteo® (teriparatide), a synthetic form of PTH, is the only agent approved by the Food and Drug Association that stimulates bone formation. Several reports have been published, investigating the molecular mechanisms that mediate both catabolic and anabolic actions of PTH, although the exact mechanisms remain unclear [Hock et al., 2002; Qin et al., 2004]. Here, we discuss recent developments on the catabolic effects of PTH on bone, focusing on the effect on osteoblast mineralization. We also draw comparisons between the effects of PTH on bone and vascular calcification.

PTH Inhibition of Osteoblast Mineralization

Biomineralization is a complex process, involving either the formation of matrix vesicles (nucleation sites for mineral formation) followed by secondary crystal growth on collagen, or direct nucleation and mineral growth within gap zones of collagen fibrils. Recent genetic studies suggest that mineralization inhibitors such as matrix Gla protein (MGP), rather than mineralization nucleators, play an active role in the regulation of biomineralization [Schinke et al., 1999]. Therefore, knowledge of factors that modulate such inhibitors is critical for understanding the mechanisms involved in biomineralization.

A major hurdle in understanding the mechanisms for the anabolic effect of PTH on bone is the apparent contradiction between the in vivo and in vitro responses to PTH. The catabolic action of PTH on bone has been associated with continuous treatment, an increase in osteoblast-mediated resorption of bone via activation of osteoclasts, and inhibition of osteoblast activity and mineralization [Tam et al., 1982; Bellows et al., 1990; Murrils et al., 1990; Lee and Loenzo, 1999; Schiller et al., 1999; Gopalakrishnan et al., 2001]. On the other hand, the anabolic effect has been associated with intermittent PTH treatment, amino-terminal PTH peptide, cyclic adenosine monophosphate (cAMP) activation, inhibition of osteoblast apoptosis, activation of Runx2, and upregulation of c-fos and insulin-like growth factor 1 [Tam et al., 1982; Canalis et al., 1989; McCarthy et al., 1989; Rixon et al., 1994; Armamento-Villareal et al., 1997; Jilka et al., 1999; Fujita et al., 2001; Demiralp et al., 2002; Krishnan et al., 2003]. Several in vitro models have shown the inhibitory effect of PTH on osteoblast differentiation and mineralization [Bellows et al., 1990; Koh et al., 1999; Schiller et al., 1999; Gopalakrishnan et al., 2001]. Schiller et al. [1999] reported an inhibitory effect on MC3T3-E1 cell mineralization, when PTH was continuously administered at an early stage of maturation (i.e. cells treated continuously between days 5 and 30, days 10 and 30, and days 15 and 30). The authors suggested that this effect was due to either a prevention of, or a delay in, the maturation of these cells. On the other hand, cells exposed to 10 nm PTH between days 20 and 25 in a 30-day culture showed an increase in mineralization. This anabolic process is not well understood and Schiller et al. [1999] noted that this effect coincided with a time at which the cAMP response to PTH would be elevated, due to elevated expression of the PTH1 receptor.

Other investigators have also observed similar inhibition of mineralization. Bellows et al. [1990] reported a dose-dependent suppression of osteoblast differentiation following PTH treatment (1 p*M* to 1 n*M*), and concluded that such suppression occurred at late stages, preventing preosteoblasts from differentiating into mature osteoblasts. Koh et al. [1999], using PTH fragments with differing cAMP-stimulating activity, showed varying effects on osteoblast differentiation and mineralization in MC3T3-E1 cells and primary calvarial osteoblasts. The authors concluded that PTH fragments that increased cAMP activity downregulated PTH1 receptor mRNA levels, which related to inhibition of osteoblast differentiation and mineralization. The inhibitory effects on osteoblast differentiation and mineralization were also mimicked by agents that altered cAMP activity, without binding to the PTH1 receptor. Wang et al. [2000] reported that PTH(1–34) suppressed mineralization in UMR 106-01 cells by activating the protein kinase A pathway. Ma et al. [2001] also noted a downregulation of osteoblast-specific markers in distal femur metaphysis of parathyroidectomized rats that had been infused with 20 μg/100 g of human PTH(1–38) for 6 h using an Azmet pump. The authors reported a 2.3-fold inhibition of Cbfa1/Runx2, a 3-fold inhibition of osteocalcin (OCN), a 2.8-fold inhibition of bone sialoprotein (BSP), and a 5-fold inhibition of type I collagen.

The use of PTH in the treatment of osteoporosis is dependent on the anabolic action of the hormone, but the exact mechanism explaining this action is not known. Recently, several investigators showed that the new bone formed following anabolic PTH treatment has lower mineral density compared with placebo groups [Misof et al., 2003; Paschalis et al., 2005]. Misof et al. [2003], using quantitative backscattered electron imaging, evaluated bone mineral densities of 26 iliac crest biopsies from osteoporosis patients before and after PTH treatment. The authors showed that the new bone formed had a lower mineral content [Misof et al., 2003]. Paschalis et al. [2005] also reported a decrease in bone mineral crystallinity and matrix mineralization in patients treated with human PTH(1–34), when compared with a placebo group. The mechanism for this effect is not clear, and a greater understanding of the mechanism will be critical for the development of an optimal therapeutic regimen using PTH.

MGP Is a Key Regulator of PTH-Mediated Inhibition of Osteoblast Mineralization

We recently reported an inhibition of mineralization in MC3T3-E1 cells following a single dose of 10^{-7} *M* PTH (fig. 1a, b) [Gopalakrishnan et al., 2001]. Using a ^{45}Ca uptake assay, we noted that PTH significantly inhibited mineralization by approximately 30% ($p < 0.05$), as early as 3 h after PTH treatment, with the largest effective reduction of approximately 50% after 6 h ($p < 0.01$) (fig. 1b). Continued inhibition was observed up to 48 h after PTH treatment. The surprising aspect of our study was that inhibition of osteoblast mineralization was observed when the cells were treated with only a single dose of PTH. Further, the osteoblasts were already fully differentiated and ready to mineralize, because of treatment with ascorbic acid (AA) for 8 days prior to treatment with a single dose of PTH (10^{-7} *M*). This prompted an investigation of the expression of key extracellular matrix (ECM) protein mRNAs known to regulate osteoblast mineralization. Of the four ECM protein mRNAs investigated, OCN, BSP, osteopontin (OPN) and MGP, only changes in MGP mRNA levels coincided with the observed time course of inhibition by PTH. We noted a peak induction of approximately 6.5-fold at 6 h following PTH treatment, which remained elevated for up to 24 h and dropped to basal levels after 48 h. Of the other bone ECM proteins, OPN mRNA levels were elevated, but were induced with a slower time course, with peak induction (approximately 4-fold) seen at 12 h after PTH addition, i.e. after the major PTH-dependent drop in mineralizing activity. On the other hand, OCN and BSP mRNA were significantly reduced after 12 h of PTH treatment. None of the changes in OPN, BSP and OCN correlated well with changes in mineralizing activity following PTH treatment, but our results do not completely exclude the participation of such ECM proteins in the PTH response.

Similar results for PTH-mediated induction of MGP mRNA expression were also noted using real-time reverse transcription polymerase chain reaction (RT-PCR) (fig. 2a). MGP mRNA expression increased, beginning at 3 h (approximately 3.5-fold compared with vehicle-treated control) of PTH treatment, with peak induction at 6 h (approximately 10-fold compared with vehicle-treated control), and remained induced at 24 h (approximately 3.3-fold compared with vehicle-treated control), before dropping to basal levels by 48 h. We also noted PTH induction of MGP mRNA expression in undifferentiated and differentiating osteoblasts (fig. 2b, c). For experiments investigating MGP expression in undifferentiated osteoblasts, MC3T3-E1 cells were plated at 50,000 cells/mm^2 and treated with 10^{-7} *M* PTH after 24 h, with total RNA isolated after 6, 12 and 24 h. MGP mRNA expression was induced at all three time points studied compared with vehicle-treated controls (1.87-fold at 6 h, 2.73-fold at 12 h, and 2.76-fold at 24 h), although to a lesser extent than after differentiation (fig 2b). For assays investigating MGP expression during osteoblast differentiation, cells were untreated or treated with AA alone, PTH alone, or both AA and PTH every other day, and cells were harvested for total RNA on days 4 and 8. MGP mRNA expression was induced with PTH treatment alone compared with untreated controls on both day 4 (1.5-fold) and day 8 (1.9-fold) (fig. 2c). MGP mRNA expression was also induced in differentiating osteoblasts with PTH treatment (1.9-fold on day 4, and 6-fold on

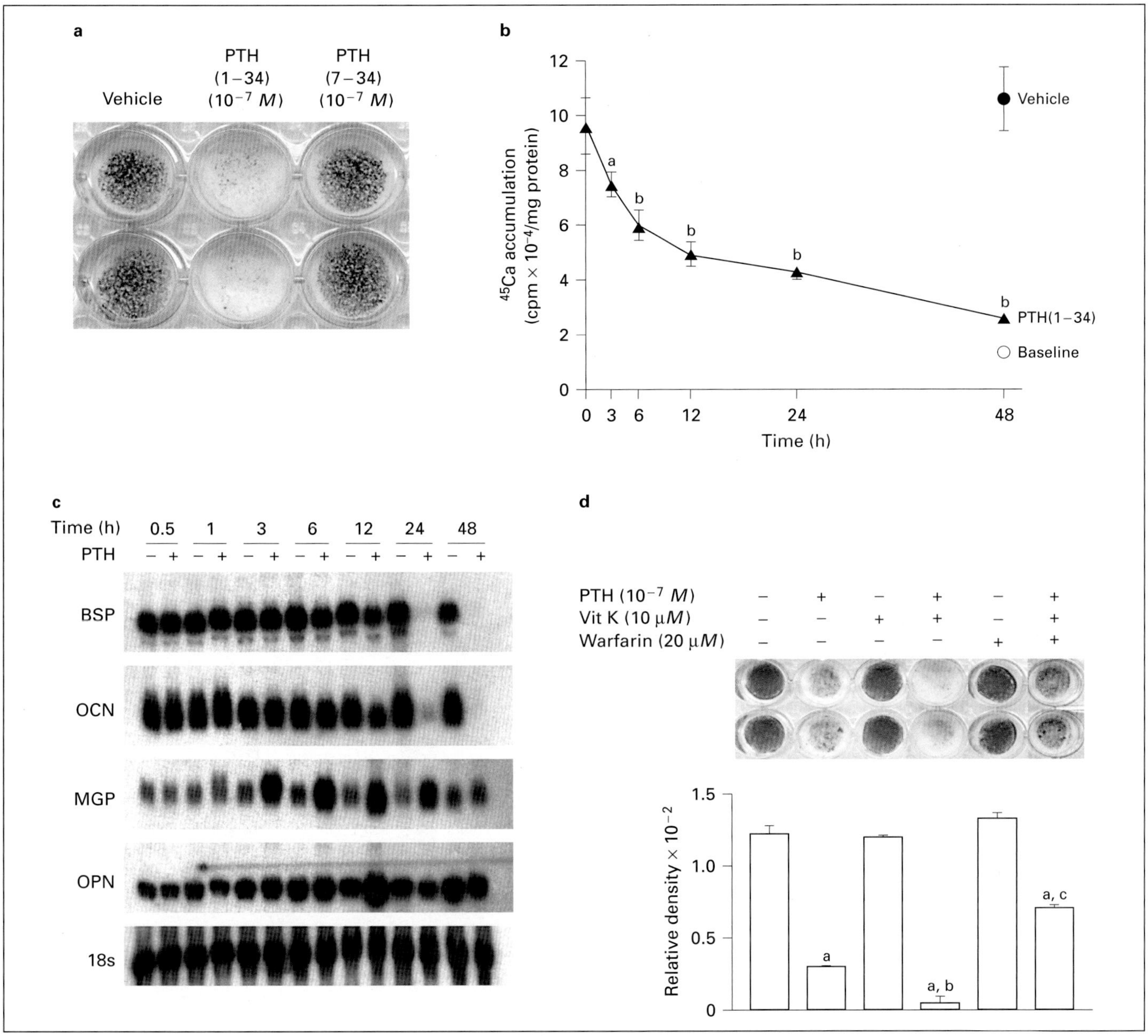

Fig. 1. Role of MGP in PTH-mediated inhibition of MC3T3-E1 osteoblast mineralization. **a** MC3T3-E1 cells were grown for 8 days in the presence of AA. Cells were treated with vehicle, PTH(1–34) and PTH(7–34), as well as mineralization induced after 48 h by addition of medium containing a total of 4.0 m*M* inorganic phosphate. Cells were stained for mineralization by von Kossa staining. **b** Time course for ^{45}Ca uptake following PTH(1–34) treatment. MC3T3-E1 cells were grown in AA for 6–8 days, followed by treatment with vehicle for 48h (●) or 10^{-7} *M* PTH(1–34) for the times indicated (▲). Initial mineralization was measured by a 3-hour incubation in medium containing 4 m*M* inorganic phosphate and ^{45}Ca. Basal ^{45}Ca accumulation in the absence of added inorganic phosphate (○). All values are mean ± SEM for triplicate samples. ^{a} $p<0.05$; ^{b} $p<0.01$ (significantly different from vehicle control). **c** Northern blot analysis of bone ECM protein mRNAs in MC3T3-E1 cells after PTH(1–34) treatment. **d** Role of γ-carboxylation in PTH-mediated inhibition of mineralization. MC3T3-E1 cells were grown under differentiating conditions for 6 days, at which time cells were treated as indicated. In the case of warfarin-treated cultures, pretreatment began on day 4 (i.e. 2 days before PTH or vitamin K treatment). On day 8, all cultures were allowed to mineralize by incubation with inorganic phosphate (final concentration, 4 m*M*) for 24 h. Mineralization was detected by von Kossa staining, and densitometric measurements (mean ± SEM) of von Kossa-stained cultures were performed using NIH image software. ^{a} $p < 0.001$, significantly different from the untreated control group; ^{b} $p < 0.005$, significantly different from the PTH-treated group; ^{c} $p < 0.001$, significantly different from PTH + vitamin K group. From Gopalakrishnan et al. [2001] with permission, Copyright 2001, The Endocrine Society.

Fig. 2. Quantitative real-time RT-PCR analysis of MGP expression in MC3T3-E1 osteoblasts. For all experiments, total RNA was isolated from cells using TRIzol reagent according to the manufacturer's directions (Invitrogen Life Technologies, Carlsbad, Calif., USA) and quantitated by UV spectroscopy. Reverse transcription was performed using 10 ng of denatured RNA and 100 pmol of random hexamers (Invitrogen Life Technologies) in a total volume of 20 μl containing 50 U Super Script reverse transcriptase (Invitrogen Life Technologies). Quantitative PCR analysis was performed using MX 3000P™ Real Time PCR System (Stratagene, La Jolla, Calif., USA) using 1 μl of the cDNA (equivalent to 0.5 ng RNA) combined with 1 × Brilliant SYBR Green Master Mix (Stratagene). MGP primer sequences were used as previously published [Newman et al., 2001]. The mRNA levels were normalized using mouse glyceraldehyde-3-phosphate dehydrogenase as housekeeping gene and compared with mRNA levels in mouse total RNA (Stratagene). **a** Representative experiment showing MGP mRNA induction by PTH after osteoblast differentiation. MC3T3-E1 cells were allowed to differentiate for 8 days in AA after which they were treated with vehicle or 10^{-7} *M* PTH(1–34). Total RNA was isolated at 1, 3, 6, 12 and 24 h after treatment. MGP mRNA expression was determined by real-time RT-PCR and presented as fold induction in the PTH-treated group over time-matched vehicle controls. **b** Representative experiment showing MGP mRNA induction by PTH in undifferentiated osteoblasts. MC3T3-E1 cells were treated with vehicle or 10^{-7} *M* PTH(1–34) 24 h after plating and total RNA isolated after 6, 12 and 24 h of treatment. MGP mRNA expression was determined by real-time RT-PCR analysis and expressed as fold induction in the PTH-treated samples over time-matched vehicle controls. **c** Representative experiment showing MGP mRNA expression during osteoblast differentiation. Osteoblast cells were treated with vehicle or PTH(1–34) in the presence or absence of AA. Media were changed every other day. Total RNA was isolated at 4 and 8 days, and real-time RT-PCR was performed to measure MGP mRNA expression. MGP mRNA expression is presented as percentage, with day 4 and day 8 controls (no AA, no PTH) considered as 100%.

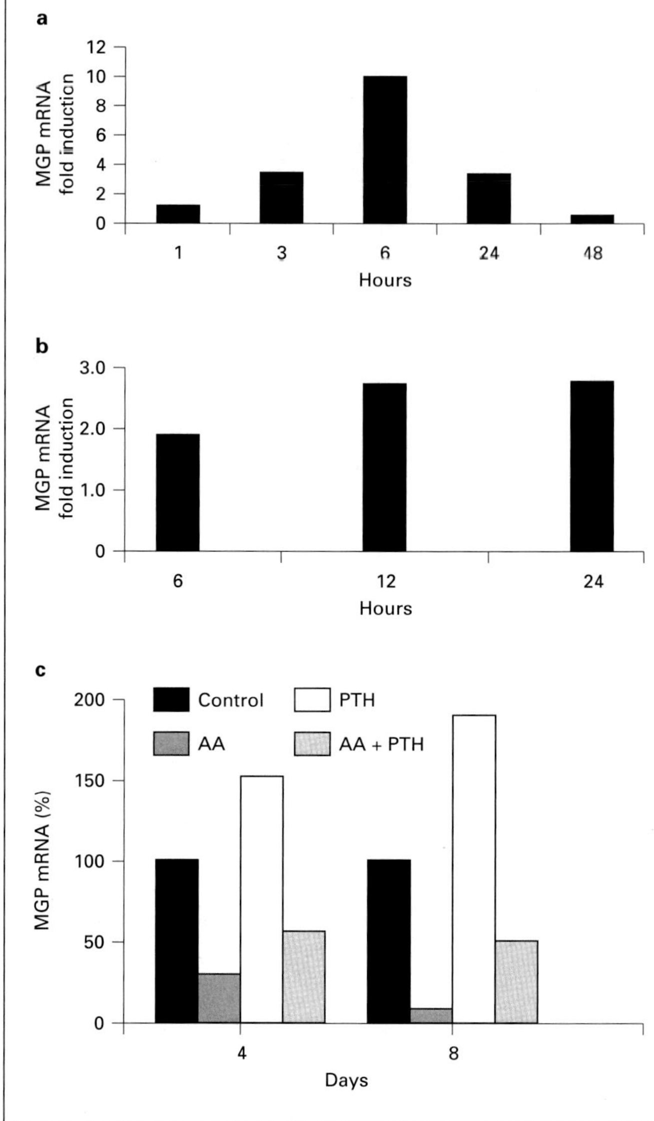

day 8). The MGP mRNA induction in the AA + PTH group on day 8 compared with the AA alone group was comparable with that reported previously by us in osteoblasts treated with a single dose of PTH after differentiation (fig.1c) [Gopalakrishnan et al., 2001].

An interesting aspect noted in the differentiation experiments is that MGP mRNA expression decreases as the osteoblasts differentiate following AA treatment. Decrease in MGP mRNA expression was more pronounced on day 8 (12-fold decrease in the AA vs. the no-AA group) compared with day 4 (3.4-fold decrease in the AA vs. the no-AA group) (fig. 2c). It is not known how MGP expression is reduced as the osteoblasts acquire phenotypic and genotypic characteristics of mature osteoblasts; this is an area of investigation in our laboratory.

MGP is a 10-kDa secreted protein initially extracted and purified from demineralized bone [Price et al., 1983]. Along with OCN, MGP belongs to the mineral-binding γ-carboxyglutamic acid (Gla)-containing protein family, which also includes numerous coagulation factors [Hauschka et al., 1989; Price, 1989]. The Gla residues are produced posttranslationally by a vitamin-K-dependent γ-carboxylation reaction of glutamyl residues [Suttie, 1985]. Although the exact mechanism is not completely understood, the Gla residues are critical for the anti-mineralizing function of MGP [Price et al., 2000; Murshed et al., 2004]. Therefore, we used warfarin, a vitamin K antagonist, to provide direct evidence for the role of MGP in PTH-mediated inhibition of mineralization. Addition of warfarin inhibits the production of Gla residues by inhibiting γ-carboxylation. Therefore, if MGP is required for PTH-dependent inhibition of mineralization, blocking γ-carboxylation with warfarin should allow mineralization to proceed, even in the presence of PTH. These results are shown in figure 1d. In these experiments, MC3T3-E1 cells were grown under differentiating conditions for 6 days, at which time cells were treated as indicated in figure 1d. In the case of warfarin-treated cultures, pretreatment began on day 4 (i.e. 2 days before PTH or vitamin K treatment). On day 8, all cultures were allowed to mineralize by incubation with inorganic phosphate (final concentration, 4 m*M*) for 24 h and mineralization was detected by von Kossa staining. Densitometric analysis of cultures was performed using NIH image. As shown, 10^{-7} *M* PTH alone inhibited mineralization by 75%, as opposed to 96% inhibition by PTH plus 10 μ*M* vitamin K_3. However, treatment with 20 μ*M* warfarin in the presence of vitamin K_3 reduced PTH-dependent inhibition of mineralization to only 42%, consistent with our hypothesis of the role of MGP in osteoblast mineralization.

Pettway et al. [2005] using a novel cell-based ectopic ossicle model showed a significant increase in MGP in 2-week-old ossicles harvested 8 h after an acute injection of PTH (20 μg) compared with vehicle controls. The authors suggested that the MGP induction by PTH might delay mineralization of ossicles early in development, facilitating osteoprogenitor cell proliferation responsible for a subsequent increase in bone mass. However, the authors observed no decrease in ossicle mineralization.

MGP and Pathologic Calcification

It is well established that MGP is a potent inhibitor of pathologic calcification. Mice deficient for the *Mgp* gene show severe vascular calcification and premature mineralization of long bones [Luo et al., 1997]. Transgenic mice overexpressing *Mgp* in osteoblasts, under the control of the *α1(I)-collagen* promoter *(α1(I)-Mgp),* exhibit a reduction in bone mineral, indicating that MGP can grossly disrupt bone formation [Murshed et al., 2004]. It has been previously reported that most tooth dentin and cementum from *α1(I)-Mgp* transgenic mice are hypomineralized [Schinke et al., 2000]. Retrovirus-induced overexpression of MGP in developing growth plates blocks endochondral ossification by delaying normal chondrocyte differentiation [Yagami et al., 1999]. Murine MGP contains four Gla residues, which are critical for MGP function. The Gla residues bind to calcium and hydroxyapatite, but the role of this effect in MGP-mediated inhibition of mineralization is not known [Hauschka et al., 1989]. The vascular calcification noted in *Mgp–/–* mice was reversed by overexpressing MGP in vascular smooth muscle cells using a *Sm22α* promoter [Murshed et al., 2004]. The rescue was dependent on local expression of MGP and not systemic expression, because mice overexpressing MGP systemically did not rescue the vascular phenotype. The potential importance of γ-carboxylation and MGP was also confirmed in experiments where rats treated with warfarin, a vitamin K antagonist, developed vascular calcification after 2–4 weeks [Price et al., 1998, 2000]. Moreover, MGP promoter polymorphisms are associated with lower MGP expression and serum levels, and such polymorphisms in humans have been associated with increased risk of myocardial infarction [Herrmann et al., 2000].

Combining results reported by various researchers, several mechanisms, which are not mutually exclusive, have been proposed for the function of MGP as an inhibitor of vascular calcification [Speer et al., 2002]. First, MGP could physically interact with, and inhibit, bone morphogenetic protein 2 (BMP2)-induced differentiation of vascular smooth muscle cells into osteoblasts and chondrocytes [Wallin et al., 2000; Bostrom et al., 2001; Zebboudj et al., 2002, 2003]. Support for this mechanism stems from several observations. For example, aortic vascular smooth muscle cells from *Mgp–/–* mice differentiated into osteoblasts and chondrocytes, MGP expression was decreased in patients with atherosclerosis and Mönckeberg sclerosis just before calcification, and vascular calcification was also noted in mice with a targeted mutation of Smad 6, a potent inhibitor of BMP signaling [Shanahan et al., 1999; Galvin et al., 2000; Bostrom et al., 2001]. Second, formation of a high-molecular-weight calcium, fetuin and MGP complex facilitates removal of these minerals through circulation, thus reducing their availability for tissue calcification [Price and Lim, 2003; Price et al., 2003]. Fetuin, a circulating protein, is a well-known inhibitor of ectopic calcification, and mice deficient in fetuin develop mineralization when fed a high calcium-phosphorus diet [Schafer et al., 2003]. Price et al. [2002] discovered a complex of calcium, phosphate, fetuin, and MGP in the serum of rats, the formation of which coincided with inhibition of mineralization following treatment with the bisphosphonate, etidronate. The authors further noted that warfarin treatment prevented the etidronate-induced increase in serum MGP levels, confirming that γ-carboxylation is required for formation of the MGP-serum-fetuin complex. Third, MGP may act via direct interaction with hydroxyapatite through the Gla residues, thereby preventing further crystal growth [Roy and Nishimoto, 2002]. Impaired carboxylation of MGP leading to reduced Gla residues has also been associated with intimal and medial calcification in patients, suggesting that γ-carboxylation is critical for MGP function [Schurgers et al., 2005]. To confirm the role of Gla residues, Murshed et al. [2004] studied transgenic mice overexpressing *Mgp* in osteoblasts using a 2.3-kb *α1(1) collagen* gene promoter, and showed a decrease in intramembranous bone mineralization. The same authors also noted that one *Mgp* transgenic line in which the Gla residues had been mutated to aspartic acid showed no change in unmineralized bone, confirming the importance of Gla residues for MGP anti-mineralization function.

Regulation of MGP

In addition to PTH, MGP is also regulated by retinoic acid, transforming growth factor-β, fibroblast growth factor 2 (FGF2), and thyroid hormone. The effect of retinoic acid is cell type dependent, as it induces MGP expression in osteoblasts, chondrocytes and fibroblasts, but decreases expression in MCF7 breast cancer and NRK52E kidney cells [Cancela and Price, 1992; Cancela et al., 1997]. The reduction in MGP mRNA in NRK52E cells was mediated through a 37-bp negative retinoic acid response element located in the human *Mgp* promoter [Kirfel et al., 1997]. FGF2 induced MGP gene expression in proliferative chondrocytes through direct action with the FGF2 response element located between –168 and –748 bp of the *Mgp* promoter [Stheneur et al., 2003]. Lung cultures exposed to transforming growth factor-β_1 adenovirus induced MGP mRNA expression in a concentration-dependent manner [Zhao et al., 1999]. Using rat aortic smooth muscle cells, Sato et al. [2005] showed that thyroid hormone (T3) induced MGP mRNA expression, and this induction was mediated via the thyroid receptor. The Fos-related antigen Fra-1 has been shown to be a direct regulator of MGP, as mice deficient in Fra-1 *(fra-1*$^{\Delta/\Delta}$*)* showed reduced expression of MGP mRNA in both calvarial osteoblasts and long bones. The authors also showed increased MGP mRNA expression in long bones of transgenic mice overexpressing *fra-1*. The authors hypothesized that the dysregulation of MGP and other bone matrix proteins in osteoblasts and chondrocytes could be partly attributed to the bone defects observed in *(fra-1*$^{\Delta/\Delta}$*)* and *fra-1* overexpressing mice [Eferl et al., 2004].

OPN and Mineralization

In addition to MGP, we also observed induction of OPN mRNA in MC3T3-E1 cells following PTH treatment [Gopalakrishnan et al., 2001]. OPN is a secreted, glycosylated phosphoprotein normally expressed in mineralized tissues such as bones and teeth. The role of OPN as an inhibitor of mineralization has been well established in both osteoblast and vascular smooth muscle cell systems. Boskey et al. [2002], using Fourier transform infrared microspectroscopy and infrared imaging, showed increased mineral content and crystal size/perfection in *Opn–/–* mice, suggesting that OPN is a potent inhibitor of mineral formation and mineral crystal growth and proliferation. Similar results were also noted in mature bones from *Opn–/–* mice during calcium deficiency, suggesting that OPN has an inhibitory effect on crystal size and proliferation [Shapses et al., 2003]. Kitahara et al. [2003] reported that intermittent PTH treatment increased the rate of periosteal bone formation and the rate of mineral apposition in *Opn–/–* mice compared with wildtype mice. They also noted increased mineral nodule formation when PTH-treated *Opn–/–* bone marrow stromal cells were differentiated into osteoblasts. These results indicated that osteoblasts were the source of OPN, following PTH treatment.

Studies have shown that pathological calcification of blood vessels shares features with normal embryonic bone formation and bone repair [Zebboudj et al., 2003; Vattikuti and Towler, 2004; Hruska et al., 2005]. The pathogenesis of vascular calcification is mediated by component cells that have developed an osteogenic phenotype with an ability to mineralize extracellular matrix. Therefore, it can be speculated that vascular calcification is regulated partly by a process similar to bone formation. Moreover, various components of mineralization such as matrix vesicles, nucleation sites, and proteins such as BMPs, OCN, MGP and OPN have been identified in atherosclerotic lesions [Tyson et al., 2003; Reynolds et al., 2004]. OPN is present in abundance in calcifications of the aortic valve and atherosclerotic plaques [Giachelli et al., 1993; O'Brien et al., 1995]. OPN has also been noted to inhibit mineralization of calcifying smooth muscle cells in vitro [Wada et al., 1999]. To evaluate the role of OPN in vascular calcification, Speer et al. [2002] crossed *Mgp+/–* mice with *Opn–/–* mice to generate *Mgp+/– Opn+/–* animals which were used as breeders to generate *Mgp–/– Opn+/+* and *Mgp–/– Opn–/–*, *Mgp–/– Opn+/–* and *Mgp+/– Opn–/–* genotypes. All of these mice died early (as early as 3–4 weeks of age), due to severe vascular calcification leading to vascular rupture followed by hemorrhage, similar to *Mgp–/–* mice. The authors noted that the *Mgp–/– Opn–/–* mice had almost twice as much calcification as *Mgp–/– Opn+/+* mice at 2 weeks, and more than three times as much at 4 weeks. Further, *Mgp+/– Opn–/–* mice showed vascular calcification at 4–8 weeks, whereas *Mgp+/– Opn+/+* mice had no calcification at any time. These studies confirmed that OPN is an inducible inhibitor of vascular calcification in vivo. The role of OPN as an inhibitor of vascular calcification was also studied by examining the effects of intermittent teriparatide injections in a diabetic low-density lipoprotein receptor-deficient mouse model. Shao et al. [2003] reported that the inhibitory effects of PTH(1–34) on vascular calcification in low-density lipoprotein receptor-deficient mice were mediated, at least in part, by suppression of Msx2 expression in vivo. The authors showed that inhibition of Msx2 expression results in increased circulating levels of OPN, leading to inhibition of osteogenic differentiation in vascular myofibroblasts [Shao et al., 2003].

Conclusion

Mineralization is a complex process controlled by the interplay between various nucleators and inhibitors of hydroxyapatite formation. Although the mechanisms involved in mineralization are not known, a recent model suggested that mineralization is a default process, and that specific inhibitors such as MGP and OPN, rather than nucleators of mineralization, may be critical determinants of this process. Knowledge of the regulation of these inhibitors of mineralization is necessary for understanding mineralization. Thus, demonstrating that MGP and OPN can mediate the mineralization inhibitory effects of PTH is significant. Moreover, several questions remain about the mechanisms involved in the anabolic and catabolic effects of PTH. Therefore, studies to investigate these mechanisms, and to determine the role of PTH and mineralization inhibitors in vascular calcification, will be essential in the development of novel and improved treatment protocols for both osteoporosis and cardiovascular disease.

Acknowledgements

This work was supported by NIH grants DE016093 (to R.G.) and DE12211 (to R.T.F.) and a grant-in-aid from the University of Minnesota Graduate School to R.G. The authors also thank all those whose work has been presented in this review.

References

Armamento-Villareal, R., K. Ziambaras, S.H. Abbasi-Jarhomi, A. Dimarogonas, L. Halstead, A. Fausto, L.V. Avioli, R. Civitelli (1997) An intact N terminus is required for the anabolic action of parathyroid hormone on adult female rats. J Bone Miner Res *12:* 384–392.

Bellows, C.G., H. Ishida, J.E. Aubin, J.N. Heersche (1990) Parathyroid hormone reversibly suppresses the differentiation of osteoprogenitor cells into functional osteoblasts. Endocrinology *127:* 3111–3116.

Black, D.M., S.L. Greenspan, K.E. Ensrud, L. Palermo, J.A. McGowan, T.F. Lang, P. Garnero, M.L. Bouxsein, J.P. Bilezikian, C.J. Rosen (2003) The effects of parathyroid hormone and alendronate alone or in combination in postmenopausal osteoporosis. N Engl J Med *349:* 1207–1215.

Boskey, A.L., L. Spevak, E. Paschalis, S.B. Doty, M.D. McKee (2002) Osteopontin deficiency increases mineral content and mineral crystallinity in mouse bone. Calcif Tissue Int *71:* 145–154.

Bostrom, K., D. Tsao, S. Shen, Y. Wang, L.L. Demer (2001) Matrix GLA protein modulates differentiation induced by bone morphogenetic protein-2 in C3H10T1/2 cells. J Biol Chem *276:* 14044–14052.

Bringhurst, F.R., G.J. Strewler (2002) Renal and skeletal actions of parathyroid hormone (PTH) and PTH-related protein; in Bilezikian, J.P., L.G. Raisz, G.A. Rodan (eds): Principles of Bone Biology. San Diego, Academic Press, pp 483–514.

Brixen, K.T., P.M. Christensen, C. Ejersted, B.L. Langdahl (2004) Teriparatide (biosynthetic human parathyroid hormone 1–34): a new paradigm in the treatment of osteoporosis. Basic Clin Pharmacol Toxicol *94:* 260–270.

Burr, D.B., T. Hirano, C.H. Turner, C. Hotchkiss, R. Brommage, J.M. Hock (2001) Intermittently administered human parathyroid hormone (1–34) treatment increases intracortical bone turnover and porosity without reducing bone strength in the humerus of ovariectomized cynomolgus monkeys. J Bone Miner Res *16:* 157–165.

Canalis, E., M. Centrella, W. Burch, T.L. McCarthy (1989) Insulin-like growth factor I mediates selective anabolic effects of parathyroid hormone in bone cultures. J Clin Invest *83:* 60–65.

Cancela, M.L., B. Hu, P.A. Price (1997) Effect of cell density and growth factors on matrix Gla protein expression by normal rat kidney cells. J Cell Physiol *171:* 125–134.

Cancela, M.L., P.A. Price (1992) Retinoic acid induces matrix Gla protein gene expression in human cells. Endocrinology *130:* 102–108.

Demiralp, B., H.L. Chen, A.J. Koh, E.T. Keller, L.K. McCauley (2002) Anabolic effects of parathyroid hormone during bone growth are dependent on c-fos. Endocrinology *143:* 4038–4047.

Eferl, R., A. Hoebertz, A.F. Schilling, M. Rath, F. Karreth, L. Kenner, M. Amling, E.F. Wagner (2004) The Fos-related antigen Fra-1 is an activator of bone matrix formation. EMBO J *23:* 2789–2799.

Fujita, T., R. Fukuyama, N. Izumo, T. Hirai, T. Meguro, H. Nakamuta, M. Koida (2001) Transactivation of core binding factor alpha1 as a basic mechanism to trigger parathyroid hormone-induced osteogenesis. Jpn J Pharmacol *86:* 405–416.

Galvin, K.M., M.J. Donovan, C.A. Lynch, R.I. Meyer, R.J. Paul, J.N. Lorenz, V. Fairchild-Huntress, K.L. Dixon, J.H. Dunmore, M.A. Gimbrone, Jr., D. Falb, D. Huszar (2000) A role for smad6 in development and homeostasis of the cardiovascular system. Nat Genet *24:* 171–174.

Giachelli, C.M., N. Bae, M. Almeida, D.T. Denhardt, C.E. Alpers, S.M. Schwartz (1993) Osteopontin is elevated during neointima formation in rat arteries and is a novel component of human atherosclerotic plaques. J Clin Invest *92:* 1686–1696.

Gopalakrishnan, R., H. Ouyang, M.J. Somerman, L.K. McCauley, R.T. Franceschi (2001) Matrix gamma-carboxyglutamic acid protein is a key regulator of PTH-mediated inhibition of mineralization in MC3T3-E1 osteoblast-like cells. Endocrinology *142:* 4379–4388.

Hauschka, P.V., J.B. Lian, D.E. Cole, C.M. Gundberg (1989) Osteocalcin and matrix Gla protein: vitamin K-dependent proteins in bone. Physiol Rev *69:* 990–1047.

Herrmann, S.M., C. Whatling, E. Brand, V. Nicaud, J. Gariepy, A. Simon, A. Evans, J.B. Ruidavets, D. Arveiler, G. Luc, L. Tiret, A. Henney, F. Cambien (2000) Polymorphisms of the human matrix gla protein (MGP) gene, vascular calcification, and myocardial infarction. Arterioscler Thromb Vasc Biol *20:* 2386–2393.

Hock, J.M., L.A. Fitzpatrick, J.P. Bilezikian (2002) Actions of parathyroid hormone; in Bilezikian, J.P., L.G. Raisz, G.A. Rodan (eds): Principles of Bone Biology. San Diego, Academic Press, pp 463–481.

Hock, J.M., I. Gera (1992) Effects of continuous and intermittent administration and inhibition of resorption on the anabolic response of bone to parathyroid hormone. J Bone Miner Res *7:* 65–72.

Hruska, K.A., S. Mathew, G. Saab (2005) Bone morphogenetic proteins in vascular calcification. Circ Res *97:* 105–114.

Jilka, R.L., R.S. Weinstein, T. Bellido, P. Roberson, A.M. Parfitt, S.C. Manolagas (1999) Increased bone formation by prevention of osteoblast apoptosis with parathyroid hormone. J Clin Invest *104:* 439–446.

Kirfel, J., M. Kelter, L.M. Cancela, P.A. Price, R. Schule (1997) Identification of a novel negative retinoic acid responsive element in the promoter of the human matrix Gla protein gene. Proc Natl Acad Sci USA *94:* 2227–2232.

Kitahara, K., M. Ishijima, S.R. Rittling, K. Tsuji, H. Kurosawa, A. Nifuji, D.T. Denhardt, M. Noda (2003) Osteopontin deficiency induces parathyroid hormone enhancement of cortical bone formation. Endocrinology *144:* 2132–2140.

Koh, A.J., C.A. Beecher, T.J. Rosol, L.K. McCauley (1999) 3′, 5′-Cyclic adenosine monophosphate avtivation in osteoblastic cells: effects on parathyroid hormone-1 receptors and osteoblastic differentiation in vitro. Endocrinology *140:* 3154–3162.

Krishnan, V., T.L. Moore, Y.L. Ma, L.M. Helvering, C.A. Frolik, K.M. Valasek, P. Ducy, A.G. Geiser (2003) Parathyroid hormone bone anabolic action requires cbfa1/runx2-dependent signaling. Mol Endocrinol *17:* 423–435.

Kurland, E.S., F. Cosman, D.J. McMahon, C.J. Rosen, R. Lindsay, J.P. Bilezikian (2000) Parathyroid hormone as a therapy for idiopathic osteoporosis in men: effects on bone mineral density and bone markers. J Clin Endocrinol Metab *85:* 3069–3076.

Lacey, D.L., E. Timms, H.L. Tan, M.J. Kelley, C.R. Dunstan, T. Burgess, R. Elliott, A. Colombero, G. Elliott, S. Scully, H. Hsu, J. Sullivan, N. Hawkins, E. Davy, C. Capparelli, A. Eli, Y.X. Qian, S. Kaufman, I. Sarosi, V. Shalhoub, G. Senaldi, J. Guo, J. Delaney, W.J. Boyle (1998) Osteoprotegerin ligand is a cytokine that regulates osteoclast differentiation and activation. Cell *93:* 165–176.

Lee, S.K., J.A. Loenzo (1999) Parathyroid hormone stimulates TRANCE and inhibits osteoprotegrin ribonucleic acid expression in murine bone marrow cultures: correlation with osteoclast-like cell formation. Endocrinology *140:* 3552–3561.

Luo, G., P. Ducy, M.D. McKee, G.J. Pinero, E. Loyer, R.R. Behringer, G. Karsenty (1997) Spontaneous calcification of arteries and cartilage in mice lacking matrix GLA protein. Nature *386:* 78–81.

Ma, Y.L., R.L. Cain, D.L. Halladay, X. Yang, Q. Zeng, R.R. Miles, S. Chandrasekhar, T.J. Martin, J.E. Onyia (2001) Catabolic effects of continuous human PTH(1–38) in vivo is associated with sustained stimulation of RANKL and inhibition of osteoprotegerin and gene-associated bone formation. Endocrinology *142:* 4047–4054.

McCarthy, T.L., M. Centrella, E. Canalis (1989) Parathyroid hormone enhances the transcript and polypeptide levels of insulin-like growth factor I in osteoblast-enriched cultures from fetal rat bone. Endocrinology *124:* 1247–1253.

Misof, B.M., P. Roschger, F. Cosman, E.S. Kurland, W. Tesch, P. Messmer, D.W. Dempster, J. Nieves, E. Shane, P. Fratzl, K. Klaushofer, J. Bilezikian, R. Lindsay (2003) Effects of intermittent parathyroid hormone administration on bone mineralization density in iliac crest biopsies from patients with osteoporosis: a paired study before and after treatment. J Clin Endocrinol Metab *88:* 1150–1156.

Murrils, R.J., L.S. Stein, C.P. Fey, D.W. Dempster (1990) The effects of parathyroid hormone (PTH) and PTH-related peptide on osteoclast resorption of bone slices in vitro: an analysis of pit size and the resorption focus. Endocrinology *127:* 2648–2653.

Murshed, M., T. Schinke, M.D. McKee, G. Karsenty (2004) Extracellular matrix mineralization is regulated locally; different roles of two gla-containing proteins. J Cell Biol *165:* 625–630.

Neer, R.M., C.D. Arnaud, J.R. Zanchetta, R. Prince, G.A. Gaich, J.Y. Reginster, A.B. Hodsman, E.F. Eriksen, S. Ish-Shalom, H.K. Genant, O. Wang, B.H. Mitlak (2001) Effect of parathyroid hormone (1–34) on fractures and bone mineral density in postmenopausal women with osteoporosis. N Engl J Med *344:* 1434–1441.

Newman, B., L.I. Gigout, L. Sudre, M.E. Grant, G.A. Wallis (2001) Coordinated expression of matrix gla protein is required during endochondral ossification for chondrocyte survival. J Cell Biol *154:* 659–666.

O'Brien, K.D., J. Kuusisto, D.D. Reichenbach, M. Ferguson, C. Giachelli, C.E. Alpers, C.M. Otto (1995) Osteopontin is expressed in human aortic valvular lesions. Circulation *92:* 2163–2168.

Paschalis, E.P., E.V. Glass, D.W. Donley, E.F. Eriksen (2005) Bone mineral and collagen quality in iliac crest biopsies of patients given teriparatide: new results from the fracture prevention trial. J Clin Endocrinol Metab *90:* 4644–4649.

Pettway, G.J., A. Schneider, A.J. Koh, E. Widjaja, M.D. Morris, J.A. Meganck, S.A. Goldstein, L.K. McCauley (2005) Anabolic actions of PTH(1–34): use of a novel tissue engineering model to investigate temporal effects on bone. Bone *36:* 959–970.

Price, P.A. (1989) Gla-containing proteins of bone. Connect Tissue Res *21:* 51–57; discussion 57–60.

Price, P.A., S.A. Faus, M.K. Williamson (1998) Warfarin causes rapid calcification of the elastic lamellae in rat arteries and heart valves. Arterioscler Thromb Vasc Biol *18:* 1400–1407.

Price, P.A., S.A. Faus, M.K. Williamson (2000) Warfarin-induced artery calcification is accelerated by growth and vitamin D. Arterioscler Thromb Vasc Biol *20:* 317–327.

Price, P.A., J.E. Lim (2003) The inhibition of calcium phosphate precipitation by fetuin is accompanied by the formation of a fetuin-mineral complex. J Biol Chem *278:* 22144–22152.

Price, P.A., T.M. Nguyen, M.K. Williamson (2003) Biochemical characterization of the serum fetuin-mineral complex. J Biol Chem *278:* 22153–22160.

Price, P.A., G.R. Thomas, A.W. Pardini, W.F. Figueira, J.M. Caputo, M.K. Williamson (2002) Discovery of a high molecular weight complex of calcium, phosphate, fetuin, and matrix gamma-carboxyglutamic acid protein in the serum of etidronate-treated rats. J Biol Chem *277:* 3926–3934.

Price, P.A., M.R. Urist, Y. Otawara (1983) Matrix Gla protein, a new gamma-carboxyglutamic acid-containing protein which is associated with the organic matrix of bone. Biochem Biophys Res Commun *117:* 765–771.

Qin, L., L.J. Raggatt, N.C. Partridge (2004) Parathyroid hormone: a double-edged sword for bone metabolism. Trends Endocrinol Metab *15:* 60–65.
Reynolds, J.L., A.J. Joannides, J.N. Skepper, R. McNair, L.J. Schurgers, D. Proudfoot, W. Jahnen-Dechent, P.L. Weissberg, C.M. Shanahan (2004) Human vascular smooth muscle cells undergo vesicle-mediated calcification in response to changes in extracellular calcium and phosphate concentrations: a potential mechanism for accelerated vascular calcification in ESRD. J Am Soc Nephrol *15:* 2857–2867.
Rixon, R.H., J.F. Whitfield, L. Gagnon, R.J. Issacs, S. Maclean, B. Chakravarthy, J.P. Durkin, W. Neugebauer, V. Ross, W. Sung, G.E. Willick (1994) Parathyroid hormone fragments may stimulate bone growth in ovariectomized rats by activating adenylyl cyclase. J Bone Miner Res *9:* 1179–1189.
Roy, M.E., S.K. Nishimoto (2002) Matrix Gla protein binding to hydroxyapatite is dependent on the ionic environment: calcium enhances binding affinity but phosphate and magnesium decrease affinity. Bone *31:* 296–302.
Sato, Y., R. Nakamura, M. Satoh, K. Fujishita, S. Mori, S. Ishida, T. Yamaguchi, K. Inoue, T. Nagao, Y. Ohno (2005) Thyroid hormone targets matrix Gla protein gene associated with vascular smooth muscle calcification. Circ Res *97:* 550–557.
Schafer, C., A. Heiss, A. Schwarz, R. Westenfeld, M. Ketteler, J. Floege, W. Muller-Esterl, T. Schinke, W. Jahnen-Dechent (2003) The serum protein alpha 2-Heremans-Schmid glycoprotein/fetuin-A is a systemically acting inhibitor of ectopic calcification. J Clin Invest *11:* 357–366.
Schiller, P.C., G. D'Ippolito, B.A. Roos, G.A. Howard (1999) Anabolic or catabolic responses of MC3T3-E1 osteoblastic cells to parathyroid hormone depend on time and duration of treatment. J Bone Miner Res *14:* 1504–1512.
Schinke, T., M.D. McKee, M. Amling, G. Karsenty (2000) Severe bone mineralization defects in transgenic mice expressing matrix Gla protein in osteoblasts. J Bone Miner Res *15:* S170.
Schinke, T., M.D. McKee, G. Karsenty (1999) Extracellular matrix calcification: where is the action? Nat Genet *21:* 150–151.
Schurgers, L.J., K.J. Teunissen, M.H. Knapen, M. Kwaijtaal, R. van Diest, A. Appels, C.P. Reutelingsperger, J.P. Cleutjens, C. Vermeer (2005) Novel conformation-specific antibodies against matrix gamma-carboxyglutamic acid (Gla) protein: undercarboxylated matrix Gla protein as marker for vascular calcification. Arterioscler Thromb Vasc Biol *25:* 1629–1633.
Shanahan, C.M., N.R. Cary, J.R. Salisbury, D. Proudfoot, P.L. Weissberg, M.E. Edmonds (1999) Medial localization of mineralization-regulating proteins in association with Monckeberg's sclerosis: evidence for smooth muscle cell-mediated vascular calcification. Circulation *100:* 2168–2176.
Shao, J.S., S.L. Cheng, N. Charlton-Kachigian, A.P. Loewy, D.A. Towler (2003) Teriparatide (human parathyroid hormone (1–34)) inhibits osteogenic vascular calcification in diabetic low density lipoprotein receptor-deficient mice. J Biol Chem *278:* 50195–50202.
Shapses, S.A., M. Cifuentes, L. Spevak, H. Chowdhury, J. Brittingham, A.L. Boskey, D.T. Denhardt (2003) Osteopontin facilitates bone resorption, decreasing bone mineral crystallinity and content during calcium deficiency. Calcif Tissue Int *73:* 86–92.
Speer, M.Y., M.D. McKee, R.E. Guldberg, L. Liaw, H.Y. Yang, E. Tung, G. Karsenty, C.M. Giachelli (2002) Inactivation of the osteopontin gene enhances vascular calcification of matrix Gla protein-deficient mice: evidence for osteopontin as an inducible inhibitor of vascular calcification in vivo. J Exp Med *196:* 1047–1055.
Stheneur, C., M.F. Dumontier, C. Guedes, M.C. Fulchignoni-Lataud, K. Tahiri, G. Karsenty, M.T. Corvol (2003) Basic fibroblast growth factor as a selective inducer of matrix Gla protein gene expression in proliferative chondrocytes. Biochem J *369:* 63–70.
Suttie, J.W. (1985) Vitamin K-dependent carboxylase. Annu Rev Biochem *54:* 459–477.
Tam, C.S., J.N. Heersche, T.M. Murray, J.A. Parsons (1982) Parathyroid hormone stimulates the bone apposition rate independently of its resorptive action: differential effects of intermittent and continuous administration. Endocrinology *110:* 506–512.
Tyson, K.L., J.L. Reynolds, R. McNair, Q. Zhang, P.L. Weissberg, C.M. Shanahan (2003) Osteo/chondrocytic transcription factors and their target genes exhibit distinct patterns of expression in human arterial calcification. Arterioscler Thromb Vasc Biol *23:* 489–494.
Vattikuti, R., D.A. Towler (2004) Osteogenic regulation of vascular calcification: an early perspective. Am J Physiol Endocrinol Metab *286:* E686–E696.
Wada, T., M.D. McKee, S. Steitz, C.M. Giachelli (1999) Calcification of vascular smooth muscle cell cultures: inhibition by osteopontin. Circ Res *84:* 166–178.
Wallin, R., D. Cain, S.M. Hutson, D.C. Sane, R. Loeser (2000) Modulation of the binding of matrix Gla protein (MGP) to bone morphogenetic protein-2 (BMP-2). Thromb Haemost *84:* 1039–1044.
Wang, A., J.A. Martin, L.A. Lembke, R.J. Midura (2000) Reversible suppression of in vitro biomineralization by activation of protein kinase A. J Biol Chem *275:* 11082–11091.
Yagami, K., J.Y. Suh, M. Enomoto-Iwamoto, E. Koyama, W.R. Abrams, I.M. Shapiro, M. Pacifici, M. Iwamoto (1999) Matrix GLA protein is a developmental regulator of chondrocyte mineralization and, when constitutively expressed, blocks endochondral and intramembranous ossification in the limb. J Cell Biol *147:* 1097–1108.
Yasuda, H., N. Shima, N. Nakagawa, K. Yamaguchi, M. Kinosaki, S. Mochizuki, A. Tomoyasu, K. Yano, M. Goto, A. Murakami, E. Tsuda, T. Morinaga, K. Higashio, N. Udagawa, N. Takahashi, T. Suda (1998) Osteoclast differentiation factor is a ligand for osteoprotegerin/osteoclastogenesis-inhibitory factor and is identical to TRANCE/RANKL. Proc Natl Acad Sci USA *95:* 3597–3602.
Zebboudj, A.F., M. Imura, K. Bostrom (2002) Matrix GLA protein, a regulatory protein for bone morphogenetic protein-2. J Biol Chem *277:* 4388–4394.
Zebboudj, A.F., V. Shin, K. Bostrom (2003) Matrix GLA protein and BMP-2 regulate osteoinduction in calcifying vascular cells. J Cell Biochem *90:* 756–765.
Zhao, J., P.J. Sime, P. Bringas, Jr., J.D. Tefft, S. Buckley, D. Bu, J. Gauldie, D. Warburton (1999) Spatial-specific TGF-beta1 adenoviral expression determines morphogenetic phenotypes in embryonic mouse lung. Eur J Cell Biol *78:* 715–725.

Cells Tissues Organs

Cells Tissues Organs 2005;181:176–188
DOI: 10.1159/000091379

Hierarchies of Extracellular Matrix and Mineral Organization in Bone of the Craniofacial Complex and Skeleton

M.D. McKee[a, b] W.N. Addison[a] M.T. Kaartinen[a, c]

[a]Faculty of Dentistry, and Departments of [b]Anatomy and Cell Biology and [c]Medicine, Faculty of Medicine, McGill University, Montreal, Canada

Key Words
Osteogenesis · Osteopontin · Bone remodeling · Biomineralization · Extracellular matrix

Abstract
Structural hierarchies are common in biologic systems and are particularly evident in biomineralized structures. In the craniofacial complex and skeleton of vertebrates, extracellular matrix and mineral of bone are structurally ordered at many dimensional scales from the macro level to the nano level. Indeed, the nanocomposite texture of bone, with nanocrystals of apatitic mineral embedded within a crosslinked matrix of fibrillar and nonfibrillar proteins, imparts to bone the very mechanical properties and toughness it needs to function in vital organ protection, musculoskeletal movement and mastication. This article focuses on how hierarchies of extracellular matrix protein organization influence bone cell behavior, tissue architecture and mineralization. Additional attention is given to recent work on the molecular determinants of mineral induction in bone, and how the mineralization process is subsequently regulated by inhibitory proteins.

Abbreviations used in this paper

ANK	progressive ankylosis
CPPD	calcium pyrophosphate dihydrate
ENPP1	ectonucleotide pyrophosphatase/phosphodiesterase 1
PHEX	phosphate-regulating gene with homologies to endopeptidases on the X chromosome
P_i	inorganic phosphate
PP_i	inorganic pyrophosphate
TG	transglutaminase
SIBLING	small integrin-binding ligand N-linked glycoprotein
TNAP	tissue non-specific alkaline phosphatase
ttw/ttw	tiptoe walking mice

Introduction

Biomineralization occurs across many phyla and consists of a hardening strategy used for a multitude of purposes by different organisms [Knoll, 2003; Weiner and Dove, 2003]. At the broadest level, practically all biomineralized structures are highly hierarchical, with structures varying across different dimensions [Currey, 2005b]. In vertebrates, while providing protection for vulnerable cell and tissue systems, other key functions include providing skeletal attachment points and weight-bearing lever arms for movement in the musculoskeletal system, and providing hard, wear-resistant teeth for mastication [Currey, 2005a]. Additional diverse roles for mineralized structures in biology include facilitating ocean buoyancy in coccolithophores [Young et al., 1992] and forming lenses to focus light onto receptor cells in deep-sea brittlestars [Aizen-

KARGER
Fax +41 61 306 12 34
E-Mail karger@karger.ch
www.karger.com

1422–6405/05/1814–0176$22.00/0

Accessible online at:
www.karger.com/cto

Marc D. McKee, PhD
Faculty of Dentistry, McGill University
3640 University Street
Montreal, QC, H3A 2B2 (Canada)
Tel. +1 514 398 7203, ext. 00041, Fax +1 514 398 8900, E-Mail marc.mckee@mcgill.ca

berg et al., 2001]. Another recent example remarkably illustrates hierarchies in biomineralized structures, where the deepwater glassy sponge *Euplectella,* with silica as its mineral phase, creates a glassy skeleton as a hollow cylinder – much like the diaphyseal shaft of long bones [Aizenberg et al., 2005]. The walls of the cylinder of the sponge, like bone, have at least 5–6 levels of structural hierarchy, whose mechanical properties collectively resist torsion and stiffen the structure. Some of these hierarchies, at selected length scales, are described herein for bone, with a focus on extracellular matrix proteins, their assembly and organization, and their ability to influence mineralization.

Biominerals almost invariably form in direct relation to organic molecules – usually proteins [Boskey, 2003]. This article also focuses on biomineralization occurring within the vertebrate skeleton where apatitic crystals are deposited within an abundant organic extracellular matrix consisting predominantly of collagen fibrils, but also containing abundant noncollagenous proteins [McKee and Sodek, 2000]. Significant progress has been made in understanding the process of extracellular matrix assembly in skeletal and dental biology, the function of individual extracellular matrix proteins in bones and teeth, and how biomineralization is regulated in the craniofacial complex and elsewhere in the skeleton.

Bone at the Macro Scale: Major Structural Variations

Variation in structure at different hierarchical levels in the skeleton creates a highly organized, robust mineralized tissue that performs a variety of functions based on the biomechanical demands placed upon it at specific anatomical sites. In the craniofacial complex, these demands are largely protective (the cranium) and masticatory (moving jaws and their teeth). At the macro scale, the bone of the craniofacial complex is organized much like that found elsewhere in the skeleton, with regions of dense cortical bone and regions of porous trabecular bone. At all sites, intermediate osseous structure is also present existing in many cases as a continuum between dense and porous architecture. Bone growth patterns and rates within the craniofacial complex are controlled by a large number of endocrine factors [Pirinen, 1995], including a significant influence of growth hormone [Pirinen et al., 1994; Ramirez-Yanez et al., 2005].

In the head, like for long bones of the limbs as well as the axial skeleton, trabecular bone spans marrow cavities found within dense cortical lamellar bone – this is evident in the diploe of the calvariae and in the tooth-supporting alveolar bone of the maxilla and mandible [Sodek and McKee, 2000]. For the periodontium, this arrangement provides the structural basis for fixation and suspension of teeth within osseous alveolar sockets via the periodontal ligament having insertion sites both within dense alveolar bone and in tooth cementum [McCulloch et al., 2000]. Such an anatomical arrangement is essential for masticatory function while simultaneously providing mechanosensory feedback during mastication.

Bone at the Micro Scale: Cells and Extracellular Matrix

Central to all bone formation processes in the craniofacial complex and elsewhere in the skeleton is continual cell activity resulting in extracellular matrix deposition, assembly and maturation by osteoblasts and osteocytes. Subsequently, extracellular matrix mineralization hardens the bone (fig. 1). Cell dynamics not only form the bone developmentally, but bone cell-signaling events provide the mechanism by which bone is constantly remodeled by osteoclasts. Bone remodeling is either stochastic, to prevent it from exceeding a predetermined age, or targeted, to replace bone based on its use and the resulting biomechanical forces placed upon it [Parfitt, 2002].

Mineralization of the extracellular matrix of bone (fig. 1, 2) [Landis, 1996] occurs as part of all developmental processes leading to mature skeletal element formation [Karsenty and Wagner, 2002]. For bone turnover, mineralization is likewise a major physiological and structural requirement produced as a result of either stochastic or targeted bone remodeling. Conversely, removal of mineral by the pH-lowering actions of osteoclasts during bone resorption is a prerequisite for extracellular matrix degradation by proteolytic enzymes [Blair, 1998]. Bone-lining cells are strategically situated at bone surfaces to transfer information from the osteocyte network regarding ever-changing stress-strain fields within the interior of the bone [Klein-Nulend et al., 2003]. The mechanosensory osteocyte network is present in bone wherever it is formed, but is particularly active in regions of bone affected by the transmission of frequent cycles of periodontal ligament tension between the teeth and the alveolar bone [McCulloch et al., 2000; Sodek and McKee, 2000]. In these regions of the craniofacial complex, bone metabolism is high and bone remodeling is extensive as evidenced by abundant cement lines (fig. 1; see below) demarcating reversal sites where bone resorption by os-

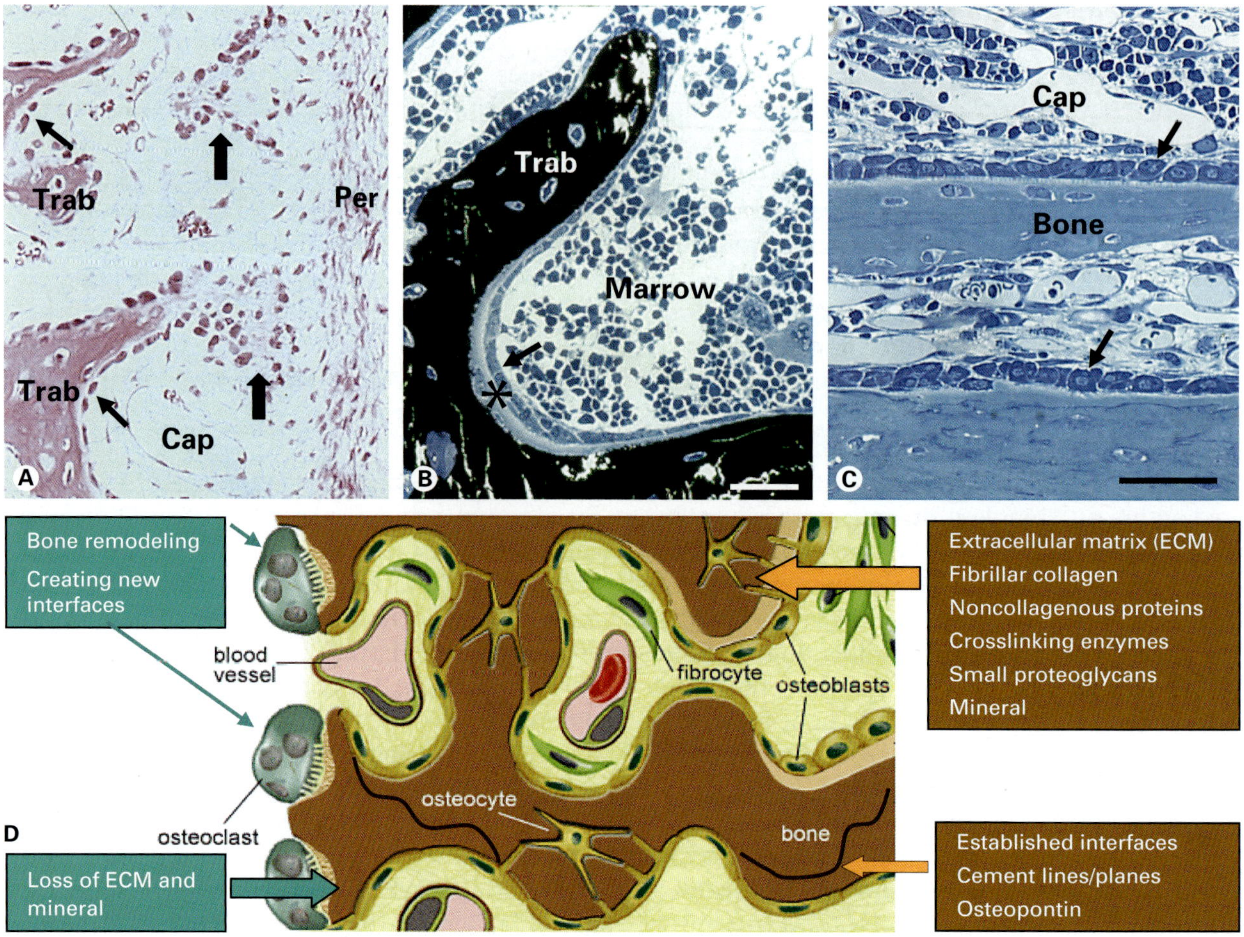

Fig. 1. Light micrographs illustrating the initiation of trabecular bone formation and osteoblast and matrix-mineral relationships in the rat. **A** During cranial growth by intramembranous ossification, and in the presence of a capillary network (Cap), committed osteoprogenitor cells derived from the periosteum (Per) condense into cell aggregates (large arrows), proliferate and further differentiate into bone-forming osteoblasts (small arrows), and begin the formation of bone trabeculae (Trab). Demineralized paraffin section stained with hematoxylin and eosin. **B** With time, abundant extracellular matrix produced by osteoblasts (arrow) thickens the trabeculae (Trab) and mineralizes the matrix (black, von Kossa staining) with an intervening, unmineralized layer of osteoid (asterisk) positioned between the osteoblasts and the mineralization front. Epoxy resin, semi-thin (1-μm) section stained for mineral with silver nitrate (von Kossa staining) and counterstained with toluidine blue. **C** Bone section after sample demineralization and staining with toluidine blue to illustrate the abundant stained extracellular matrix of bone after removal of mineral, and to show the contiguous layer of osteoblasts (arrows) at the surface of the growing bone. Cap = Capillary. Epoxy resin, semi-thin (1-μm) section. Scale bars = 50 μm. **D** Diagram illustrating bone cell types, cell-matrix relationships and extracellular matrix compartments and interfaces in bone as depicted partially in panels **A–C** and as discussed in this review.

teoclasts was immediately followed by bone deposition by osteoblasts [McKee and Nanci, 1995]. These reversal sites are indicative of high bone turnover in response to various signals and biomechanical demands, and represent an important interfacial boundary between older remodeled bone and newly deposited bone [McKee and Nanci, 1996a]. At the microscopic level, osteonal bone remodeling creates centrally located (within cortical bone), cylindrical Haversian systems, typically aligned with the long axis of long bones, which impart an additional level of strengthening architectural hierarchy. Hemi-osteonal remodeling occurring at the surface of tra-

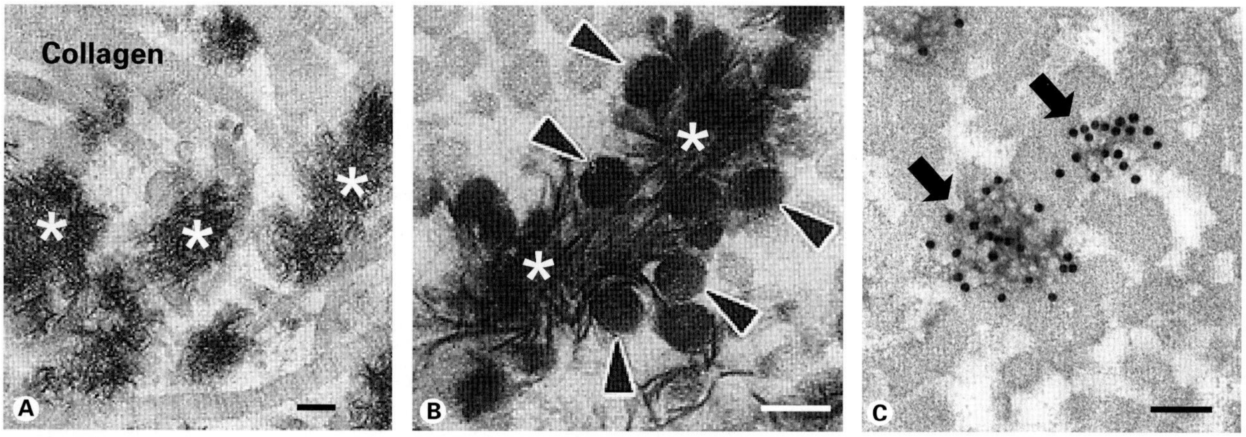

Fig. 2. Transmission electron micrographs showing bone as an organic-inorganic nanocomposite material consisting of a nanocrystalline mineral phase embedded within an organic, extracellular matrix. **A**, **B** Crystals of apatite are found within bone extracellular matrix, either between the collagen fibrils (interfibrillarly; asterisks) or within the collagen fibrils (arrowheads). Interfibrillar crystals are notably larger than those within the collagen fibrils. Epoxy resin, thin (80-nm) sections stained with uranyl acetate and lead citrate. **C** Post-embedding, colloidal-gold immunolocalization of osteopontin in rat bone using anti-osteopontin primary antibody followed by protein A-colloidal gold conjugate. Osteopontin localizes to protein aggregates (arrows) between the collagen fibrils that coincide with small mineralization foci at an early stage of mineralization near the mineralization front. LR White acrylic resin, thin section (80 nm) immunostained for osteopontin and conventionally counterstained with uranyl acetate and lead citrate. Scale bars = 100 nm.

becular bone and at the outer (and inner) surfaces of cortical bone ensures turnover and replacement of bone at surface sites [Parfitt, 2002]. Collectively, these microscale changes orchestrated locally by cell signaling, and more distally by release and systemic circulation of hormones, result in layered macro and micro (lamellar) bone structure whose spatial configuration meets local biomechanical demands. An additional function of this hierarchical arrangement in bone, like in other biologic and synthetic composite materials, is most certainly to prevent catastrophic material failure by creating interfaces that deflect microcracks and thus resist crack propagation leading to fracture [O'Brien et al., 2005].

Bone as a Nanocomposite Organic-Inorganic Hybrid Material

The collagen fibrils, noncollagenous protein assemblies, interconnected pores within the structured extracellular matrix, and the apatitic crystals of bone all have nanoscale dimensions. Calcium- and phosphate-containing mineral is nucleated not only in nanoscale volumes within fibrillar collagens, but also interfibrillarly where crystal dimensions are slightly larger and where noncollagenous proteins are abundant (fig. 2) [McKee and Nanci, 1993]. These two extracellular compartments provide different biochemical constraints on biomineralization, yet at each site, mineral is nucleated and crystal growth is subsequently regulated such that bone crystals do not grow beyond the nanometer range. This exquisite biological control over bone mineralization is thought to be regulated by mineral-nucleating and mineral-inhibiting proteins [Hunter et al., 1996], or by the local removal of inhibitors, such as inorganic pyrophosphate (PP_i), from the extracellular matrix (see below). Abundant evidence exists to show that in various mineralized tissues (including pathologically mineralizing soft tissues), once initiated, crystal growth is regulated (inhibited) by direct binding of inhibitory proteins (such as osteopontin) to crystal surfaces [McKee and Nanci, 1993; Giachelli, 2005]. Irrespective of the mechanisms involved, in bone, osteoblasts produce an extracellular matrix that becomes fully impregnated with mineral, both intra- and interfibrillarly (with respect to collagen fibrils), thus forming a nanocomposite organic-inorganic hybrid material.

The molecular determinants guiding mineralization during osteogenesis result in the production of either woven or lamellar bone whose intrafibrillar apatitic crystals typically orient with their C-axis aligned with the long axis of collagen fibrils [Landis, 1999]. Much less is known regarding the orientation, size and shape of the interfibrillar crystals, but their heterogeneous nucleation and abundance is likely more important to the mechanical proper-

Fig. 3. TG-mediated extracellular matrix crosslinking in bone. **A** Illustration of the isopeptide bond/crosslink created via the TG-mediated transamidation reaction. The crosslink forms between a lysine and a glutamine residue within, or between, proteins. **B, C** MC3T3-E1/C14 murine calvarial osteoblasts were cultured in the presence of monodansylcadaverine (MDC), a primary amine that is incorporated into glutamine residues of TG substrate proteins by the activity of TG. Monodansylcadaverine was detected with anti-dansyl primary antibody (Invitrogen) and secondary anti-rabbit Alexa Fluor 568 (Invitrogen). **B** Cells cultured without ascorbic acid, a cofactor required for collagen post-translational modification and deposition, remain undifferentiated, do not assemble an extracellular matrix, and incorporate the label only intracellularly. **C** On the other hand, in MC3T3-E1/C14 osteoblasts cultured with ascorbic acid to promote collagen deposition and cell differentiation, monodansylcadaverine is incorporated into the fibrillar extracellular matrix. Scale bars = 50 μm. **D** Von Kossa staining of MC3T3-E1/C14 osteoblast cultures that were treated with ascorbic acid (AA; 50 μg/ml) and AA + β-glycerophosphate (βGP; 10 m*M*) for 12 days to induce matrix formation and mineralization. Cells were treated with the TG inhibitor cystamine (CYS; 5 m*M*) for either the full 12-day period (0–12), the first 6-day period (0–6) that represents the early cell differentiation phase, or the last 6-day period that represents the late cell differentiation phase. Blocking of TG-mediated crosslinking of the matrix by cystamine resulted in a complete lack of mineralization in cultures treated with cystamine for 12 days and for the early 0- to 6-day differentiation phase, but not in the cultures treated with cystamine for the last 6 days (a time when extracellular matrix had already formed). NT =Non-treated.

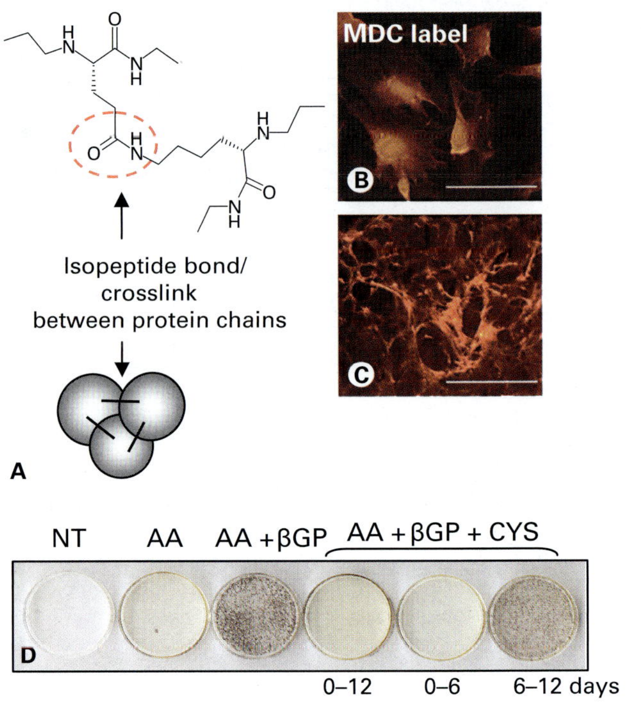

ties of woven bone than of lamellar, dense cortical bone. Indeed, the noncollagenous proteins thought to influence the interfibrillar mineralization are in greater abundance in woven bone [Gorski, 1998]. Interfacial forces and characteristics reflecting the composite nature of bone span across many dimensional scales starting from the protein/organic-nanocrystal interface and extending to the cement line and beyond into the anatomical macro-scale structure of bones.

De novo Construction of Bone by Osteoblasts: Extracellular Matrix Proteins and Crosslinking Enzymes

In addition to its serving as a scaffolding for mineralization, the extracellular matrix of bone functions as a substratum for bone cell adhesion and differentiation. Once engaged with the matrix, bone cells sense deformation and other changes within the bone (matrix-cell crosstalk) [Klein-Nulend et al., 2003] and, conversely, they may interact with their surroundings by anchoring and pulling on the matrix, as has been shown for other cell types (cell-matrix crosstalk) [Discher et al., 2005]. Thus, cell differentiation events occurring early in osteoblast lineage progression in response to assembled extracellular matrix molecules ultimately result in terminally differentiated bone cells with important roles in mechanobiology.

Whereas the hardness of bone derives predominantly from its mineral phase, the abundant organic matrix increases its elastic modulus and toughness. Bone extracellular matrix proteins undergo a number of post-translational modifications which stabilize their structure and modulate their functions. The best known example of this is the lysyl oxidase-mediated, enzymatic conversion of lysines and hydroxylysines in the α-chains of type I collagen into aldehyde group-containing allysines. This triggers the spontaneous formation of pyridinoline and pyrrole crosslinks that stabilize the quarter-staggered molecular arrangement characteristic of triple-helical, type I collagen fibrils. These crosslinks substantially strengthen the collagen fibrils, thus imparting important functional, biomechanical properties to bone. Crosslink formation is an important step in type I collagen fibrillogenesis, which in turn is important in cell adhesion and mineralization

[McKee and Kaartinen, 2002]. More specifically for mineralization, it has been shown that collagen fibril maturation and elevated levels of lysylpyridinoline crosslinks correlate with mineralization [Wassen et al., 2000].

Like collagen in bone, noncollagenous bone matrix proteins are also covalently crosslinked. This is performed by transglutaminases (TGs), a family of enzymes that catalyze the formation of isopeptide crosslinks in a Ca^{2+}-dependent acyl transfer reaction between polypeptide-bound glutamine residues and primary amines [Lorand and Graham, 2003]. The amines, predominantly acting as acyl acceptors, are protein-bound lysine residues and polyamines such as putrescine and spermidine. This enzymatic reaction is exclusively performed by TGs and takes place in the cytosol, at the cell surface, and/or extracellularly. The resulting crosslink is a covalent γ-(glutamyl)-ε-lysyl bond (an isopeptide crosslink/bond) which can form intra- or intermolecularly within, or between, substrate proteins (fig. 3). In both cases, conformational and structural changes have been shown to occur in the substrate [Kaartinen et al., 1999; Murthy et al., 2000; Lorand and Graham, 2003]. Intermolecular covalent crosslinking of noncollagenous substrate proteins results in the formation of high-molecular-weight protein polymers and macromolecular assemblies [Lorand and Graham, 2003]. The isopeptide crosslinks are resistant to normal proteolysis, and thus, their presence is considered to enhance the biochemical stability and cohesive integrity of extracellular matrix in normal tissues and in wound healing and scarring [Lorand and Graham, 2003; Verderio et al., 2005].

Osteoblasts secrete fibronectin, osteopontin and bone sialoprotein, all of which are TG substrate proteins. The latter two proteins are members of the SIBLING (small integrin-binding ligand N-linked glycoprotein) family [Fisher and Fedarko, 2003]. They all form homotypic protein polymers [Kaartinen et al., 1997; Gaudry et al., 1999; Kaartinen et al., 1999, 2002], and heterotypic crosslinking between osteopontin and fibronectin has also been reported in vitro [Beninati et al., 1994]. Crosslinking of fibronectin and osteopontin to type I collagen has been shown in vitro [Mosher and Schad, 1979; Kaartinen et al., 1999], but similar data are still lacking from in vivo studies. This crosslinking between fibrillar and nonfibrillar matrix proteins would likely contribute to the strength and toughness of bone.

TG-crosslinked protein polymers are abundant in bone and in osteoblast cultures (mouse primary osteoblasts and the MC3T3-E1 osteoblast cell line). Polymerization of noncollagenous proteins in bone results from the activity of two TG enzymes – TG2 and Factor XIIIA [Al-Jallad et al., 2006; Nurminskaya and Kaartinen, 2006]. The crosslinking activity provides a critical maturational step in early osteoblast differentiation by crosslinking fibronectin in an event which appears to promote interaction between a fibronectin network and the earliest collagen fibrils. Inhibition of TG activity early during osteoblast differentiation prevents the formation of this initial matrix network and completely blocks further matrix production (both mRNA and protein) and mineralization in the cultures (fig. 3) [Al-Jallad et al., 2006]. Therefore, the formation of this initial extracellular matrix network, and its stabilization by TGs, appears to be critical for further osteoblast differentiation, collagen deposition and matrix mineralization.

Interestingly, TGs have been linked to cell adhesion, cell-matrix crosstalk and signaling in fibroblasts, where the TG family member TG2 (also expressed by osteoblasts) acts as a β_1- and β_3-integrin-binding coreceptor for fibronectin on the cell surface [Gaudry et al., 1999; Akimov et al., 2000]. Based on these findings, it is plausible that TG-mediated crosslinking of nascent bone matrix secreted by osteoblasts signals back to the cells via integrins and thus affects gene transcription. Cell adhesion experiments on monomeric versus polymeric fibronectin reveal that the crosslinking modification significantly alters the ability of fibronectin to support osteoblast adhesion and promotes integrin clustering at the cell surface [Kaartinen et al., unpubl. results]. Since osteopontin and bone sialoprotein are also RGD-containing cell adhesion proteins, and since they accumulate at cell-matrix interfaces, their crosslinking might similarly affect osteoblast behavior.

Molecular Determinants of Bone Mineralization

Bone mineral is present in the form of a carbonate-substituted hydroxyapatite [Rey, 1990]. In recent years, it has become evident that the ratio of inorganic phosphate (P_i) to pyrophosphate (PP_i) plays a key role in the regulation of extracellular matrix mineralization [Terkeltaub, 2001]. The PP_i anion consists of two phosphate molecules linked by a high-energy ester bond. It is present in the extracellular matrix of almost all tissues where it acts as an endogenous inhibitor of both physiologic and pathologic mineral formation. PP_i levels in plasma are sufficient to inhibit the growth of apatite crystals in vitro [Russell et al., 1971], where PP_i binds with high affinity to the growing crystals and prevents further apposition of mineral ions (fig. 4) [Fleisch et al., 1966; Moreno et al., 1987].

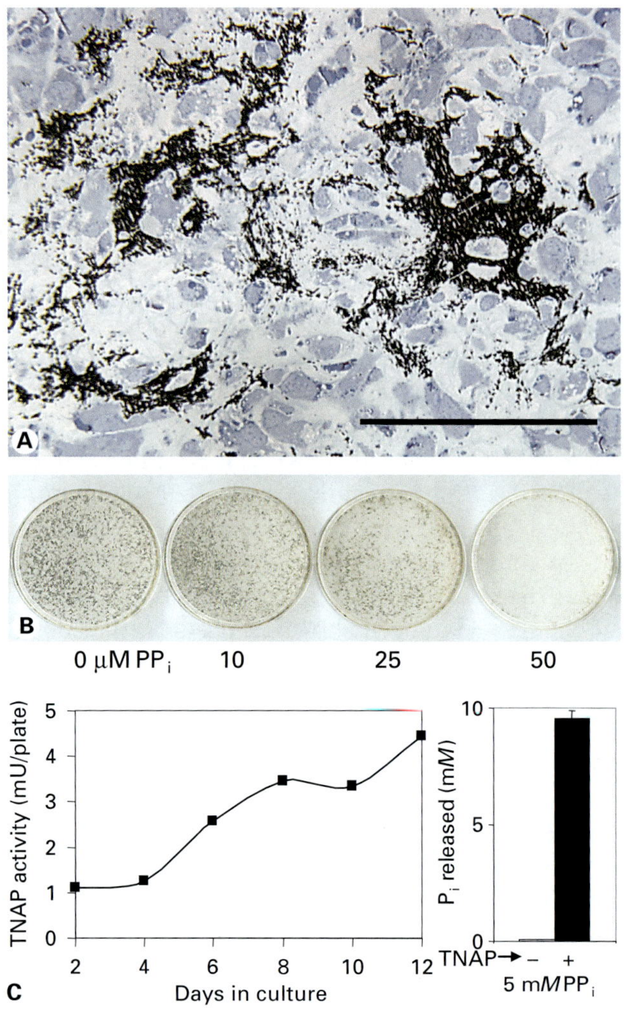

Fig. 4. Pyrophosphate inhibits mineralization in cell cultures of MC3T3-E1 murine calvarial osteoblasts. **A** Semi-thin (1-µm), epoxy-resin section cut parallel to the cell culture dish surface of a 12-day mineralized MC3T3-E1 osteoblast culture showing mineral deposition between osteoblasts and within a collagen-rich extracellular matrix (confirmed by electron microscopy, data not shown). Von Kossa staining for mineral (black), and counterstaining with toluidine blue. Scale bar = 100 µm. **B** Inhibition of osteoblast mineralization in vitro by increasing doses of pyrophosphate (0–50 µM PP$_i$). MC3T3-E1 osteoblasts were cultured in α-modified minimum essential medium supplemented with 10% FBS, inorganic phosphate (5 mM; a phosphate source for mineralization), ascorbic acid (50 µg/ml; a cofactor required for collagen fibrillogenesis) and increasing concentrations of PP$_i$ (a mineralization/crystal growth inhibitor). Medium was replaced every 48 h and after 12 days, mineral was stained by silver nitrate staining (von Kossa staining). **C** TNAP activity increases with time in differentiating MC3T3-E1 osteoblast cultures and correlates with extracellular matrix accumulation and mineralization over 12 days. Cells were incubated in α-modified minimum essential medium supplemented with 10% FBS, β-glycerophosphate (10 mM) and ascorbic acid (50 µg/ml). At the indicated time points, cultures were harvested in 10 mM Tris-HCl (pH 7.4), 0.2% Igepal^{TM} detergent and 2 mM PMSF. After sonication and centrifugation, TNAP activity in the supernatant was measured colorimetrically using *p*-nitrophenylphosphate as a substrate (left panel). TNAP hydrolysis of 5 mM PP$_i$ produces 10 mM P$_i$. For this experiment, 5 mM PP$_i$ dissolved in 10 mM Tris-HCl (pH 8.8) containing 10 mM $MgCl_2$ was incubated for 1 h with or without 2 µg/µl TNAP, at 37°C. Following incubation, P$_i$ released was measured colorimetrically using the ammonium molybdate complex method (right panel).

Release of PP$_i$ into the extracellular matrix of bone is controlled to a large extent by two genes/proteins – *ecto-nucleotidepyrophosphatase/phosphodiesterase 1 (ENPP1)* and the *progressive ankylosis* gene *(ANK).* These two genes are ubiquitously expressed in all tissues but they are most abundant in bone. It is likely that ubiquitous expression ensures that PP$_i$ levels in soft tissues and organs are sufficiently high to prevent ectopic mineralization. Indeed, although lowering extracellular P$_i$ concentrations decreases matrix mineralization, increasing extracellular P$_i$ is not sufficient to cause ectopic mineral formation [Murshed et al., 2005].

ENPP1 is a membrane-bound ectoenzyme that catalyzes the hydrolysis of the phosphodiester I bond of nucleoside triphosphates to produce PP$_i$ [Chern et al., 1969; Huang et al., 1994]. *Enpp1* expression correlates with cell differentiation in cultured mouse osteoblasts [Johnson et al., 1999]. The natural substrate of ENPP1 is believed to be ATP, and the release of ATP into the extracellular matrix by chondrocytes has been demonstrated [Graff et al., 2000]. Osteoblast cultures overexpressing *Enpp1* contain elevated amounts of PP$_i$ and show reduced mineral formation [Johnson et al., 1999]. Further evidence supporting the role of *ENPP1* in preventing ectopic mineralization has been documented by the recent discovery of gene mutations in this protein occurring in idiopathic infantile arterial calcification [Rutsch et al., 2003]. Rutsch et al. [2001] reported decreased levels of ENPP1 protein and decreased PP$_i$ levels, associated with peri-articular and arterial calcification in an individual with this disease. In *tiptoe walking mice (ttw/ttw),* a nonsense mutation causing a premature stop codon in *Enpp1* results in hyperossification of articulating joints and spinal ligaments [Okawa et al., 1998].

Transport of PP_i into the extracellular matrix occurs by means of ANK, an integral multi-pass transmembrane protein [Ho et al., 2000]. PP_i is generated in the intracellular compartment as a byproduct of mitochondrial metabolism and nucleic acid synthesis reactions [Rachow and Ryan, 1988]. Because of its charged and polar nature, intracellular PP_i cannot diffuse passively across the plasma membrane, and functional studies have shown that ANK regulates intra- and extracellular PP_i levels by means of an anion transport mechanism [Ho et al., 2000; Wang et al., 2005]. In situ hybridization studies detected high levels of ANK mRNA in both osteogenic and chondrogenic cells of developing long bones and in articular cartilage of limb joints [Sohn et al., 2002]. An autosomal recessive mutation in the *progressive ankylosis* mouse *(ank/ank)* results in an extracellular PP_i deficiency and severe ankylosis of peripheral and axial joints [Ho et al., 2000]. In humans, craniometaphyseal dysplasia, characterized by overgrowth and thickening of craniofacial bones, is caused by mutations in the *ANK* gene [Nurnberg et al., 2001; Reichenberger et al., 2001]. In contrast to these loss-of-function mutations, dominant *ANK* mutations in humans afflicted with calcium pyrophosphate dihydrate (CPPD) deposition disease results from ANK overactivity and an excess of extracellular PP_i which is then deposited ectopically in articular cartilage as CPPD crystals [Zaka and Williams, 2005].

Homeostatic levels of PP_i thus appear to regulate physiologic mineralization, with perturbations resulting in excess hydroxyapatite formation (PP_i deficiency) or CPPD deposition (elevated PP_i). The high levels of *ENPP1* and *ANK* expression in bone that result in increased extracellular PP_i suggest that mineralization of bone extracellular matrix cannot occur unless this PP_i is removed. PP_i is a substrate for osteoblast-produced tissue non-specific alkaline phosphatase (TNAP) (fig. 4), a well-known enzymatic marker of the osteoblast lineage [Hui and Tenenbaum, 1998]. TNAP is a membrane-bound ectoenzyme phosphatase that plays an essential role in mineralization [Narisawa et al., 1997]. TNAP-mediated hydrolysis of mineralization-inhibiting PP_i results in two molecules of P_i which likely serve as a source of P_i for subsequent hydroxyapatite formation [Eaton and Moss, 1968]. Inactivating mutations of *TNAP* in humans or in mice are characterized by hyperosteoidosis, hypophosphatasia and elevated PP_i levels [Russell et al., 1971; Whyte, 1994; Waymire et al., 1995; Narisawa et al., 1997]. The role of TNAP is therefore antagonistic to ENPP1 with respect to PP_i metabolism [Hessle et al., 2002]. The elevated PP_i levels and hyperosteoidosis of *Tnap*-deficient mice are normalized in *Tnap;Enpp1* double-knockout mice [Hessle et al., 2002; Anderson et al., 2005]. Some of these observations are summarized in figure 5.

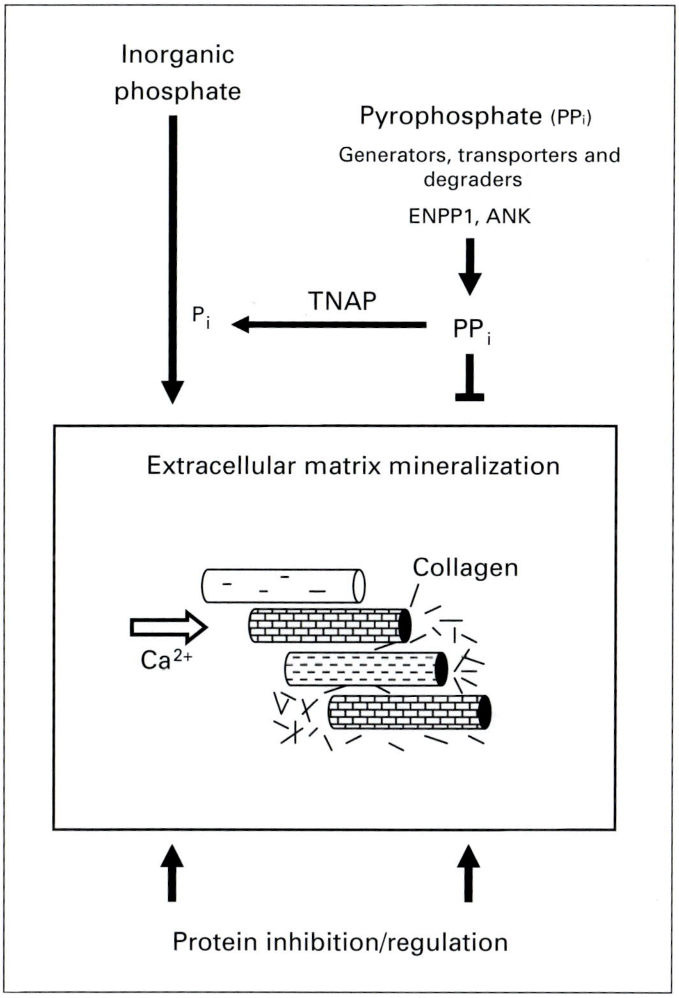

Fig. 5. Schematic diagram illustrating the interplay between various molecular determinants of mineralization in an extracellular matrix. Induction of mineralization in bone, at least in part, results from the activities of proteins and enzymes that generate, transport and degrade the crystal growth inhibitor pyrophosphate (PP_i) within the extracellular compartment/matrix. Enzymatic cleavage of crystal growth-inhibiting pyrophosphate by TNAP is proposed to generate phosphate ions (P_i) that are subsequently used for crystal growth in the extracellular matrix in the presence of calcium ions (Ca^{2+}). Once mineral is nucleated, inhibition of crystal growth by proteins occurs to determine characteristic, bone-specific crystal size, shape and orientation.

Table 1. Extracellular matrix interfaces in mineralized tissues

Hard tissue interfaces in skeletal biology	
Intramembranous ossification (initial)[1]	no substratum required
Endochondral ossification	cartilage substratum
Bone remodeling	bone substratum
Ligament/tendon insertions	bone/fibrocartilage substratum
Osseointegration, orthopedic implants	metal/ceramic substratum
Hard tissue interfaces in the periodontium	
Dentinogenesis	no substratum required
Cementogenesis	dentin substratum
Amelogenesis	dentin substratum
Alveolar bone remodeling	bone substratum
Tooth root resorption	dentin/cementum substratum
Periodontal ligament insertions	bone/cementum substratum
Osseointegration, dental implants	metal/ceramic substratum

[1] During development from cell condensations in mesenchyme. Subsequent appositional growth is onto a substratum of existing bone.

The role of PP_i as an inhibitor of mineralization may not be limited to its crystal-binding properties. PP_i also has a direct effect on osteoblast gene expression [Harmey et al., 2004], and recent data have shown that PP_i inhibits the enzymatic activity of PHEX (phosphate-regulating gene with homologies to endopeptidases on the X chromosome) [Boileau et al., 2001] – an enzyme whose gene mutations lead to the osteomalacia (hypomineralization) associated with X-linked hypophosphatasia in humans [Tenenhouse, 1999]. Thus, PP_i may also function indirectly in regulating mineralization by acting upon mineral-regulating enzymes.

Bone Formation during Physiological Skeletal Remodeling: The Cement Line

Bone cell adhesion events and mineralization occur not only during 'bulk' bone formation and maturation, but also at specific interfacial sites where bone is deposited by osteoblasts directly onto a substratum (table 1). Perhaps the best known example arises during bone remodeling. The reversal phase of the bone remodeling cycle occurs when osteoclasts terminate their bone-resorptive activity. Bone resorption by osteoclasts involves acidification of the resorption pit to dissolve mineral and the release of enzymes to degrade extracellular matrix proteins. The reversal phase is characterized by the loss of resorptive activity, detachment of osteoclasts from the bone surface, and their death by apoptosis. While some additional enzymatic modifications of the resorbed bone surface may then occur by adjacent bone-lining cells [Everts et al., 2002], the resorption pit is invariably populated by committed osteoblast progenitors. This differentiation pathway includes an initial secretion event that creates a three-dimensional cement plane, seen histologically in two dimensions as a cement line, on the surface of the resorbed bone [McKee et al., 1993; McKee and Nanci, 1995]. The cement line is created by the secretory activity of osteoblasts that deposit at the surface of the resorbed bone a planar coating of extracellular matrix deficient in collagen but rich in other proteins. The proteins in the cement line include osteopontin (fig. 6) and variable amounts of bone sialoprotein [Chen et al., 1994].

Concomitant with cement line deposition is its immediate mineralization. This is followed by further osteoblast differentiation into type I collagen (Col1a1)-producing cells synthesizing, secreting and assembling a network of collagen fibrils to form an extended extracellular matrix incorporating abundant additional noncollagenous proteins. This secretory process embeds the cement line deep within the bone and creates an important interface where newer bone contacts older bone, and where microcrack propagation is known to frequently terminate [Qiu et al., 2005]. Understanding the interfacial properties of cement lines/planes, where temporo-spatially distinct bone matrices meet and bond, and where osteopontin is concentrated and bone microfracturing is aborted, represents a key area for further investigation [McKee and Nanci, 1996a]. To this end, we have reported on osteopontin-osteopontin homotypic interactions using a protein-coated bead rheoscope assay and dynamic light scattering [Goldsmith et al., 2002].

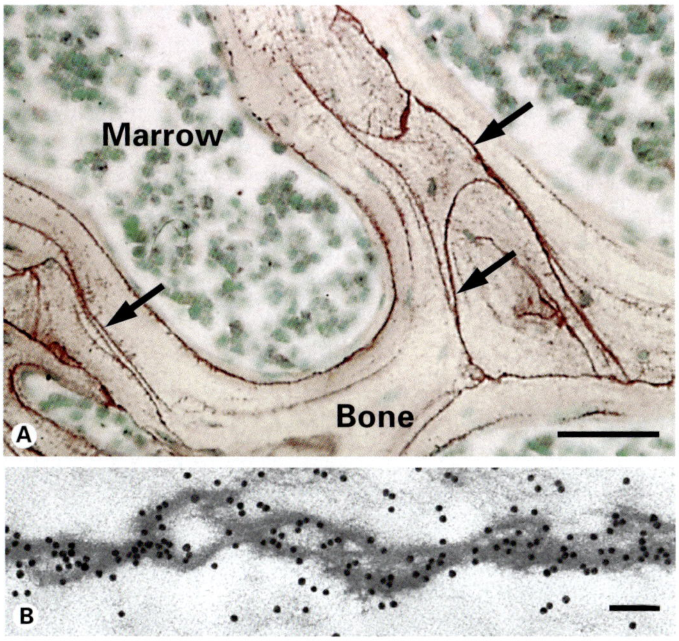

Fig. 6. Micrographs showing osteopontin immunolocalization in rat bone. **A** Paraffin section of decalcified bone after immunohistochemistry for osteopontin and after counterstaining with methyl green. Osteopontin (red) is predominantly localized to cement lines (arrows) – sites representing the reversal phase in which osteoclastic resorption terminates and is followed by bone deposition by osteoblasts. Scale bar = 50 μm. **B** Post-embedding, colloidal-gold immunocytochemistry and transmission electron microscopy reveal abundant gold particles marking sites of osteopontin accumulation at the protein-rich, electron-dense cement line. LR White acrylic resin, thin section (80 nm) immunostained for osteopontin and conventionally counterstained with uranyl acetate and lead citrate. Scale bar = 100 nm.

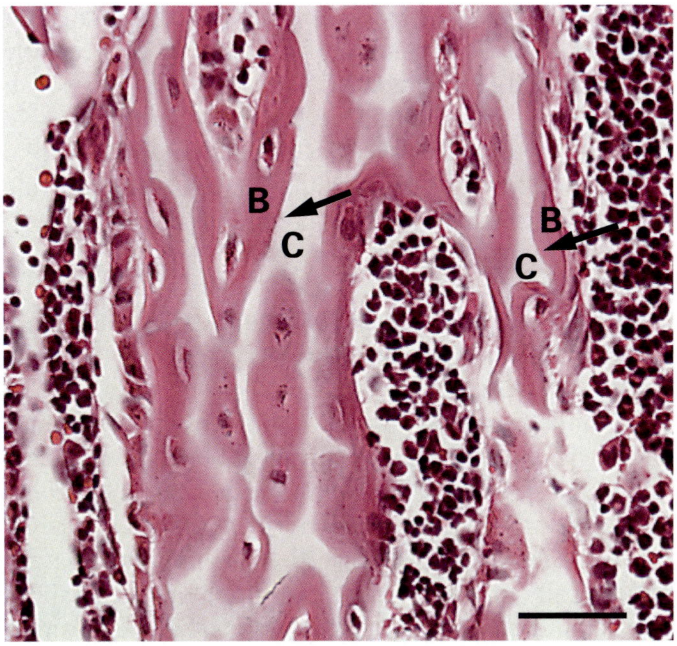

Fig. 7. Paraffin section of the metaphyseal region of a rat tibia, just distal to the proximal growth plate, after conventional staining with hematoxylin and eosin. Bone (B) stains pink, and cartilage cores (C) remain unstained, with the interface between these two distinct extracellular matrices being indicated by arrows. Scale bar = 50 μm.

Bone Formation onto Calcified Cartilage in the Epiphyseal Growth Plate

In addition to cement lines at bone-bone interfaces, another important interface develops during skeletogenesis where a similar sequence of secretory events is mediated by osteoblasts to create a structurally similar cement line. This arises during endochondral ossification and occurs when bone is deposited by osteoblasts onto a scaffolding of calcified cartilage (fig. 7) most readily observed and best documented in the epiphyseal growth plate of growing long bones [Poole et al., 2000]. The structure and extracellular matrix composition of the cement line at the bone-calcified cartilage interface appears in most ways similar to that seen at the bone-bone interface and is likely created by the same sequence of secretory activity from osteoblasts [McKee and Nanci, 1996a]. Some investigators have referred to this structure not as a cement line, but as a lamina limitans [Scherft, 1972]. While not predicated by an osteoclastic resorptive event, the calcified cartilage spicules that emerge from the cartilaginous growth plate and extend into the marrow cavity of the metaphysis are immediately exposed to osteoblast precursors that derive from the developing marrow and the vascular invasion occurring in this region. Lee et al. [1995] have described cartilage (uncalcified)-resorbing cells in this region called septoclasts that express collagenases and other enzymes. Their resorptive activity immediately adjacent to the calcified cartilage may in some ways be likened to osteoclast resorption during bone remodeling. In this context, their enzymatic activity may precondition the calcified cartilage surface for the deposition of the cement line by resident osteoblasts.

Like for bone-bone interfacial cement lines, the bone-calcified cartilage cement line is rich in osteopontin and is structurally similar at the ultrastructural level [McKee and Nanci, 1996a]. While many of the central mixed (bone and calcified cartilage) spicules in the metaphysis are resorbed by osteo/chondroclasts as part of the endochondral process, those peripheral mixed spicules of the growth plate form an important adhesive boundary for the long bone at the anatomical junction between the epiphysis and the metaphysis. Thus, interfaces between mineralized tissues at this location might similarly help to maintain skeletal integrity at a site otherwise known to be prone to fracture [Forriol and Shapiro, 2005] during long bone growth prior to closure of the growth plate.

Bone Formation at Other Osseous Interfaces: Bone Repair and Implants

Orthopedic and dental interventions often involve surgeries where drilling and/or cutting of bone is performed. Such surgeries necessarily produce a new interface where bone deposition is desired during the post-surgery healing process. Likewise, osseointegration of implanted materials, typically for bone being either titanium, metal alloys or calcium-based ceramics, requires that bone deposition occurs directly on the implant surface in a manner that potentiates osseointegration rather than fibrous encapsulation. Numerous electron microscopic studies have reported the formation of a collagen-deficient, but protein-rich, cement line (also called a lamina limitans on occasion) at the bone-implant interface [De Lange et al., 1990; Sennerby et al., 1991; de Bruijn et al., 1992; Nanci et al., 1994; Irie et al., 1998]. We have reported that this structure is similar to other cement lines and contains abundant osteopontin [McKee and Nanci, 1996a]. Likewise, we have made similar observations for cement lines that form as part of the bone wound healing process and are found at the margins of surgically drilled bone, with the additional observation that macrophages may contribute osteopontin to initial cement line formation [McKee and Nanci, 1996b]. Given these similarities in cement line formation, structure and composition in various bone healing models, we have postulated that cement line formation during bone healing is similar to that shown physiologically for bone remodeling and during endochondral ossification. Cement line formation at this interfacial boundary likely represents a key event in integrating and bonding one mineralized extracellular matrix with another (or with an implant). Table 1 summarizes these and additional interfaces in skeletal and dental biology, making a distinction between those where bone deposition occurs onto a substrate, and those where it does not. Additional studies are required to test adhesive forces across these interfaces and to determine the contributions made by the proteins residing in cement lines.

Acknowledgements

This work was supported by grants from the Canadian Institutes of Health Research to M.D.M. and M.T.K. The authors thank all those who contributed in one way or another to the work presented in this review, and in particular, M.D.M. would like to thank Drs. Antonio Nanci, William Landis and Gerard Karsenty for many stimulating past and present collaborations. M.D.M. and M.T.K. are scholars of the Fonds de la Recherche en Santé du Quebec and members of the Fonds de la Recherche en Santé du Quebec Oral Health Research Network and the McGill Centre for Bone and Periodontal Research. Figure 1D was prepared with the help of Justin Stephens and the McGill Molson Medical Informatics Project.

References

Aizenberg, J., A. Tkachenko, S. Weiner, L. Addadi, G. Hendler (2001) Calcitic microlenses as part of the photoreceptor system in brittlestars. Nature *412:* 819.

Aizenberg, J., J.C. Weaver, M.S. Thanawala, V.C. Sundar, D.E. Morse, P. Fratzl (2005) Skeleton of *Euplectella* sp: structural hierarchy from the nanoscale to the macroscale. Science *309:* 275–278.

Akimov, S.S., D. Krylov, L.F. Fleischman, A.M. Belkin (2000) Tissue transglutaminase is an integrin-binding adhesion coreceptor for fibronectin. J Cell Biol *148:* 825–838.

Al-Jallad, H.F., Y. Nakano, J.L.Y. Chen, E. McMillan, C. Lefebvre, M.T. Kaartinen Transglutaminase activity regulates osteoblast differentiation and matrix mineralization in MC3T3-E1 osteoblast cells. Matrix Biol, in press.

Anderson, H.C., D. Harmey, N.P. Camacho, R. Garimella, J.B. Sipe, S. Tague, X. Bi, K. Johnson, R. Terkeltaub, J.L. Millan (2005) Sustained osteomalacia of long bones despite major improvement in other hypophosphatasia-related mineral deficits in tissue nonspecific alkaline phosphatase/nucleotide pyrophosphatase phosphodiesterase 1 double-deficient mice. Am J Pathol *166:* 1711–1720.

Beninati, S., D.R. Senger, E. Cordella-Miele, A.B. Mukherjee, I. Chackalaparampil, V. Shanmugam, K. Singh, B.B. Mukherjee (1994) Osteopontin: its transglutaminase-catalyzed post-translational modifications and cross-linking to fibronectin. J Biochem (Tokyo) *115:* 675–682.

Blair, H.C. (1998) How the osteoclast degrades bone. Bioessays *20:* 837–846.

Boileau, G., H.S. Tenenhouse, L. Desgroseillers, P. Crine (2001) Characterization of PHEX endopeptidase catalytic activity: identification of parathyroid-hormone-related peptide107–139 as a substrate and osteocalcin, PP_i and phosphate as inhibitors. Biochem J *355:* 707–713.

Boskey, A.L. (2003) Biomineralization: an overview. Connect Tissue Res *44(suppl 1):* 5–9.

Chen, J., M.D. McKee, A. Nanci, J. Sodek (1994) Bone sialoprotein mRNA expression and ultrastructural localization in fetal porcine calvarial bone: comparisons with osteopontin. Histochem J *26:* 67–78.

Chern, C.J., A.B. MacDonald, A.J. Morris (1969) Purification and properties of a nucleoside triphosphate pyrophosphohydrolase from red cells of the rabbit. J Biol Chem *244:* 5489–5495.

Currey, J.D. (2005a) Bone architecture and fracture. Curr Osteoporos Rep *3:* 52–56.

Currey, J.D. (2005b) Hierarchies in biomineral structures. Science *309:* 253–254.
de Bruijn, J.D., C.P. Klein, K. de Groot, C.A. van Blitterswijk (1992) The ultrastructure of the bone-hydroxyapatite interface in vitro. J Biomed Mater Res *26:* 1365–1382.
De Lange, G.L., C. De Putter, F.L. De Wijs (1990) Histological and ultrastructural appearance of the hydroxyapatite-bone interface. J Biomed Mater Res *24:* 829–845.
Discher, D.E., P. Janmey, Y.L. Wang (2005) Tissue cells feel and respond to the stiffness of their substrate. Science *310:* 1139–1143.
Eaton, R.H., D.W. Moss (1968) Kinetic studies on the orthophosphatase and inorganic pyrophosphatase activities of human alkaline phosphatase. Enzymologia *35:* 168–178.
Everts, V., J.M. Delaisse, W. Korper, D.C. Jansen, W. Tigchelaar-Gutter, P. Saftig, W. Beertsen (2002) The bone lining cell: its role in cleaning Howship's lacunae and initiating bone formation. J Bone Miner Res *17:* 77–90.
Fisher, L.W., N.S. Fedarko (2003) Six genes expressed in bones and teeth encode the current members of the SIBLING family of proteins. Connect Tissue Res *44(suppl 1):* 33–40.
Fleisch, H., R.G. Russell, F. Straumann (1966) Effect of pyrophosphate on hydroxyapatite and its implications in calcium homeostasis. Nature *212:* 901–903.
Forriol, F., F. Shapiro (2005) Bone development: interaction of molecular components and biophysical forces. Clin Orthop Relat Res *432:* 14–33.
Gaudry, C.A., E. Verderio, D. Aeschlimann, A. Cox, C. Smith, M. Griffin (1999) Cell surface localization of tissue transglutaminase is dependent on a fibronectin-binding site in its N-terminal beta-sandwich domain. J Biol Chem *274:* 30707–30714.
Giachelli, C.M. (2005) Inducers and inhibitors of biomineralization: lessons from pathologic calcification. Orthod Craniofac Res *8:* 229–231.
Goldsmith, H.L., J.M. Labrosse, F.A. McIntosh, P.H. Maenpaa, M.T. Kaartinen, M.D. McKee (2002) Homotypic interactions of soluble and immobilized osteopontin. Ann Biomed Eng *30:* 840–850.
Gorski, J.P. (1998) Is all bone the same? Distinctive distributions and properties of non-collagenous matrix proteins in lamellar vs woven bone imply the existence of different underlying osteogenic mechanisms. Crit Rev Oral Biol Med *9:* 201–223.
Graff, R.D., E.R. Lazarowski, A.J. Banes, G.M. Lee (2000) ATP release by mechanically loaded porcine chondrons in pellet culture. Arthritis Rheum *43:* 1571–1579.
Harmey, D., L. Hessle, S. Narisawa, K.A. Johnson, R. Terkeltaub, J.L. Millan (2004) Concerted regulation of inorganic pyrophosphate and osteopontin by akp2, enpp1, and ank: an integrated model of the pathogenesis of mineralization disorders. Am J Pathol *164:* 1199–1209.
Hessle, L., K.A. Johnson, H.C. Anderson, S. Narisawa, A. Sali, J.W. Goding, R. Terkeltaub, J.L. Millan (2002) Tissue-nonspecific alkaline phosphatase and plasma cell membrane glycoprotein-1 are central antagonistic regulators of bone mineralization. Proc Natl Acad Sci USA *99:* 9445–9449.
Ho, A.M., M.D. Johnson, D.M. Kingsley (2000) Role of the mouse ank gene in control of tissue calcification and arthritis. Science *289:* 265–270.
Huang, R., M. Rosenbach, R. Vaughn, D. Provvedini, N. Rebbe, S. Hickman, J. Goding, R. Terkeltaub (1994) Expression of the murine plasma cell nucleotide pyrophosphohydrolase PC-1 is shared by human liver, bone, and cartilage cells. Regulation of PC-1 expression in osteosarcoma cells by transforming growth factor-beta. J Clin Invest *94:* 560–567.
Hui, M., H.C. Tenenbaum (1998) New face of an old enzyme: alkaline phosphatase may contribute to human tissue aging by inducing tissue hardening and calcification. Anat Rec *253:* 91–94.
Hunter, G.K., P.V. Hauschka, A.R. Poole, L.C. Rosenberg, H.A. Goldberg (1996) Nucleation and inhibition of hydroxyapatite formation by mineralized tissue proteins. Biochem J *317:* 59–64.
Irie, K., S. Zalzal, H. Ozawa, M.D. McKee, A. Nanci (1998) Morphological and immunocytochemical characterization of primary osteogenic cell cultures derived from fetal rat cranial tissue. Anat Rec *252:* 554–567.
Johnson, K., A. Moffa, Y. Chen, K. Pritzker, J. Goding, R. Terkeltaub (1999) Matrix vesicle plasma cell membrane glycoprotein-1 regulates mineralization by murine osteoblastic MC3T3 cells. J Bone Miner Res *14:* 883–892.
Kaartinen, M.T., S. El-Maadawy, N.H. Rasanen, M.D. McKee (2002) Tissue transglutaminase and its substrates in bone. J Bone Miner Res *17:* 2161–2173.
Kaartinen, M.T., A. Pirhonen, A. Linnala-Kankkunen, P.H. Maenpaa (1997) Transglutaminase-catalyzed cross-linking of osteopontin is inhibited by osteocalcin. J Biol Chem *272:* 22736–22741.
Kaartinen, M.T., A. Pirhonen, A. Linnala-Kankkunen, P.H. Maenpaa (1999) Cross-linking of osteopontin by tissue transglutaminase increases its collagen binding properties. J Biol Chem *274:* 1729–1735.
Karsenty, G., E.F. Wagner (2002) Reaching a genetic and molecular understanding of skeletal development. Dev Cell *2:* 389.
Klein-Nulend, J., P.J. Nijweide, E.H. Burger (2003) Osteocyte and bone structure. Curr Osteoporos Rep *1:* 5–10.
Knoll, A.H. (2003) Biomineralization and evolutionary history; in Dove, P.M., J.J. De Yoreo, S. Weiner (eds): Reviews in Mineralogy and Geochemistry. St Louis, Mineralogical Society of America and Geochemical Society, vol 54, pp 329–356.
Landis, W.J. (1996) Mineral characterization in calcifying tissues: atomic, molecular and macromolecular perspectives. Connect Tissue Res *34:* 239–246.
Landis, W.J. (1999) An overview of vertebrate mineralization with emphasis on collagen-mineral interaction. Gravit Space Biol Bull *12:* 15–26.
Lee, E.R., L. Lamplugh, N.L. Shepard, J.S. Mort (1995) The septoclast, a cathepsin B-rich cell involved in the resorption of growth plate cartilage. J Histochem Cytochem *43:* 525–536.
Lorand, L., R.M. Graham (2003) Transglutaminases: crosslinking enzymes with pleiotropic functions. Nat Rev Mol Cell Biol *4:* 140–156.
McCulloch, C.A.G., P. Lekic, M.D. McKee (2000) Role of physical forces in regulating the form and function of the periodontal ligament. Periodontology *24:* 56–72.
McKee, M.D., M.C. Farach-Carson, W.T. Butler, P.V. Hauschka, A. Nanci (1993) Ultrastructural immunolocalization of noncollagenous (osteopontin and osteocalcin) and plasma (albumin and alpha 2HS-glycoprotein) proteins in rat bone. J Bone Miner Res *8:* 485–496.
McKee, M.D., M.T. Kaartinen (2002) Regulation of biomineralization by proteins and their assembly into extracellular matrices: bone and the osseointegrated implant interface; in Zarb, G., U. Lekholm, T. Albrektsson, H. Tenenbaum (eds): Aging, Osteoporosis and Dental Implants. Carol Stream, Quintessence Publishing, pp 191–205.
McKee, M.D., A. Nanci (1993) Ultrastructural, cytochemical and immunocytochemical studies on bone and its interfaces. Cell Mater *3:* 219–243.
McKee, M.D., A. Nanci (1995) Osteopontin and the bone remodeling sequence. Colloidal-gold immunocytochemistry of an interfacial extracellular matrix protein. Ann N Y Acad Sci *760:* 177–189.
McKee, M.D., A. Nanci (1996a) Osteopontin at mineralized tissue interfaces in bone, teeth, and osseointegrated implants: ultrastructural distribution and implications for mineralized tissue formation, turnover, and repair. Microsc Res Tech *33:* 141–164.
McKee, M.D., A. Nanci (1996b) Secretion of osteopontin by macrophages and its accumulation at tissue surfaces during wound healing in mineralized tissues: a potential requirement for macrophage adhesion and phagocytosis. Anat Rec *245:* 394–409.
McKee, M.D., J. Sodek (2000) Bone matrix proteins; in Henderson, J.E., D. Goltzman (eds): The Osteoporosis Primer. Cambridge, Cambridge University Press, pp 46–63.
Moreno, E.C., T. Aoba, H.C. Margolis (1987) Pyrophosphate adsorption onto hydroxyapatite and its inhibition of crystal growth. Compend Suppl *8:* S256–S258, S260, S262–S266.
Mosher, D.F., P.E. Schad (1979) Cross-linking of fibronectin to collagen by blood coagulation Factor XIIIa. J Clin Invest *64:* 781–787.

Murshed, M., D. Harmey, J.L. Millan, M.D. McKee, G. Karsenty (2005) Unique coexpression in osteoblasts of broadly expressed genes accounts for the spatial restriction of ECM mineralization to bone. Genes Dev *19:* 1093–1104.

Murthy, S.N., J.H. Wilson, T.J. Lukas, Y. Veklich, J.W. Weisel, L. Lorand (2000) Transglutaminase-catalyzed crosslinking of the alpha and gamma constituent chains in fibrinogen. Proc Natl Acad Sci USA *97:* 44–48.

Nanci, A., G.F. McCarthy, C. Clokie, H. Warshawsky, S. Zalzal, M.D. McKee (1994) Tissue response to titanium implants in the rat tibia: ultrastructural, immunocytochemical and lectin-cytochemical characterization of the bone-titanium interface. Cell Mater *4:* 1–30.

Narisawa, S., N. Frohlander, J.L. Millan (1997) Inactivation of two mouse alkaline phosphatase genes and establishment of a model of infantile hypophosphatasia. Dev Dyn *208:* 432–446.

Nurminskaya, M., M.T. Kaartinen (2006) Transglutaminases in mineralized tissues. In press. http://www.bioscience.org/.

Nurnberg, P., H. Thiele, D. Chandler, W. Hohne, M.L. Cunningham, H. Ritter, G. Leschik, K. Uhlmann, C. Mischung, K. Harrop, J. Goldblatt, Z.U. Borochowitz, D. Kotzot, F. Westermann, S. Mundlos, H.S. Braun, N. Laing, S. Tinschert (2001) Heterozygous mutations in ANKH, the human ortholog of the mouse progressive ankylosis gene, result in craniometaphyseal dysplasia. Nat Genet *28:* 37–41.

O'Brien, F.J., O. Brennan, O.D. Kennedy, T.C. Lee (2005) Microcracks in cortical bone: how do they affect bone biology? Curr Osteoporos Rep *3:* 39–45.

Okawa, A., I. Nakamura, S. Goto, H. Moriya, Y. Nakamura, S. Ikegawa (1998) Mutation in Npps in a mouse model of ossification of the posterior longitudinal ligament of the spine. Nat Genet *19:* 271–273.

Parfitt, A.M. (2002) Targeted and nontargeted bone remodeling: relationship to basic multicellular unit origination and progression. Bone *30:* 5.

Pirinen, S. (1995) Endocrine regulation of craniofacial growth. Acta Odontol Scand *53:* 179–185.

Pirinen, S., A. Majurin, H.L. Lenko, K. Koski (1994) Craniofacial features in patients with deficient and excessive growth hormone. J Craniofac Genet Dev Biol *14:* 144–152.

Poole, A.R., S. Laverty, F. Mwale (2000) Endochondral bone formation and development in the axial and appendicular skeleton; in Henderson, J.E., D. Goltzman (eds): The Osteoporosis Primer. Cambridge, Cambridge University Press, pp 3–17.

Qiu, S., D. Sudhaker Rao, D.P. Fyhrie, S. Palnitkar, A.M. Parfitt (2005) The morphological association between microcracks and osteocyte lacunae in human cortical bone. Bone *37:* 10–15.

Rachow, J.W., L.M. Ryan (1988) Inorganic pyrophosphate metabolism in arthritis. Rheum Dis Clin North Am *14:* 289–302.

Ramirez-Yanez, G.O., J.R. Smid, W.G. Young, M.J. Waters (2005) Influence of growth hormone on the craniofacial complex of transgenic mice. Eur J Orthod *27:* 494–500.

Reichenberger, E., V. Tiziani, S. Watanabe, L. Park, Y. Ueki, C. Santanna, S.T. Baur, R. Shiang, D.K. Grange, P. Beighton, J. Gardner, H. Hamersma, S. Sellars, R. Ramesar, A.C. Lidral, A. Sommer, C.M. Raposo do Amaral, R.J. Gorlin, J.B. Mulliken, B.R. Olsen (2001) Autosomal dominant craniometaphyseal dysplasia is caused by mutations in the transmembrane protein ANK. Am J Hum Genet *68:* 1321–1326.

Rey, C. (1990) Calcium phosphate biomaterials and bone mineral. Differences in composition, structures and properties. Biomaterials *11:* 13–15.

Russell, R.G., S. Bisaz, A. Donath, D.B. Morgan, H. Fleisch (1971) Inorganic pyrophosphate in plasma in normal persons and in patients with hypophosphatasia, osteogenesis imperfecta, and other disorders of bone. J Clin Invest *50:* 961–969.

Rutsch, F., N. Ruf, S. Vaingankar, M.R. Toliat, A. Suk, W. Hohne, G. Schauer, M. Lehmann, T. Roscioli, D. Schnabel, J.T. Epplen, A. Knisely, A. Superti-Furga, J. McGill, M. Filippone, A.R. Sinaiko, H. Vallance, B. Hinrichs, W. Smith, M. Ferre, R. Terkeltaub, P. Nurnberg (2003) Mutations in ENPP1 are associated with 'idiopathic' infantile arterial calcification. Nat Genet *34:* 379.

Rutsch, F., S. Vaingankar, K. Johnson, I. Goldfine, B. Maddux, P. Schauerte, H. Kalhoff, K. Sano, W.A. Boisvert, A. Superti-Furga, R. Terkeltaub (2001) PC-1 nucleoside triphosphate pyrophosphohydrolase deficiency in idiopathic infantile arterial calcification. Am J Pathol *158:* 543–554.

Scherft, J.P. (1972) The lamina limitans of the organic matrix of calcified cartilage and bone. J Ultrastruct Res *38:* 318–331.

Sennerby, L., L.E. Ericson, P. Thomsen, U. Lekholm, P. Astrand (1991) Structure of the bone-titanium interface in retrieved clinical oral implants. Clin Oral Implants Res *2:* 103–111.

Sodek, J., M.D. McKee (2000) Molecular and cellular biology of alveolar bone. Periodontology 2000 *24:* 99–126.

Sohn, P., M. Crowley, E. Slattery, R. Serra (2002) Developmental and TGF-beta-mediated regulation of Ank mRNA expression in cartilage and bone. Osteoarthritis Cartilage *10:* 482.

Tenenhouse, H.S. (1999) X-linked hypophosphataemia: a homologous disorder in humans and mice. Nephrol Dial Transplant *14:* 333–341.

Terkeltaub, R.A. (2001) Inorganic pyrophosphate generation and disposition in pathophysiology. Am J Physiol Cell Physiol *281:* C1–C11.

Verderio, E.A., T.S. Johnson, M. Griffin (2005) Transglutaminases in wound healing and inflammation. Prog Exp Tumor Res *38:* 89–114.

Wang, W., J. Xu, B. Du, T. Kirsch (2005) Role of the progressive ankylosis gene (ank) in cartilage mineralization. Mol Cell Biol *25:* 312–323.

Wassen, M.H.M., J. Lammens, J.M. Tekoppele, R.J.B. Sakkers, Z. Liu, A.J. Verbout, R.A. Bank (2000) Collagen structure regulates fibril mineralization in osteogenesis as revealed by cross-link patterns in calcifying callus. J Bone Miner Res *15:* 1776–1785.

Waymire, K.G., J.D. Mahuren, J.M. Jaje, T.R. Guilarte, S.P. Coburn, G.R. MacGregor (1995) Mice lacking tissue non-specific alkaline phosphatase die from seizures due to defective metabolism of vitamin B-6. Nat Genet *11:* 45–51.

Weiner, S., P.M. Dove (2003) An overview of biomineralization processes and the problem of the vital effect; in Dove, P.M., J.J. De Yoreo, S. Weiner (eds): Reviews in Mineralogy and Geochemistry. St Louis, Mineralogical Society of America and Geochemical Society, vol 54, pp 1–29.

Whyte, M.P. (1994) Hypophosphatasia and the role of alkaline phosphatase in skeletal mineralization. Endocr Rev *15:* 439–461.

Young, J.R., J.M. Didymus, P.R. Brown, B. Prins, S. Mann (1992) Crystal assembly and phylogenetic evolution in heterococcoliths. Nature *356:* 516.

Zaka, R., C.J. Williams (2005) Genetics of chondrocalcinosis. Osteoarthritis Cartilage *13:* 745.

Cells
Tissues
Organs

Cells Tissues Organs 2005;181:189–195
DOI: 10.1159/000091380

Essential Roles of Ameloblastin in Maintaining Ameloblast Differentiation and Enamel Formation

Satoshi Fukumoto[a] Aya Yamada[a] Kazuaki Nonaka[a] Yoshihiko Yamada[b]

[a]Section of Pediatric Dentistry, Division of Oral Health, Growth and Development, Faculty of Dental Science, Kyushu University, Fukuoka, Japan; [b]Craniofacial Developmental Biology and Regeneration Branch, National Institute of Dental and Craniofacial Research, National Institutes of Health, Bethesda, Md., USA

Key Words
Ameloblastin · Amelogenin · Enamel matrix protein

Abstract
During tooth development, dental epithelial cells interact with extracellular matrix components, such as the basement membrane and enamel matrix. Ameloblastin, an enamel matrix protein, plays a crucial role in maintaining the ameloblast differentiation state and is essential for enamel formation. Ameloblastin-null mice developed severe enamel hypoplasia. In mutant mice, dental epithelial cells started to differentiate into ameloblasts, but ameloblasts soon lost cell polarity, proliferated, and formed multiple cell layers, indicative of some aspects of preameloblast phenotypes. In addition, the expression of amelogenin, another component of the enamel matrix, was specifically reduced in mutant ameloblasts. More than 20% of amelobastin-null mice developed odontogenic tumors. We also found that recombinant ameloblastin specifically bound to ameloblasts and inhibited proliferation of dental epithelial cells. These results suggest that ameloblastin is an important regulator to maintain the differentiation state of ameloblasts.

Overview of Extracellular Matrix in Tooth Development

The extracellular matrix plays a critical role in tissue development and homeostasis by mediating cell growth, migration, differentiation, apoptosis, and gene expression [Damsky and Werb, 1992; Lin et al., 1993]. Tooth development is regulated by sequential and reciprocal interactions between the neural crest-derived mesenchyme and oral ectoderm [Thesleff and Hurmerinta, 1981; Ruch, 1987; Lumsden, 1988]. Although the precise molecular mechanisms that mediate the interactions between epithelia and mesenchyme remain unknown, the basement membrane between epithelial and mesenchymal cells has been reported to play a critical role in the induction and maintenance of cellular differentiation phenotypes [Adams and Watt, 1993]. The basement membrane is a specialized extracellular matrix that mainly consists of various forms of laminin, type IV collagen, perlecan, and nidogen, and provides a scaffolding for epithelium and signaling for cellular differentiation in a variety of tissues through interactions between specific cellular receptors [Timpl, 1996]. Type IV collagen and laminins are present in the dental basement membrane during early mouse tooth development but disappear at a later stage by proteolytic enzymes [Lesot et al., 1981; Sahlberg et al., 1992].

KARGER

Fax +41 61 306 12 34
E-Mail karger@karger.ch
www.karger.com

Accessible online at:
www.karger.com/cto

Satoshi Fukumoto, DDS
Section of Pediatric Dentistry, Division of Oral Health, Growth and Development
Faculty of Dental Science, Kyushu University, 3-1-1 Maidashi, Higashi-ku
Fukuoka 812-8582 (Japan)
Tel. +81 92 642 6401, Fax +81 95 849 6468, E-Mail fukumoto@dent.kyushu-u.ac.jp

Dental epithelium differentiates into ameloblasts through distinct steps, including presecretory, secretory, and maturation stages [Fincham et al., 1999]. Evidence for each of these differentiation stages can be seen in the incisors of adult rodents, because they continuously grow and erupt throughout the life span. In the presecretory stage, the basement membrane matrix separates the dental epithelium (preameloblast) and mesenchyme (preodontoblast) [Thesleff and Hurmerinta, 1981; Adams and Watt, 1993]; however, the basement membrane disappears during the secretory stage and is replaced by the enamel matrix, which supports secretory ameloblasts [Smith, 1998]. Secretory-stage ameloblasts produce and secrete specific proteins in the enamel matrix that are replaced by calcium and phosphorous during the maturation stage for enamel formation.

Expression and Localization of Enamel Matrix in the Tooth Germ

The major secretory proteins synthesized by ameloblasts can be divided into two categories, amelogenin and nonamelogenin. Ameloblastin (also known as sheathlin and amelin) and enamelin are well known members of the nonamelogenin proteins [Deutsch et al., 1991; Cerny et al., 1996; Fong et al., 1996; Fukae et al., 1996; Krebsbach et al., 1996; Hu et al., 1997]. Amelogenin, the major component of the mineralizing enamel matrix, has been shown to be critical for enamel formation [Fincham et al., 1999; Gibson et al., 2001; Moradian-Oldak, 2001]. These findings are supported by the analysis of a group of inherited disorders with defective enamel formation called amelogenesis imperfecta. Ameloblastin was identified by three groups and reported to code for an anionic protein that is rich in proline, glycine, and leucine [Fong et al., 1996; Krebsbach et al., 1996; Hu et al., 1997]. Enamelin, the largest enamel protein, contains hydrophobic, acidic, and basic domains in different regions of its molecule [Uchida et al., 1991; Fukae et al., 1996; Hu et al., 1998]. Immunohistochemistry demonstrates that enamelin concentrates at the growing tips of enamel crystallites, while proteolytically cleaved products become localized in the rod and interrod enamel.

Immunodetection analysis shows that amelogenin is expressed in the extracellular matrix prior to ameloblastin [Nanci et al., 1998]. At the presecretory stage, when the basement membrane is still present between ameloblasts and odontoblasts, only amelogenin is detectable in secretory granules. Typically, the dispersed presence of amelogenin can be observed in the extracellular matrix prior to the disappearance of the basement membrane. Ameloblastin is not detectable extracellularly at this early stage but later appears as patches of electron-dense matrix in the dentin mantle. At the secretory stage, amelogenin and ameloblastin are produced by secretory ameloblasts (fig. 1). In this stage, ameloblastin is present over the saccules of the Golgi apparatus, in secretory granules in the Golgi region, in Tomes' process, and over multivesicular bodies [Uchida et al., 1997; Nanci et al., 1998]. During the early maturation stage, amelogenin and ameloblastin are still positive for immunoreactivity over the Golgi apparatus, secretory granules, and endosome/lysosome structures of ameloblasts. In addition, as in the secretory stage, antibodies for amelogenin and ameloblastin yield differential immunostaining in the enamel. Anti-amelogenin antibody is immunoreactive throughout the enamel layer, except near the cell surface, whereas anti-ameloblastin antibody shows a decreasing gradient away from the cell surface (fig. 1) [Nanci et al., 1998]. At the late maturation stage, amelogenin and ameloblastin are still present, though they are significantly reduced as compared with the early maturation stage. Additionally, at this late stage, anti-ameloblastin antibody shows very weak immunolabeling on the enamel surface, and almost no immunogold particles can be found in the matrix in deeper regions. The distribution of ameloblastin and amelin is different even though they are the same extract protein, because the epitopes of the antibodies were different. Furthermore, an antibody to the C terminus of amelogenin gives the opposite results to that illustrated in figure 1. The reason for this is that enamel proteins are processed by several kinds of protease, including enamelysin, into many cleavage products, each with a different distribution [Nanci et al., 1998].

Tooth Phenotypes of Ameloblastin-Null Mutants

Ameloblastin overexpression in transgenic mice results in abnormal enamel crystallite formation and enamel rod morphology [Paine et al., 2003]. These findings suggest that enamel crystallite formation and rod morphology are influenced by the temporal and spatial expression of ameloblastin and imply that the ameloblastin gene locus may be involved in the etiology of a number of undiagnosed hereditary amelogenesis imperfecta [MacDougall et al., 2000]. To better characterize the function of ameloblastin during enamel formation,

Fig. 1. Different localizations of ameloblastin and amelogenin in the enamel matrix layer. Ameloblastin is a tooth-specific glycoprotein. The most abundant expression of ameloblastin occurs at the secretory stage, and its expression is diminished at the maturation stage. In the secretory stage, ameloblastin protein is localized near the ameloblast cell surface. On the other hand, amelogenin is broadly localized throughout the enamel layer, but not around the cell surface. Differences in the distribution pattern suggest that ameloblastin and amelogenin have different functions in amelogenesis.

Fig. 2. Defect in maintaining the differentiation state of ameloblasts in ameloblastin-null tooth. In wildtype tooth, dental epithelium is differentiated through the interaction between preameloblasts and the basement membrane in the presecretory (PS) stage. In this stage, the epithelium is proliferating. In the secretory (S) stage, ameloblasts stop proliferation and start to secrete enamel matrix proteins. In this stage, basement membrane (BM) components collagen IV and laminin, and their receptor integrin α_6, disappear, and ameloblastin is secreted, binds secretory stage ameloblasts, maintains cell polarity, and inhibits cell proliferation. In ameloblastin-null mice, dental epithelial cells are normal in the presecretory stage. At the secretory stage, preameloblasts start to differentiate into ameloblasts. However, later ameloblasts depolarize, detach from the matrix, and proliferate. Ameloblasts in mutant mice are round, form multicell layers, and secrete abnormal matrix vesicles.

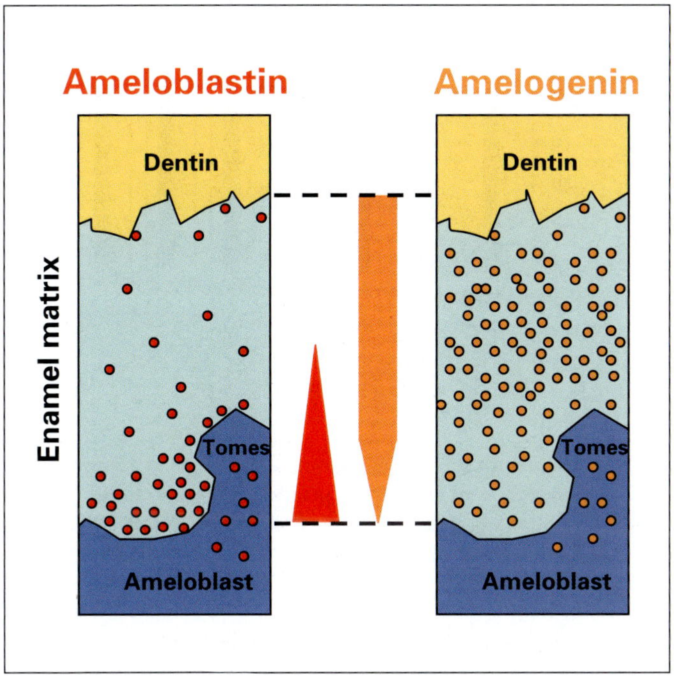

1

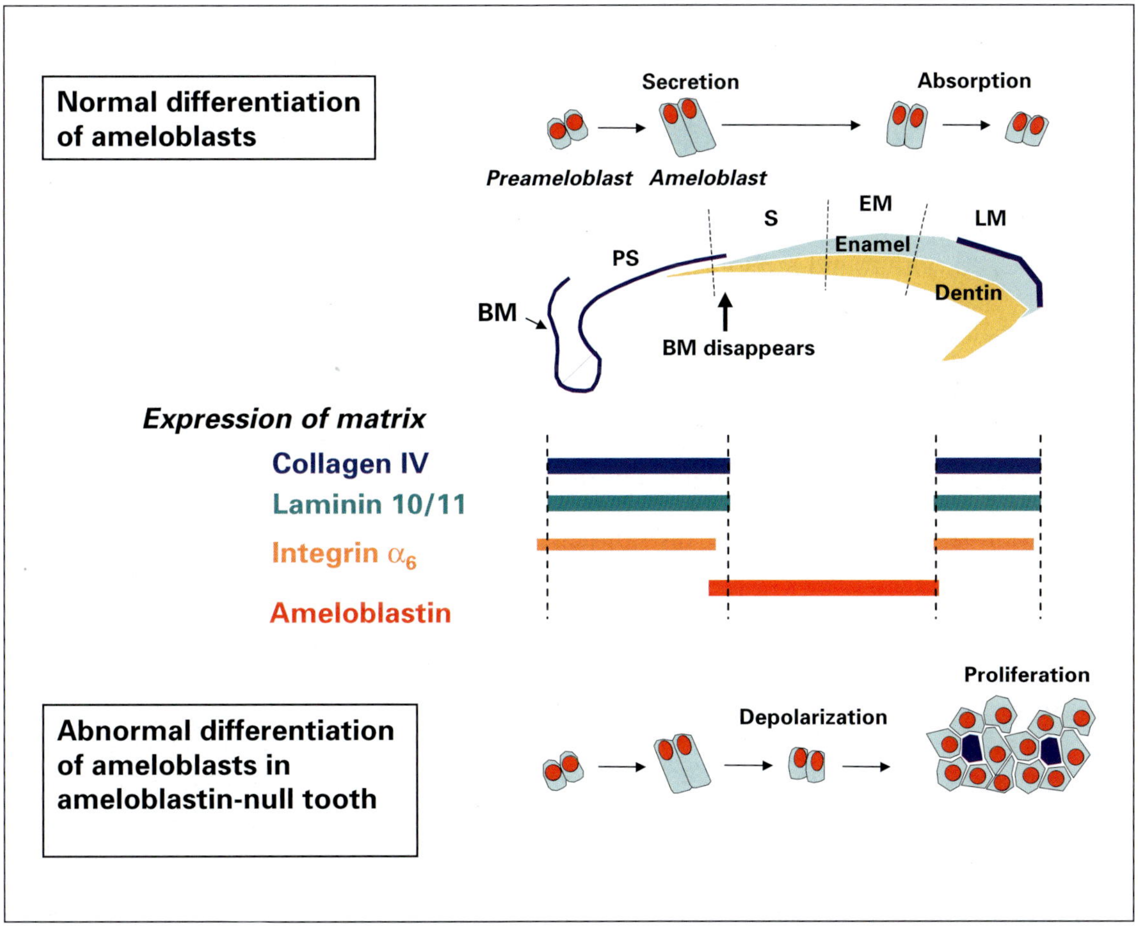

2

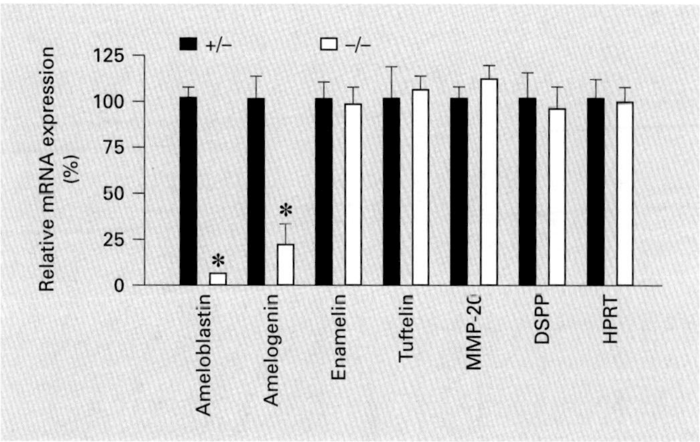

Fig. 3. Downregulation of amelogenin expression in ameloblastin-null tooth. mRNA isolated from postnatal day 3 mandibular first molar was subject to real-time reverse transcription polymerase chain reaction using specific primer sets. Amelogenin expression was reduced in ameloblastin-null tooth germs. These experiments were repeated at least three times with similar results. DSPP = Dentin sialophosphoprotein; HPRT = hypoxanthine-guanine phosphoribosyltransferase. Statistical analysis was performed using ANOVA (* $p < 0.01$).

we created ameloblastin-null mice by a conventional gene-targeting approach [Fukumoto et al., 2004]. The ameloblastin-null mice are born normally and fertile; however, mutant mice develop severe enamel hypoplasia as expected, with round incisor tips and a flat occlusal plane. These phenotypes are similar to those of human amelogenesis imperfecta. Microradiographic analysis of ameloblastin-deficient tooth shows normal development of both the craniofacial bone and outward appearance of the teeth. It was previously reported that ameloblastin is transiently expressed in Hertwig's root sheath, and recombinant ameloblastin enhanced the proliferation of cells derived from the epithelial root sheath of Hertwig's but not periodontal ligament cells. However, root formation in ameloblastin-null mice was normal. On the other hand, the tooth roots in aged amelogenin-null mice showed irregular resorption [Hatakeyama et al., 2003]. Further, root resorption was not observed in aged ameloblastin-null mutants, while there was sever enamel hypoplasia compared with amelogenin-null mice. These results suggest that amelogenin, but not ameloblastin, is important for the maintenance of the root surface.

Histological analysis revealed that dental epithelium differentiation was normal during the presecretory stage, and at the early secretory stage, dental epithelial cells started to differentiate into ameloblasts. However, ameloblasts later detached from the matrix and dentin surface, lost cell polarity, and accumulated to form a multiple layer, in contrast to the single layer of ameloblasts in normal tooth (fig. 2) [Fukumoto et al., 2004]. In mutant mice, multilayered cells were round and positive for immunostaining for enamelin and tuftelin, while amelogenin was weak, indicating that these cells were derived from ameloblasts and not other types of epithelium, such as stratum intermedium and stellate reticulum cells. In mutant mice, ameloblasts in the multilayers were proliferating, while those in wildtype mice stopped proliferating. These results suggest that ameloblasts in the mutant mice lose cell polarity, change morphology, and resume proliferation (fig. 2). In addition, the expression of amelogenin in ameloblasts in the mutant tooth was dramatically reduced in RT-PCR (fig. 3) and Western blot analyses [Fukumoto et al., 2004]. Thus, ameloblastin may indirectly regulate the expression of amelogenin.

Cell-Binding Activity of Ameloblastin

The finding that ameloblasts in ameloblastin-null mice detach from the matrix suggests that ameloblastin normally has cell-binding activity. Ameloblastin contains a DGEA motif, which is a potential integrin-binding site of collagen I [Staatz et al., 1991; Cerny et al., 1996], as well as a thrombospondin-like cell adhesion motif, VTKG [Yamada and Kleinman, 1992]. We found that recombinant ameloblastin produced in mammalian cells specifically binds primary dental epithelial cells but not other cell types such as NIH3T3, HeLa, epithelial MDCK, COS, 293EBNA, and rat chondrosarcoma cells [Fukumoto et al., 2004].

Primary dental epithelial cells contain mixed epithelial cell populations. To determine the differentiation stage at which dental epithelial cells bind ameloblastin, we used stage-specific antibodies to distinguish cell types in binding assays. For example, presecretory ameloblasts express the cell adhesion molecule integrin α_6, a receptor for laminin, but not amelogenin or ameloblastin (fig. 2), while secretory-stage ameloblasts express amelogenin and ameloblastin, but not integrin α_6. Using these antibodies, we found that ameloblastin specifically binds ameloblasts but not preameloblasts. We also examined the substrate specificity of ameloblast adhesion and found that secretory ameloblasts (integrin negative) adhered to recombinant ameloblastin, but not laminin or fibronec-

Fig. 4. A model for the roles of ameloblastin in amelogenesis. Ameloblastin binds ameloblasts and inhibits the expression of p21 and p27, inhibitors for cell cycle progression. Ameloblastin also downregulates the expression of p75, which is normally expressed by preameloblasts. Ameloblastin also inhibits the expression of Msx2, a negative regulator of amelogenin expression, by directly binding to the promoter region of the amelogenin gene. The expression of these molecules is downregulated in secretory ameloblasts in wildtype tooth. In ameloblastin-null tooth, p27, p75 and Msx2 are expressed in ameloblasts. These results suggest that in the absence of ameloblastin, dental epithelium regains some early phenotypes of the undifferentiated dental epithelial cells.

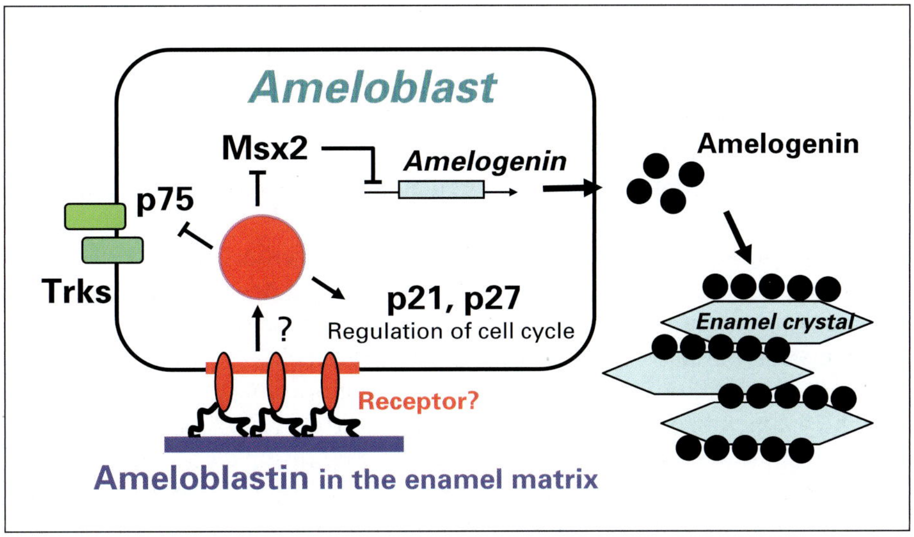

tin. In contrast, presecretory ameloblasts (integrin positive) were found to adhere to fibronectin and laminin, but not ameloblastin. These results suggest that ameloblasts, but not preameloblasts, preferentially adhere to ameloblastin. However, DGEA and VTKG peptide motifs are conserved only in rodents. There is little or no conservation of those motifs across other species including human, pig, bovine, and caiman. Further, integrin expression disappeared in differentiated ameloblasts, indicating that other motifs in ameloblastin protein may be important for the cell adhesion.

Since ameloblasts in ameloblastin-deficient mice continue to proliferate, ameloblastin may inhibit ameloblast proliferation in wildtype teeth. We tested this possibility in cell culture. We found that proliferation of ameloblasts from ameloblastin-null mice was completely inhibited by recombinant ameloblastin, while proliferation of other cell types, such as MDCK cells, was not affected by exogenous ameloblastin. These results suggest that ameloblastin regulates the proliferation of ameloblasts.

Tumor Formation in Ameloblastin-Null Mice

Ameloblastin-null mutant mice develop soft tissue tumors in the buccal vestibules of both the maxilla and mandibula with age. About 20–30% of the homozygous mice developed lesions, with the earliest at 26 weeks old [Fukumoto et al., 2004]. This type of tumor is similar to a human calcified epithelial odontogenic tumor. Human ameloblastoma is the most common type of odontogenic tumor and is thought to be of dental epithelial origin, primarily because of the histological similarities with the developing tooth germ. A recent report described potential mutations in the ameloblastin transcript that resulted in substitutions and a deletion of ameloblastin [Toyosawa et al., 2000], though those mutations may not cause primary ameloblastoma. In fact, histological analysis showed that none of the tumor specimens from ameloblastin-null mice was similar to human ameloblastoma. More recently, the association of ameloblastin gene mutations with epithelial odontogenic tumors was reported [Perdigao et al., 2004]. Although the mechanism of tumor formation in the ameloblastin-null mice is not clearly understood, deregulation of ameloblast differentiation due to a lack of ameloblastin function is likely the primary cause of these tumors.

Regulation of Intracellular Signaling Associated with Amelogenin Expression

In ameloblastin-null mice, amelogenin, but not enamelin or tuftelin, dramatically reduced the expression of ameloblasts, suggesting that ameloblastin regulates the expression of amelogenin, perhaps indirectly. Msx2, a homeobox-containing transcription factor expressed in preameloblasts, is downregulated in secretory ameloblasts [Mass and Bei, 1997]. In ameloblastin-null mice, Msx2 was expressed in presecretory ameloblasts, similar to wildtype mice; however, Msx2 was also expressed in multilayered ameloblasts [Satokata et al., 2000]. Although amelogenin was expressed in mutant ameloblasts, the level was significantly reduced. Msx2 has been shown to inhibit the promoter activity of the amelogenin gene in a DNA transfection analysis [Zhou et al., 2000]. Thus, the abnormal expression of Msx2 in mutant ameloblasts is potentially responsible for the downregulation of amelogenin expression (fig. 4).

Deficiencies of several molecules, such as amelogenin and Msx2, have been reported to cause amelogenesis defects, and amelogenin-null mice develop less severe enamel defects compared with ameloblastin-null mutants [Satokata et al., 2000; Gibson et al., 2001]. In amelogenin-null mice, ameloblasts differentiate normally and do not detach from the matrix or form multicell layers [Gibson et al., 2001]. In addition, tooth germs in Msx2-null mice develop normally until the cap stage; however, by postnatal day 1, the stratum intermedium becomes reduced, and stratified epithelial cells accumulate in the intercuspal region and about the ameloblast layers [Satokata et al., 2000]. It appears that there is no detachment of the ameloblast layer from the matrix in Msx2 knockout mice. Thus, ameloblastin has a distinct role in amelogenesis.

It was also reported that Msx1 and Msx2 increase the expression of cyclin D1 and inhibit cell differentiation [Hu et al., 2001]. In wildtype mice, cyclin-dependent kinase inhibitor p27 is strongly expressed in secretory ameloblasts, whereas its expression is weak in mutant ameloblasts. Downregulation of p27 and upregulation of Msx2 and p75 in ameloblasts of mutant mice likely cause the proliferative activity of ameloblasts detached from the matrix due to the lack of ameloblastin.

The ameloblastin promoter functions in a cell type-specific manner and contains *cis*-acting elements that function to both enhance and suppress transcription [Dhamija et al., 1999]. Cbfa1, essential for the transcription of other mineralized tissue genes, is also required for ameloblastin transcription. A previous study found that site-directed mutagenesis of the Cbfa1-binding site of the ameloblastin promoter decreased ameloblastin promoter activity by more than 50% in ameloblast-like cells [Dhamija et al., 2001]. Further, zinc finger transcription factor Sp3-null mice showed downregulation of ameloblastin gene expression and ameloblast differentiation [Bouwman et al., 2000], indicating that Cbfa1 and Sp3 may be important for the regulation of ameloblastin gene expression. However, these transcription factors are not tooth specific, and others may be involved in the tooth-specific expression of ameloblastin and also amelogenin regulation.

Acknowledgments

We would like to thank Dr. K. Yuasa and E. Fukumoto for their careful reading of the manuscript.

References

Adams, J.C., F.M. Watt (1993) Regulation of development and differentiation by the extracellular matrix. Development *117:* 1183–1198.

Bouwman, P., H. Gollner, H.P. Elsasser, G. Eckhoff, A. Karis, F. Grosveld, S. Philipsen, G. Suske (2000) Transcription factor Sp3 is essential for post-natal survival and late tooth development. EMBO J *19:* 655–661.

Cerny, R., I. Slaby, L. Hammarstrom, T. Wurtz (1996) A novel gene expressed in rat ameloblasts codes for proteins with cell binding domains. J Bone Miner Res *11:* 883–891.

Damsky, C.H., Z. Werb (1992) Signal transduction by integrin receptors for extracellular matrix: cooperative processing of extracellular information. Curr Opin Cell Biol *4:* 772–781.

Deutsch, D., A. Palmon, L.W. Fisher, N. Kolodny, J.D. Termine, M.F. Young (1991) Sequencing of bovine enamelin ("tuftelin") a novel acidic enamel protein. J Biol Chem *206:* 16021–16028.

Dhamija, S., Y. Liu, Y. Yamada, M.L. Snead, P.H. Krebsbach (1999) Cloning and characterization of the murine ameloblastin promoter. J Biol Chem *274:* 20738–20743.

Dhamija, S., P.H. Krebsbach (2001) Role of Cbfa1 in ameloblastin gene transcription. J Biol Chem *276:* 35159–35164.

Fincham, A.G., J. Moradian-Oldak, J.P. Simmer (1999) The structural biology of the developing dental enamel matrix: cooperative processing of extracellular information. Curr Opin Cell Biol *4:* 772–781.

Fong, C.D., I. Slaby, L. Hammarstrom (1996) Amelin: an enamel-related protein, transcribed in the cells of epithelial root sheath. J Bone Miner Res *11:* 892–898.

Fukae, M., T. Tanabe, C. Murakami, N. Dohi, T. Uchida, M. Shimizu (1996) Primary structure of the procine 89-kDa enamelin. Adv Dent Res *10:* 111–118.

Fukumoto, S., T. Kiba, B. Hall, N. Iehara, T. Nakamura, G. Longenecker, P.H. Krebsbach, A. Nanci, A.B. Kulkarni, Y. Yamana (2004). Ameloblastin regulates cell adhesion and differentiation states of dental epithelium and is essential for amelogenesis. J Cell Biol *167:* 973–983.

Gibson, C.W., Z.A. Yuan, B. Hall, G. Longenecker, E. Chen, T. Thyagarajan, T. Sreenath, J.T. Wright, S. Decker, R. Piddington, G. Harrison, A.B. Kulkarni (2001) Amelogenin-deficient mice display an amelogenesis imperfecta phenotype. J Biol Chem *276:* 31871–31875.

Hatakeyama, J., T. Sreenath, Y. Hatakeyama, T. Thyagarajan, L. Shum, C.W. Gibson, J.T. Wright, A.B. Kulkarni (2003) The receptor activator of nuclear factor-kappa B ligand-mediated osteoclastogenic pathway is elevated in amelogenin-null mice. J Biol Chem *278:* 35743–35748.

Hu, C.C., M. Fukae, T. Uchida, Q. Qian, C.H. Zhang, O.H. Ryu, T. Tanabe, Y. Yamakoshi, C. Murakami, N. Dohi, M. Shimizu, J.P. Simmer (1997) Sheathlin: cloning, cDNA/polypeptide sequences and immunolocalization of porcine enamel sheath proteins. J Dent Res *76:* 648–657.

Hu, C.C., J.P. Simmer, J.D. Bartlett, Q. Qian, C. Zhang, O.H. Ryu, J. Xue, M. Fukae, T. Uchida, M. MacDougall (1998) Murine enamelin: cDNA and derived protein sequences. Connect Tissue Res *39:* 47–61.

Hu, G., H. Lee, S.M. Price, M.M. Shen, C. Abate-Shen (2001) Msx2 homeobox genes, inhibit differentiation through upregulation of cyclin D1. Development *128:* 2373–2384.
Kin, C.Q., M.J. Bissell (1993) Multi-faceted regulation of cell differentiation by extracellular matrix. FASEB J *7:* 737–743.
Krebsbach, P.H., S.K. Lee, Y. Matsuki, C.A. Kozak, K.M. Yamada, Y. Yamada (1996) Full-length sequence, localization, and chromosomal mapping of ameloblastin. A novel tooth-specific gene. J Biol Chem *271:* 4431–4435.
Lesot, H., M. Osman, J.V. Ruch (1981) Immunofluorescent localization of collagens, fibronectin, and laminin during terminal differentiation of odontoblasts. Dev Biol *82:* 371–381.
Lin, C.Q., M.J. Bissell (1993) Multi-faceted regulation of cell differentiation by extracellular matrix. FASEB J *7:* 737–743.
Lumsden, A.G. (1988) Spatial organization of the epithelium and the role of neural crest cells in the initiation of the mammalian tooth germ. Development *103(suppl):* 155–169.
MacDougall, M., D. Simmones, T.T. Gu, K. Forsman-Semb, C.K. Marbach, N. Forest, P.H. Krebsbach, Y. Yamada, A. Berdal (2000) Cloning, characterization and immunolocalization of human ameloblastin. Eur J Oral Sci *108:* 303–310.
Mass, R., M. Bei (1997) The genetic control of early tooth development. Crit Rev Oral Biol Med *8:* 4–39.
Moradian-Oldak, J. (2001) Amelogenins: assembly, processing and control of crystal morphology. Matrix Biol *20:* 293–305.
Nanci, A., Z.P. Lavoie, M. Kunikata, W.Y. Chen. P.H. Krebsbach, Y. Yamada, L. Hammarstrom, J.P. Simmer, A.G. Fincham, M.L. Snead, C.E. Smith (1998) Comparative immunochemical analyses of the developmental expression and distribution of ameloblastin and amelogenin in rat incisors. J Histochem Cytochem *46:* 911–934.
Paine, M.L., H.J. Wang, W. Luo, P.H. Krebsbach, M.L. Snead (2003) A transgeneic animal model resembling amelogenesis imperfecta related to ameloblastin overexpression. J Biol Chem *278:* 19447–19452.
Ruch, J.V. (1987) Determinisms of odontogenesis. Revis Biol Celular *14:* 1–99.
Perdigao, P.F., R.S. Gomez, F.J.G.S. Pimenta, L. De Marco (2004) Ameloblastin gene (AMBN) mutations associated with epithelial odontogenic tumor. Oral Oncol *40:* 841–846.
Sahlberg, C., P. Reponen, K. Tryggvason, I. Thesleff (1922) Association between the expression of murine 72 kDa type IV collagenase by odontoblasts and basement membrane degradation during mouse tooth development. Arch Oral Biol *37:* 1021–1030.
Satokata, I., L. Ma, H. Ohshima, M. Bei, I. Woo, K. Nishikawa, T. Maeda, Y. Takano, M. Uchiyama, S. Heaney, H. Peters, Z. Tang, R. Maxson, R. Mass (2000) Msx2 deficiency in mice causes pleiotropic defects in bone growth and ectodermal organ formation. Nat Genet *24:* 391–395.
Smith, C.E. (1998) Cellular and chemical events during enamel maturation. Crit Rev Oral Biol Med *9:* 128–161.
Staatz, W.D., K.F. Fok, M.M. Zutter, S.P. Adams, B.A. Rodriguez, S.A. Santoro (1991) Identification of a tetrapeptide recognition sequence for the alpha2 beta1 integrin in collagen. J Biol Chem *266:* 7363–7367.
Thesleff, I., K. Hurmerinta (1981) Tissue interactions in tooth development. Differentiation *18:* 75–88.
Timpl, R. (1996) Macromolecular organization of basement membranes. Curr Opin Cell Biol *8:* 618–624.
Toyosawa, S., T. Fujiwara, T. Ooshima, S. Shintani, A. Sato, Y. Ogawa, S. Sobue, N. Ijuhin (2000) Cloning and characterization of the human ameloblastin gene. Gene *256:* 1–11.
Uchida, T., T. Tanabe, M. Fukae, M. Shimizu (1991) Immunocytochemical and immunochemical detection of a 32 kDa nonamelogenin and related proteins in porcine tooth germs. Arch Histol Cytol *54:* 527–538.
Uchida, T., C. Murakami, N. Dohi, K. Wakida, T. Satoda, O. Takahashi (1997) Synthesis, secretion, degradation, and fate of ameloblastin during the matrix formation stage of the rat incisor as shown by immunocytochemistry and immunochemistry using region-specific antibodies. J Histochem Cytochem *45:* 1329–1340.
Yamada, Y., H.K. Kleinman (1992) Functional domains of cell adhesion molecules. Curr Opin Cell Biol *4:* 819–823.
Zhou, Y.L., Y. Lei, M.L. Snead (2000) Functional antagonism between Msx2 and CCAAT/enhancer-binding protein alpha in regulating the mouse amelogenin gene expression is mediated by protein-protein interaction. J Biol Chem *275:* 29066–29075.

Cells
Tissues
Organs

Cells Tissues Organs 2005;181:196–201
DOI: 10.1159/000091381

The Use of Animal Models to Explore Amelogenin Variants in Amelogenesis Imperfecta

Carolyn W. Gibson[a] Ashok B. Kulkarni[b] J. Timothy Wright[c]

[a]Department of Anatomy and Cell Biology, School of Dental Medicine, University of Pennsylvania, Philadelphia, Pa., [b]Functional Genomics Unit, Craniofacial Developmental Biology and Regeneration Branch, National Institute of Dental and Craniofacial Research, National Institute of Health, Bethesda, Md., and [c]Department of Pediatric Dentistry, School of Dentistry, University of North Carolina, Chapel Hill, N.C., USA

Key Words
Amelogenin · Amelogenesis imperfecta · Enamel proteins · *Arhgap6* · Nested genes

Abstract
Amelogenin proteins are secreted by ameloblast cells during tooth development. Because of extensive alternative splicing of the amelogenin primary RNA transcript, and because systematic proteolysis results in many additional peptides during enamel maturation, it has been difficult to assign function to individual amelogenins. Targeted deletions and transgenic mice have been generated in order to better understand amelogenin protein function in vivo. From these murine models, we have determined that amelogenins are responsible for normal enamel thickness and structure, but not for initiation of enamel mineral formation at the dentin-enamel junction. Although it is now clear that the amelogenin *(AmelX)* gene exists in a nested orientation and that *AmelX* is expressed at a low level in various developing tissues, the significance of these findings is incompletely understood. Future studies are expected to answer remaining questions concerning structure/function relationships among these 'enamel proteins'.

Introduction

Amelogenins and other enamel proteins are secreted by ameloblast cells prior to tooth eruption. The amelogenin proteins have a conserved amino acid sequence, which has been reported for at least 26 mammalian lineages [Delgado et al., 2005]. These proteins comprise nearly 90% of the extracellular matrix of developing dental enamel [Termine et al., 1980], and analysis of human and murine gene mutations indicates that amelogenins are responsible for the unique properties of dental enamel, which is the hardest tissue in the body. Antisense or ribozyme-mediated inhibition of amelogenin expression also led to enamel mineral defects, in agreement with the human and animal model results [Diekwisch et al., 1993; Lyngstadaas et al., 1995].

In addition to secretion of the enamel extracellular matrix, ameloblasts are also responsible for the orderly proteolytic degradation of the organic matrix as the mineral

Abbreviations used in this paper

AI	Amelogenesis imperfecta
LRAP	Leucine-rich amelogenin protein

KARGER

Fax +41 61 306 12 34
E-Mail karger@karger.ch
www.karger.com

Accessible online at:
www.karger.com/cto

Carolyn W. Gibson, PhD
Department of Anatomy and Cell Biology, University of Pennsylvania
School of Dental Medicine, 240 S. 40th Street
Philadelphia, PA 19104 (USA)
Tel. +1 215 898 6660, Fax +1 215 573 2324, E-Mail gibson@biochem.dental.upenn.edu

crystals grow to form mature enamel found on the crown of the erupted tooth [Smith, 1998; Bartlett and Simmer, 1999; Simmer and Hu, 2002]. Only small amounts of the organic matrix remain within enamel following eruption of the tooth into the oral cavity.

Studies of the appearance of enamel from kindreds with mutations in genes encoding secreted enamel proteins showed that several of these proteins are necessary for normal enamel structure. At least 14 mutations have been reported in the *AmelX* gene [Hart et al., 2002; Kim et al., 2004], but affected kindreds have a spectrum of phenotypic characteristics, leading to the suggestion that mutations in the N or C terminus of amelogenin may cause different functional defects [Snead, 2003; Wright et al., 2003]. Mutations within autosomal genes encoding enamelin, kallikrein 4 and matrix metalloproteinase 20 also lead to enamel defects [Kida et al., 2002; Mardh et al., 2002; Hart et al., 2004; Nusier et al., 2004; Kim et al., 2005], and in general, all of these inherited enamel defects are referred to as amelogenesis imperfecta (AI). The enamel-specific AI phenotype has been classified according to genetic inheritance (autosomal or X linked) and by enamel appearance. The phenotypic categories are hypoplasia, which is a deficiency in the normal enamel thickness, hypocalcification, a defect in the structure of the mineral, and hypomaturation, in which elevated levels of protein remain in mature enamel [Witkop and Sauk, 1976]. The AI phenotypic heterogeneity seems to be due to the gene carrying a mutation, the position of the mutation within the protein coding sequence, and gender in X-linked forms of AI.

The Amelogenins

The functions of amelogenin proteins have been difficult to decipher for a number of reasons:

(1) The *AmelX* primary RNA transcript is alternatively spliced into at least 14 messages, each capable of being translated into a protein [Gibson et al., 1991; Simmer et al., 1994; Li et al., 1995; Hu et al., 1997].

(2) Each amelogenin protein is subject to proteolytic cleavage, which is thought to be highly regulated during development, and leads to a large number of additional peptides [Simmer and Hu, 2002]. It is assumed and in some cases demonstrated that cleavage could substantially alter function.

(3) The *AmelX* gene is highly conserved and localized to the X chromosome, but in some species, including humans, an *AmelY* gene is also found on the Y chromosome. The Y-chromosomal gene in humans is 87% similar to the one on the X chromosome [Salido et al., 1992], and the Y-specific translated protein is also subject to proteolytic cleavage, adding to the expected protein heterogeneity.

(4) The individual mRNAs differ in amount, and for some, the amount varies during development [Couwenhoven and Snead, 1994; Yuan et al., 1996].

Because of the heterogeneity in the clinical phenotype in AI patients and the alternative splicing of the RNA, it is predicted that the location within the *AmelX* gene of a mutation could affect some of the amelogenin proteins but not others. To better understand the function of the individual amelogenin proteins, a mouse was generated with an *AmelX* null mutation, in which none of the amelogenin proteins were expressed [Gibson et al., 2001]. Our goal is to mate this null mouse with transgenic mice that express single normal or mutated amelogenin proteins for rescue experiments.

AmelX Null Mice

The *AmelX* null mice were generated by deleting part of *AmelX* exon 2 and intron 2, thus removing the signal sequence required for secretion of the proteins. Amelogenin proteins were not detected in the enamel of these mice. The teeth were chalky white in appearance, indicating a defect in the mineral. Analysis by light microscopy revealed a hypoplastic enamel layer, with approximately 10–20% of the normal enamel thickness. By scanning electron microscopy, the enamel appeared porous and lacked the normal highly regular rod or prismatic structure. Heterozygote murine females have ridges on the enamel surface similar to that seen in human females with AI, which is thought to be due to lyonization in which X inactivation randomly silences one of the X chromosomes [Collier et al., 1997] (fig. 1). In general, the murine phenotype is similar to that seen in the dentition of some AI patients and also reveals unambiguously that amelogenins are not required for initiation of mineral formation, as mineral is clearly evident in the enamel of these null mice [Gibson et al., 2001].

Function of Leucine-Rich Amelogenin Protein

Leucine-rich amelogenin protein (LRAP) is one of the two most abundant of the amelogenin proteins [Fincham, 1983] and results from the skipping of *AmelX* exon 4 and

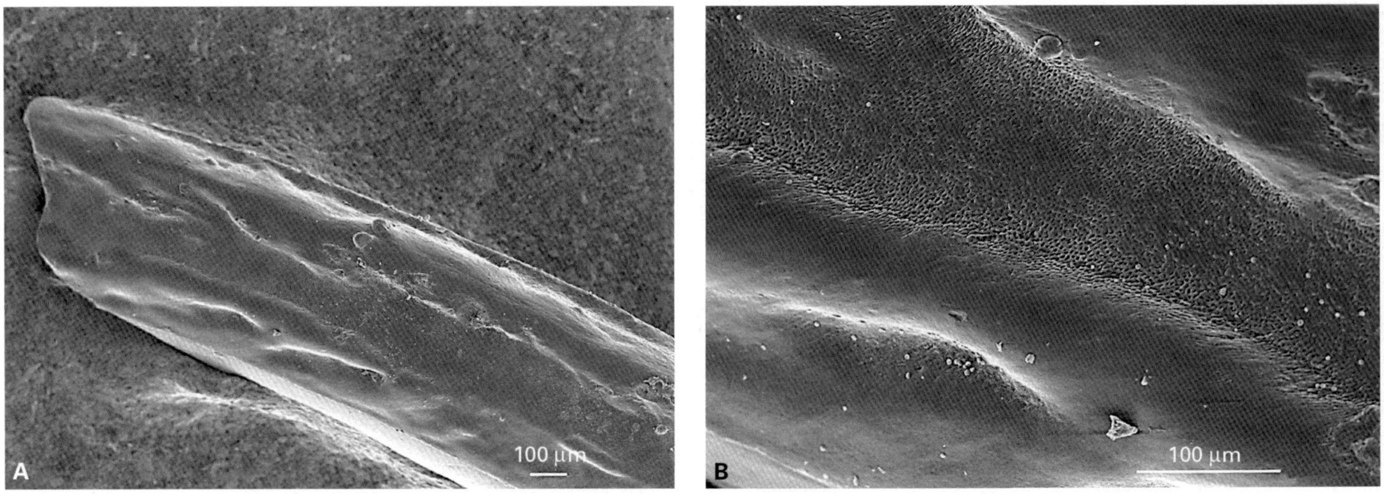

Fig. 1. Scanning electron micrographs of an incisor from an *AmelX* heterozygote female. **A** Ridges in the enamel surface indicate areas of normal and defective enamel, due to lyonization. **B** At higher magnification, the hypoplastic regions retain the surface imprint of the ameloblasts, appearing as small black indentations.

splicing out of most of exon 6, resulting in a 59-amino-acid amelogenin [Gibson et al., 1991]. Transgenic mice were generated in which LRAP was targeted for ameloblast-specific expression, as the transgene was under control of the *AmelX* promoter and upstream region [Chen et al., 2003]. These transgenic mice expressed abundant LRAP protein and had a normal enamel structure, but with a slightly irregular enamel surface. It was speculated that the surface was slightly pitted because excess LRAP protein was produced by these mice. Since they have a wildtype genomic background, they would also have the normal complement of active *AmelX* genes in addition to the transgene. It is possible that the maturation stage ended before proteolysis was complete, leaving excess protein at the external surface and disrupting the final maturation stage.

Mice have only one *AmelX* gene and no corresponding gene on the Y chromosome [Lau et al., 1989], which is an advantage for the rescue experiment. In a typical experiment, a null female is mated to a transgenic male (fig. 2). The progeny are heterozygous females, null males (transgene negative) or null males (transgene positive). It is hypothesized that comparison of male mice with and without the transgene in an *AmelX* null background would provide insight into normal function of LRAP, the transgenic protein.

However, the cross between the *AmelX* null female and LRAP transgenic male mice did not result in detectable rescue of the enamel defect in male transgenic pups

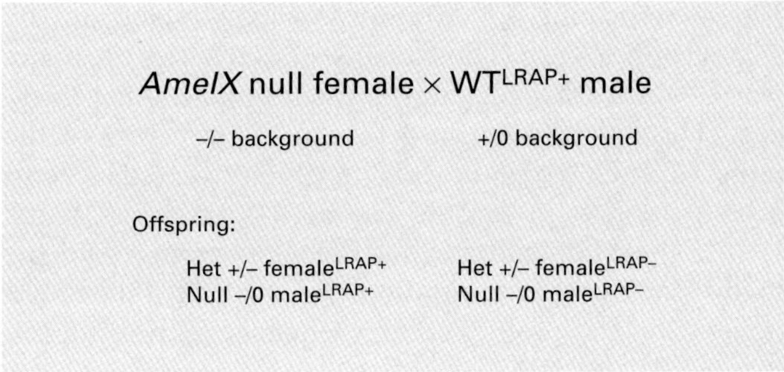

Fig. 2. Scheme for a rescue experiment. The offspring of this mating have a heterozygote (Het) (+/–) or null genetic background, with or without the LRAP transgene.

with the null genetic background [Chen et al., 2003]. Immunohistochemistry and Western blot indicated that LRAP was appropriately expressed in teeth of the offspring. Although at first this result was unexpected, it has recently been shown that LRAP, although long considered an 'enamel protein', can play a role in intercellular signaling [Veis et al., 2000; Veis, 2003]. When LRAP protein was injected into rat muscle, collagen gene expression was altered and ectopic bone formed [Nebgen et al., 1999]. It is not clear at this time whether LRAP functions during epithelial-mesenchymal interactions in the developing tooth, or why a relatively large amount of this protein is produced during tooth development if its sole role

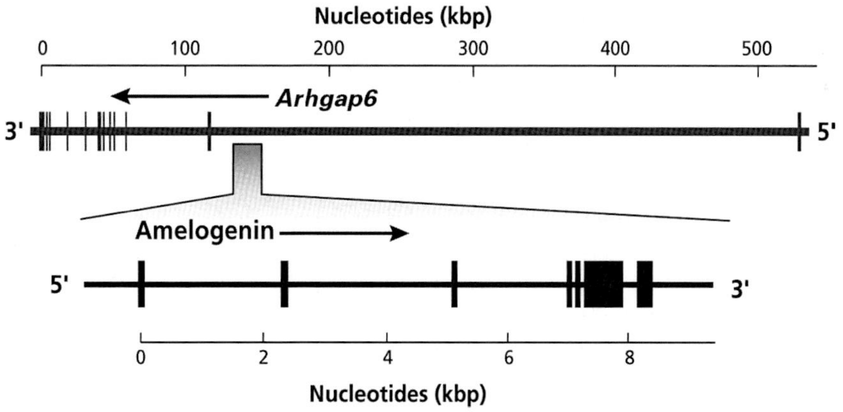

Fig. 3. *Arhgap6/AmelX* nested genes. *AmelX* is found in the opposite orientation in intron 1 of *Arhgap6* in mouse and humans.

is in signal transduction. The finding that LRAP is expressed at low levels by dental papilla and periodontal cells [Nebgen et al., 1999; Hatekeyama et al., 2003] adds a further complication, but in general, it is felt that amelogenins other than LRAP are essential for normal enamel appearance and structure [Chen et al., 2003].

A recent development is the finding that LRAP is expressed at a low level in non-dental tissues in pups between newborn and 5 days of age. LRAP mRNA has been detected in calvariae, long bones, brain, eye and skin [Li et al., in press]. Therefore, LRAP has the potential to be a multifunctional protein, which could play a role in both mineralizing and non-mineralizing tissues.

Gene Nesting

During the course of these experiments, it was determined that the *AmelX* gene is located within an intron of a much larger gene [Prakash et al., 2000; Gibson et al., 2005]. *AmelX* in the human and murine genomes is located in intron 1 of the *Arhgap6* gene in the opposite orientation (fig. 3).

Therefore, when a deletion was generated within the *AmelX* gene, a deletion in *Arhgap6* intron 1 also resulted. Although it is not clear whether the *Arhgap6* deletion contributes to the *AmelX* null phenotype, *Arhgap6* expression detected with reverse transcription polymerase chain reaction primers targeted to the 3′ end of the gene appears to be unaffected in null mice [Yuan and Gibson, unpubl.].

We also evaluated a mouse with a deletion of the entire 1.1-Mb genomic region including both *Arhgap6* and *AmelX*, generated using Cre-lox technology [Prakash et al., 2005]. As expected, these mice also have chalky white enamel, which is hypoplastic and disorganized. In addition, the Cre-lox mice have an unusual surface layer in their enamel (fig. 4); we hope to generate additional mice to better understand the importance of the Arhgap6 protein in enamel development.

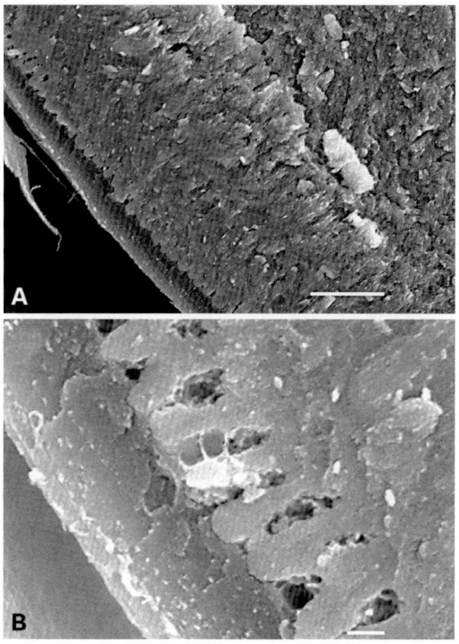

Fig. 4. Enamel from the incisor of a male mouse with a 1.1-Mb genomic deletion which removed both *Arhgap6* and *AmelX* [Prakash et al., 2005]. **A** Scanning electron micrograph of a mineralized thin section reveals abnormal enamel structure. Scale bar = 10 μm. **B** Higher magnification shows gaps within the enamel and an unusual surface layer of mineralized enamel. Scale bar = 10 μm.

Arhgap6 encodes a RhoGAP, which is a negative regulatory protein for RhoA [Prakash et al., 2000]. One of the roles of RhoA is to regulate the actin cytoskeleton [Settleman, 2000], which is significantly altered as ameloblasts change their appearance, size and shape during the stages of differing function [Nishikawa and Josephsen, 1987]. An inactivating mutation in the *Arhgap6* coding sequence would be expected to elevate RhoA and increase the F-actin/G-actin ratio, which could interfere with functions that depend on cytoskeletal integrity. Examination of mice with a targeted *Arhgap6* mutation that does not affect *AmelX* may shed light on this hypothesis and lead to an explanation for the unusual surface layer in mice with the 1.1-Mb deletion in this genomic region.

Future Perspectives and Questions

Generation of additional transgenic mice and crossing them with the *AmelX* null mice is expected to provide further insight into amelogenin protein function, and these experiments are currently in progress. Additional questions to be answered are:

- (1) Why are there so many amelogenin proteins, and does each protein have a unique function but perhaps with some functional overlap?
- (2) What are the consequences of the *AmelX* nested position? Does a deletion within *AmelX* affect expression of *Arhgap6?*
- (3) What is the significance of *AmelX* expression in tissues other than enamel?

Conclusions

Since amelogenin proteins were first described more than 40 years ago [Eastoe, 1964], there has been speculation concerning their function. Some amelogenins have been produced in *Escherichia coli* and other systems and used in biophysical analyses for studies of in vitro assembly [Fincham et al., 1994; Paine et al., 1998]. In addition, the ability of some amelogenins to affect gene expression in vitro has been reported, as well as effects on tissue regeneration in rats [Goldberg et al., 2003; Viswanathan et al., 2003; Boabaid et al., 2004]. Also, the product Emdogain®, which is an extract of developing porcine tooth enamel containing predominantly amelogenins, has been used clinically as an aid to periodontal regeneration and for in vitro studies [Gestrelius et al., 2000; Schwartz et al., 2000; Van der Pauw et al., 2000]. Both clinical studies and animal models have yielded information about the importance of amelogenins in the development of the exquisite prismatic structure of mature enamel. Because of recent developments, we know that there is still much to learn as the amelogenin story unfolds and as answers emerge to the questions concerning structure/function relationships for this interesting group of 'enamel proteins'.

Acknowledgments

We acknowledge Symposium Co-Chair M. Young for her pioneering work on amelogenins. We thank B. Daly for the scanning electron micrograph, and colleagues from the authors' laboratories for their fruitful discussions. Support for this work was provided by National Institute of Dental and Craniofacial Research grant DE011089 (to C.W.G.) and the Division of Intramural Research of the National Institute of Dental and Craniofacial Research (to A.B.K.). Permission has been obtained for use of figures 3 and 4.

References

Bartlett, J.D., J.P. Simmer (1999) Proteinases in developing dental enamel. Crit Rev Oral Biol Med *10:* 425–441.

Boabaid, F., C.W. Gibson, M.A. Kuehl, J.E. Berry, M.L. Snead, F.H. Nociti, E. Katchburian, M.J. Somerman (2004) Leucine-rich amelogenin peptide: a candidate signaling molecule during cementogenesis. J Periodontol *75:* 1126–1136.

Chen, E., Z.A. Yuan, J.T. Wright, S.P. Hong, Y. Li, P.M. Collier, B. Hall, M. D'Angelo, S. Decker, R. Piddington, W.R. Abrams, A.B. Kulkarni, C.W. Gibson (2003) The small bovine amelogenin LRAP fails to rescue the amelogenin null phenotype. Calcif Tissue Int *73:* 487–495.

Collier, P.M., J.J. Sauk, J. Rosenbloom, Z.A. Yuan, C.W. Gibson (1997) An amelogenin gene defect associated with human X-linked amelogenesis imperfecta. Arch Oral Biol *42:* 235–242.

Couwenhoven, R.I., M.L. Snead (1994) Early determination and permissive expression of amelogenin transcription during mouse mandibular first molar development. Dev Biol *164:* 290–299.

Delgado, S., M. Girondot, J.Y. Sire (2005) Molecular evolution of amelogenin in mammals. J Mol Evol *60:* 12–30.

Diekwisch, T., S. David, P. Bringas, Jr., V. Santos, H.C. Slavkin (1993) Antisense inhibition of AMEL translation demonstrates supramolecular controls for enamel HAP crystal growth during embryonic mouse molar development. Development *117:* 471–482.

Eastoe, J.E. (1964) The chemical composition of bone and tooth. Adv Fluor Res Dent Caries Prev *3:* 5–17.

Fincham, A.G., A.B. Belcourt, J.D. Termine, W.T. Butler, W.C. Cothran (1983) Amelogenins. Sequence homologies in enamel-matrix proteins from three mammalian species. Biochem J *211:* 149–154.

Fincham, A.G., J. Moradian-Oldak, J.P. Simmer, P. Sarte, E.C. Lau, T. Diekwisch, H.C. Slavkin (1994) Self-assembly of a recombinant amelogenin protein generates supramolecular structures. J Struct Biol *112:* 103–109.

Gestrelius, S., S.P. Lyngstadaas, L. Hammarstrom (2000) Emdogain – periodontal regeneration based on biomimicry. Clin Oral Invest *4:* 120–125.

Gibson, C.W., E.E. Golub, W. Ding, H. Shimokawa, M. Young, J. Termine, J. Rosenbloom (1991) Identification of the leucine-rich amelogenin peptide (LRAP) as the translation product of an alternatively spliced transcript. Biochem Biophys Res Commun *174:* 1306–1312.

Gibson, C.W., N.H. Thomson, W.R. Abrams, J. Kirkham (2005) Nested genes: biological implications and use of AFM for analysis. Gene *350:* 15–23.

Gibson, C.W., Z.A. Yuan, B. Hall, G. Longenecker, E. Chen, T. Thyagarajan, T. Sreenath, J.T. Wright, S. Decker, R. Piddington, G. Harrison, A.B. Kulkarni (2001) Amelogenin-deficient mice display an amelogenesis imperfecta phenotype. J Biol Chem *276:* 31871–31875.

Goldberg, M., N. Six, F. Decup, J.J. Lasfargues, E. Salih, K. Tompkins, A. Veis (2003) Bioactive molecules and the future of pulp therapy. Am J Dent *16:* 66–76.

Hart, P.S., T.C. Hart, M.D. Michalec, O.H. Ryu, D. Simmons, S. Hong, J.T. Wright (2004) Mutation in kallikrein 4 causes autosomal recessive hypomaturation amelogenesis imperfecta. J Med Genet *41:* 545–549.

Hart, P.S., T.C. Hart, J.P. Simmer, J.T. Wright (2002) A nomenclature for X-linked amelogenesis imperfecta. Arch Oral Biol *47:* 255–260.

Hatakeyama, J., T. Sreenath, Y. Hatakeyama, T. Thyagarajan, L. Shum, C.W. Gibson, J.T. Wright, A.B. Kulkarni (2003) The receptor activator of nuclear factor-kappaB ligand-mediated osteoclastogenic pathway is elevated in amelogenin-null mice. J Biol Chem *278:* 35743–35748.

Hu, C.C., O.H. Ryu, Q. Qian, C.H. Zhang, J.P. Simmer (1997) Cloning, characterization and heterologous expression of exon 4-containing amelogenin mRNAs. J Dent Res *76:* 641–647.

Kida, M., T. Ariga, T. Shirakawa, H. Oguchi, Y. Sakiyama (2002) Autosomal-dominant hypoplastic form of amelogenesis imperfecta caused by an enamelin gene mutation at the exon-intron boundary. J Dent Res *81:* 738–742.

Kim, J.W., J.P. Simmer, T.C. Hart, P.S. Hart, M.D. Ramaswami, J.D. Bartlett, J.C. Hu (2005) MMP-20 mutation in autosomal recessive pigmented hypomaturation amelogenesis imperfecta. J Med Genet *42:* 271–275.

Kim, J.W., J.P. Simmer, Y.Y. Hu, B.P. Lin, C. Boyd, J.T. Wright, C.J. Yamada, S.K. Rayes, R.J. Feigal, J.C. Hu (2004) Amelogenin p.M1T and p.W4S mutations underlying hypoplastic X-linked amelogenesis imperfecta. J Dent Res *83:* 378–383.

Lau, E.C., T.K. Mohandas, L.J. Shapiro, H.C. Slavkin, M.L. Snead (1989) Human and mouse amelogenin gene loci are on the sex chromosomes. Genomics *4:* 162–168.

Li, R., W. Li, P.K. DenBesten (1995) Alternative splicing of amelogenin mRNA from rat incisor ameloblasts. J Dent Res *74:* 1880–1885.

Li, Y., Z.A. Yuan, M.A. Aragon, A.B. Kulkarni, C.W. Gibson: Comparison of body weight and gene expression in amelogenin null and wild-type mice. Eur J Oral Sci, in press.

Lyngstadaas, S.P., S. Risnes, B.S. Sproat, P.S. Thrane, H.P. Prydz (1995) A synthetic, chemically modified ribozyme eliminates amelogenin, the major translation product in developing mouse enamel in vivo. EMBO J *14:* 5224–5229.

Mardh, C.K., B. Backman, G. Holmgren, J.C. Hu, J.P. Simmer, K. Forsman-Semb (2002) A nonsense mutation in the enamelin gene causes local hypoplastic autosomal dominant amelogenesis imperfecta (AIH2). Hum Mol Genet *11:* 1069–1074.

Nebgen, D.R., H. Inoue, B. Sabsay, K. Wei, C.S. Ho, A. Veis (1999) Identification of the chondrogenic-inducing activity from bovine dentin (bCIA) as a low-molecular-mass amelogenin polypeptide. J Dent Res *78:* 1484–1494.

Nishikawa, S., K. Josephsen (1987) Cyclic localization of actin and its relationship to junctional complexes in maturation ameloblasts of the rat incisor. Anat Rec *219:* 21–31.

Nusier, M., O. Yassin, T.C. Hart, A. Samimi, J.T. Wright (2004) Phenotypic diversity and revision of the nomenclature for autosomal recessive amelogenesis imperfecta. Oral Surg Oral Med Oral Pathol Oral Radiol Endod *97:* 220–230.

Paine, M.L., P.H. Krebsbach, L.S. Chen, C.T. Paine, Y. Yamada, D. Deutsch, M.L. Snead (1998) Protein-to-protein interactions: criteria defining the assembly of the enamel organic matrix. J Dent Res *77:* 496–502.

Prakash, S.K., C.W. Gibson, J.T. Wright, C. Boyd, T. Cormier, R. Sierra, Y. Li, W.R. Abrams, M.A. Aragon, Z.A. Yuan, I.B. Van den Veyver (2005) Tooth enamel defects in mice with a deletion at the Arhgap6/AmelX locus. Calcif Tissue Int *77:* 23–29.

Prakash, S.K., R. Paylor, S. Jenna, N. Lamarche-Vane, D.L. Armstrong, B. Xu, M.A. Mancini, H.Y. Zoghbi (2000) Functional analysis of ARHGAP6, a novel GTPase-activating protein for RhoA. Hum Molec Genet *9:* 477–488.

Salido, E.C., P.H. Yen, K. Koprivnikar, L.C. Yu, L.J. Shapiro (1992) The human enamel protein gene amelogenin is expressed from both the X and Y chromosomes. Am J Hum Genet *50:* 303–316.

Schwartz, Z., D.L. Carnes, R. Pulliam, C.H. Lohmann, V.L. Sylvia, Y. Liu, D.D. Dean, D.L. Cochran, B.D. Boyan (2000) Porcine fetal enamel matrix derivative stimulates proliferation but not differentiation of pre-osteoblastic 2T9 cells, inhibits proliferation and stimulates differentiation of osteoblast-like MG63 cells and increases proliferation and differentiation of normal human osteoblast NHOst cells. J Periodontol *71:* 1287–1296.

Settleman, J. (2000) Getting in shape with Rho. Nat Cell Biol *3:* E7–E9.

Simmer, J.P., J.C. Hu (2002) Expression, structure, and function of enamel proteinases. Connect Tissue Res *43:* 441–449.

Simmer, J.P., C.C. Hu, E.C. Lau, P. Sarte, H.C. Slavkin, A.G. Fincham (1994) Alternative splicing of the mouse amelogenin primary RNA transcript. Calcif Tissue Int *55:* 302–310.

Smith, C. (1998) Cellular and chemical events during enamel maturation. Crit Rev Oral Biol Med *9:* 128–161.

Snead, M.L. (2003) Amelogenin protein exhibits a modular design: implications for form and function. Connect Tissue Res *44(suppl 1):* 47–51.

Termine, J.D., A.B. Belcourt, P.J. Christner, K.M. Conn, M.U. Nylen (1980) Properties of dissociatively extracted fetal tooth matrix proteins. 1. Principal molecular species in developing bovine enamel. J Biol Chem *255:* 9760–9768.

Van der Pauw, M.T., T. Van den Bos, V. Everts, W. Beertsen (2000) Enamel matrix-derived protein stimulates attachment of periodontal ligament fibroblasts and enhances alkaline phosphatase activity and transforming growth factor beta1 release of periodontal ligament and gingival fibroblasts. J Periodontol *71:* 31–43.

Veis, A., K. Tompkins, K. Alvares, K. Wei, L. Wang, X.S. Wang, A.G. Brownell, S.M. Jengh, K.E. Healy (2000) Specific amelogenin gene splice products have signaling effects on cells in culture and in implants in vivo. J Biol Chem *275:* 41263–41272.

Veis, A. (2003) Amelogenin gene splice products: potential signaling molecules. Cell Mol Life Sci *60:* 38–55.

Viswanathan, H.L., J.E. Berry, B.L. Foster, C.W. Gibson, Y. Li, A.B. Kulkarni, M.L. Snead, M.J. Somerman (2003) Amelogenin: a potential regulator of cementum-associated genes. J Periodontol *74:* 1423–1431.

Witkop, C.J., J.J. Sauk (1976) Heritable defects of enamel; in Stewart, R.E., G.H. Prescott (eds): Oral Facial Genetics. Mosby, St Louis, pp 151–226.

Wright, J.T., P.S. Hart, M.J. Aldred, K. Seow, P.J. Crawford, S.P. Hong, C.W. Gibson, T.C. Hart (2003) Relationship of phenotype and genotype in X-linked amelogenesis imperfecta. Connect Tissue Res *44:* 2–8.

Yuan, Z.A., P.M. Collier, J. Rosenbloom, C.W. Gibson (1996) Analysis of amelogenin mRNA during bovine tooth development. Arch Oral Biol *41:* 205–213.

Cells
Tissues
Organs

Cells Tissues Organs 2005;181:202–218
DOI: 10.1159/000091382

Amelogenin Supra-Molecular Assembly in vitro Compared with the Architecture of the Forming Enamel Matrix

Janet Moradian-Oldak[a] Michel Goldberg[b]

[a]Center for Craniofacial Molecular Biology, University of Southern California School of Dentistry, Los Angeles, Calif., USA; [b]Oral Biology, Faculté de Chirurgie Dentaire, Université Paris V, Montrouge, France

Key Words

Biomineralization · Amelogenin · Enamel · Apatite · Macromolecular assembly

Abstract

Tooth enamel is formed in the extracellular space within an organic matrix enriched in amelogenin proteins. Amelogenin nanosphere assembly is a key factor in controlling the oriented and organized growth of enamel apatite crystals. Recently, we have reported the formation of higher ordered structures resulting from organized association and self-orientation of amelogenin nanospheres in vitro. This remarkable hierarchical organization includes self-assembly of amelogenin molecules into subunits of 4–6 nm in diameter followed by their assembly to form nanospheres of 15–25 nm in radii. Chains of >100 nm length are then formed as the result of nanosphere association. These linear arrays of nanospheres assemble to form the microribbons that are hundreds of microns in length, tens of microns in width, and a few microns in thickness. Here, we review the step by step process of amelogenin self-assembly during the formation of microribbon structures in vitro. Assembly properties of selected amelogenins lacking the hydrophilic C terminus will then be reviewed. We will consider amelogenin as a template for the organized growth of crystals in vitro. Finally, we will compare the structures formed in vitro with globular and periodic structures observed earlier, in vivo, by different sample preparation conditions. We propose that the alignment of amelogenin nanospheres into long chains is evident in vivo, and is an important indication for the function of this protein in controlling the oriented and elongated growth of apatite crystals during enamel biomineralization.

Introduction

Living organisms ranging from bacteria to mammals produce a wide variety of biominerals that each fulfill a specific function. The mineralized tissues exhibit remarkable characteristics in terms of their shape, organization,

Abbreviations used in this paper

AFM	atomic force microscopy
DLS	dynamic light scattering
MMP	matrix metalloproteinase
NMR	nuclear magnetic resonance
OCP	octacalcium phosphate
R_H	hydrodynamic radii
SEM	scanning electron microscopy
TEM	transmission electron microscopy

KARGER
Fax +41 61 306 12 34
E-Mail karger@karger.ch
www.karger.com

Accessible online at:
www.karger.com/cto

Janet Moradian-Oldak, PhD
Center for Craniofacial Molecular Biology
University of Southern California School of Dentistry
2250 Alcazar St., CSA 103, Los Angeles, CA 90033 (USA)
Tel. +1 323 442 1759, Fax +1 323 442 2981, E-Mail joldak@usc.edu

hierarchical structures, and mechanical properties [Lowenstam and Weiner, 1989]. Typical examples of minerals formed in the biological environment are ferrous oxide in the magnetotactic bacteria, calcium oxalate in tomato leaves, calcium carbonate in mollusk shells and sea urchin spines, silicates in plants, and calcium phosphates in bone and teeth. In what has been termed as 'matrix-mediated' mineralization, the components of the organic matrix framework (proteins, polysaccharides, and enzymes) control the mineral type, shape, size, and orientation of the inorganic phase. Among many extra- and intracellular processes, macromolecular assembly is a common and critical event in biological mineralization [Addadi et al., 2002]. Self-assembly of proteins is the result of interactions and self-organization of the protein molecules via noncovalent interactions. The supramolecular assembly of collagen in bone and teeth, β-chitin in mollusk shells, and amelogenin in mineralizing enamel are associated with the organized architecture of these mineralized tissues. Enamel is different in that the vast majority of the organic matrix disappears with the completion of mineralization [Eastoe, 1979]. This paper will consider the assembly of the major protein component of forming enamel, namely amelogenin, as the 'temporary organic matrix' framework that controls the shape, mineral phase, and most importantly, the orientation and organization of the minerals during the development of dental enamel.

Enamel as a Mineralizing System

Tooth enamel, the hardest bioceramic composite in the vertebrate body is the result of a cascade of intra- and extracellular events [Eastoe, 1964]. A single layer of epithelially derived ameloblasts, which are elongated along the dentin-enamel junction, forms enamel. Upon maturation, enamel possesses a unique combination of mechanical functions including wear resistance and fracture resistance [Habelitz et al., 2001]. These excellent mechanical properties arise inherently from the action of a series of extracellular matrix protein products whose spatial expression and temporal secretion are genetically controlled [Paine et al., 2001; Cuy et al., 2002]. The programmed expression, secretion, assembly, and degradation of the ameloblast gene products eventually result in the controlled nucleation and growth of a highly organized mineral structure comprised of elongated and oriented carbonate hydroxyapatite crystals [Robinson et al., 1998; Smith, 1998; Fincham et al., 1999].

Many chemical and biological events during enamel development and mineralization are comparable with other biomineralizing systems described previously [Lowenstam and Weiner, 1989; Fincham et al., 1999; Addadi et al., 2002]. The zone between an ameloblast cell layer and dentin is the confined space where enamel mineralization occurs. Ameloblasts secrete a group of extracellular proteins (amelogenins, enamelins, and ameloblastins) that assemble to provide the temporary organic framework for the controlled nucleation and oriented growth of carbonated hydroxyapatite crystals. Amelogenins constitute the primary structural entity (>90%) of the developing dental enamel extracellular matrix. Control of crystal orientation, modulation of crystal morphology, and subsequent crystal elongation are the proposed physiological functions for amelogenin proteins [Diekwisch et al., 1993; Simmer and Fincham, 1995; Moradian-Oldak et al., 1998b; Robinson et al., 1998; Iijima et al., 2002]. Amelogenin has also been proposed to function as spacers between the tiny apatite crystals to prevent their lateral fusion [Warshawsky, 1989; Moradian-Oldak et al., 1998b]. Enamelin was proposed to be involved in controlling the nucleation and possibly growth modulation of the crystallites [Uchida et al., 1997; Hu and Yamakoshi, 2003; Bouropoulos and Moradian-Oldak, 2004]. Ameloblastins have been hypothesized to be involved in the control of the prismatic structure of enamel [Krebsbach et al., 1996]. A recent report on ameloblastin-null mice has documented that ameloblastin functions as a cell adhesion protein controlling the differentiation state of the ameloblasts [Fukumoto et al., 2004]. As documented by recent transgenic and null mice model studies as well as linkage analysis of human pedigrees in cases of amelogenesis imperfecta, amelogenin, enamelin, ameloblastin, and enamelysin – matrix metalloproteinase (MMP-20) – have been shown to be critical for normal enamel formation [Lagerstrom-Fermer and Landegren, 1995; Gibson et al., 2001; Caterina et al., 2002; Paine et al., 2003; Fukumoto et al., 2004; Masuya et al., 2005].

There are a number of physiological events that distinguish tooth enamel from other matrix-mediated biomineralizing systems. The extracellular matrix is 'a forming matrix' and not a 'preformed matrix' as it was defined for other mineralizing tissues. The amelogenin-rich organic matrix is continuously secreted, assembled, processed, and mineralized during enamel development. The extracellular 'organic matrix framework' is processed in a stepwise and controlled manner (during the initial stage), rapidly degraded (during maturation stage), and eventually removed from the extracellular space [Eastoe,

1960; Smith et al., 1989]. During maturation, massive protein degradation events occur simultaneously with the completion of mineralization. These activities transform the matrix that contains, by weight, approximately 30% mineral with the remainder being organic material and water to a highly organized structure, which is almost completely inorganic (>99%) [Robinson et al., 1978]. Mature enamel crystals (carbonate-containing fluoridated hydroxyapatite) are different from those of dentin and bone in that they are extremely long in the c-axial direction with an aspect ratio of approximately 1,000 [Daculsi and Kerebel, 1978; Daculsi et al., 1984]. Nucleation of the initial crystals occurs within a zone where another mineralized tissue (underlying dentin) already exists. The question as to whether enamel crystals are initiated on the surface of dentin, or independently, on a preformed structural framework made of an enamel extracellular matrix is still open for investigation [Arsenault and Robinson, 1989].

Amelogenins as the Major Component of the Enamel Extracellular Matrix

It has been more than 60 years since the existence of an organic component in forming tooth enamel was confirmed by chemical analysis [Stack, 1954, 1956; Geller, 1958]. Although it was known that the material was not of a collagenous nature, the main component of the organic matrix was not defined until the early 60s when Eastoe [1960] reported the unique composition of 'amelogenins' as being enriched in Pro, His, and Glu residues. While the 'core' of the amelogenin sequence is enriched with the hydrophobic amino acids, the majority of the charged residues of the sequence are concentrated at the C-terminal region [Snead et al., 1985]. Such a distribution of amino acids provides the molecule with a hydrophobic-hydrophilic polarity that plays an important role in the self-assembly of amelogenin (see below). Human amelogenins are encoded mainly (90%) by the amelogenin gene located on the X chromosome (AMEX) which contains seven exons [Lau et al., 1990]. Extensive alternative splicing of exon 2 through 7 results in the formation of different isoforms that contribute to the heterogeneity of secreted amelogenins. Recently, two additional exons (8 and 9) have been reported in rats and mice [Papagerakis et al., 2005]. An additional factor contributing to the heterogeneity of amelogenins is post-transitional proteolytic processing [Simmer and Hu, 2002]. Amelogenin sequences at both carboxy- and amino-terminal regions across species are highly homologous suggesting that these regions play specific functional roles during the matrix-mediated enamel biomineralization [Toyosawa et al., 1998]. The trityrosine motif (PYPSYGYEPMGGW) on the tyrosine-rich amelogenin polypeptide region has been reported to have lectin-like properties. This region might be involved in amelogenin-cell or amelogenin-nonamelogenin interactions [Ravindranath et al., 1999; Paine et al., 2001]. Three independent strategies have been embraced by investigators to evaluate the loss of function of amelogenin proteins in animal and organ culture models. These include specific inhibition of amelogenin gene expression by means of a chemically modified ribozyme in newborn mice [Lyngstadaas et al., 1995], antisense inhibition of amelogenin translation in organ culture [Diekwisch et al., 1993], and a recent null mice model [Gibson et al., 2001]. All these studies have supported the hypothesis that amelogenin functions to control the organization and growth of enamel crystals, and its presence is therefore critical for normal enamel formation.

Amelogenin Self-Assembly in vitro

Nanospheres and Their Subunits

The notion that the protein components of the enamel matrix appear as polymerizing multi- or single components was first reported by Katz et al. [1965], using proteins isolated from embryonic bovine enamel. A sedimentation equilibrium study of bovine enamel proteins revealed the detection of unusually high-molecular-weight complexes ranging from 1 to 4 million daltons [Katz et al., 1969]. Protein aggregates consisting mainly of amelogenins were found to be stable even in chaotropic agents such as guanidine hydrochloride [Mechanic et al., 1967].

The problem of enamel protein 'aggregation' has limited studies concerning amelogenin structure and function. Heterogeneity in the matrix and the complexity of isolating and purifying homogeneous preparations of the protein have also contributed to these difficulties. Several attempts have been made to obtain secondary and tertiary structural information for amelogenin. These included poorly resolved X-ray diffraction images of a developing bovine tooth enamel matrix, possibly showing a β- or a cross-β-structure [Bonar et al., 1965]; circular dichroism and nuclear magnetic resonance (NMR) studies have led to suggestions that the molecule contains both β-structures and β-turns [Renugopalakrishnan et al., 1989; Goto et al. 1993], but other work has indicated a highly mobile structure [Termine et al., 1979].

Following the cDNA cloning of amelogenin and subsequent expression of a recombinant form in *Escherichia coli,* there has been a significant advance in understanding the primary structure as well as the 'aggregative' behavior of this hydrophobic protein [Snead et al., 1985; Simmer et al., 1994]. Amelogenin 'nanospheres' were first described, in vitro, in 1994 when the self-assembly properties of a recombinant mouse amelogenin (rM179) were studied employing dynamic light scattering (DLS), size exclusion chromatography, atomic force (AFM) and transmission electron microscopy (TEM) [Fincham et al., 1994, 1995; Moradian-Oldak et al., 1994, 2004]. It was then reported that full-length amelogenin molecules undergo a self-assembly process to generate spherical structures of 15–20 nm in hydrodynamic radii (R_H). It was proposed that the nanospheres were formed through intermolecular hydrophobic interactions when the hydrophilic segment is exposed on the surface of the nanospheres. The self-assembly process of amelogenin to form nanospheres is sensitive to temperature, solution pH, and protein concentration [Moradian-Oldak et al., 1998a]. Under physiological pH, the homogeneity of nanosphere assemblies with sizes of 15–20 nm was achieved at protein concentrations higher than 100 μg/ml [Wen et al., 2001]. Figure 1 is a tapping mode AFM image in air of amelogenin nanospheres adsorbed on a mica surface and fixed by Karnovsky fixative. In other studies, Leytin et al. [1998] have applied Cryo-TEM to confirm the formation of nanospheres by a recombinant human amelogenin in a vitreous ice system.

In a series of independent studies, employing the yeast two-hybrid system, it was found that amelogenin-amelogenin interactions occur through the amino-terminal 42 residues called A domain [Paine and Snead, 1997]. In addition, it was reported that the self-assembly can be affected by the 17-residue domain in the carboxyl-terminal region called B domain. Alteration of these self-assembly domains in transgenic animals has resulted in the formation of enamel with defective structural organization supporting the view that amelogenin self-assembly into nanospheres is a key factor in controlling normal enamel biomineralization [Paine et al., 2000]. Formation of nanospheres by a native porcine amelogenin isolated from scrapings of fourth mandibular molars has also been confirmed [Moradian-Oldak et al., 2002]. The native protein P173 (the '25 kDa') formed larger nanospheres than the recombinant rP172. This difference may be related to the presence of phosphate on serine 16 of the native amelogenin [Fincham and Moradian-Oldak, 1993] or it could be the result of the presence of minor impurities in the protein preparation.

We have proposed a schematic model for amelogenin folding and assembly based on the sequence for porcine amelogenin and the chemical and physical properties of the amino acids in the primary structure (fig. 2). Parameters such as the hydrophilicity [Hopp and Woods, 1981], polarity [Grantham, 1974], and conformational parameter for β-turn secondary structure [Chou and Fasman, 1978] were considered. Amelogenin molecules show a bipolar nature with a short hydrophilic block at the C terminus and the remaining overall hydrophobic block. A closer examination of the hydrophobic part suggested a pattern of alternating lower-higher hydrophobic blocks that roughly matches the pattern of alternating blocks with higher-lower polarity. The potential β-turn-forming sites are mostly located at the higher polar blocks or at the interface of lower-higher polar blocks. These patterns suggest the possibility of multiple folding and a compact structure for the hydrophobic bulk of the molecule in an aqueous environment. Those blocks with higher polarity and lower hydrophobicity tend to be exposed at the surface of the folded molecule. This prediction can be partly supported by controlled proteolysis studies [Moradian-Oldak et al., 2001]. The primary cleavage sites (fig. 2, yellow lines) that were recognized within a short-term (5-min) enzymatic digest are likely to be exposed at the surface of the molecule. Besides those sites at C and N termini, there are two sites inside the hydrophobic core of the molecule that are indeed located in the less hydrophobic and higher polar blocks. The surface exposure of the C-terminal hydrophilic segment and some residues at the N terminus has also been revealed in several other experiments including ^{1}H-NMR photo-chemically induced dynamic nuclear polarization [Aoba et al., 1990] and N-acetylglucosamine-binding studies [Ravindranath et al., 1999]. In a yeast two-hybrid assay experiment, two domains in N (A domain) and C termini (B domain) have been identified to interact during amelogenin self-assembly, either directly or indirectly [Paine and Snead, 1997]. Based on the above data, we propose a model in which the highly flexible C terminus can be narrowed down into a 7-amino-acid sequence (-TKREEVD) that is acidic and conserved among species. Therefore, we predict that the full-length amelogenin molecule can fold into a unique globular form that preserves its bipolar nature from the primary structure. Support for the hypothesis that the nanospheres are in average negatively charged was given by the streaming potential measurements (zeta potential) of a rM179 protein solution [Moradian-Oldak et al., 2004]. Assuming an ideal hard-sphere type for the hydrophobic body (fig. 2, grey sphere), its diameter is calcu-

Table 1. Analysis of amelogenin nanosphere subunits detected by DynaPro MSX/TC DLS in rP172 solutions using a 10-second acquisition time

Solvent	C_{rP172}, mg/ml	R_H, nm	MW, kDa	N_{MW}
Acetate buffer pH 4.5	0.0125, 0.025, 0.05, 0.1, 0.3, 1, 5, 10	6.4	255	13.0
		9.2	600	30.7
		9.9	711	36.3
		13.2, 13.9	1,414, 1,590	72.2, 81.2
Water pH approximately 6.5	0.05, 0.1, 0.2, 1	5.8	206	10.5
		8.4	485	24.8
		9.4, 9.7	645, 684	33.0, 34.9
		12.1, 12.6	1,142, 1,269	58.3, 64.8
		13.1, 13.6	1,386, 1,513	70.8, 77.3
Aqueous acetonitrile 60% (v/v)	0.025, 0.05, 0.1	2.2	22	1.1
		3.2	51	2.6
		3.5	65	3.3
		4.6	120	6.1
		5.5	181	9.2
		6.6	283	14.5
		7.3	351	17.9
		7.5, 7.9	372, 376	19.0, 19.2
		9.6	666	34.0
		10.5	831	42.5
		11.7	1,070	54.7
		13.8	1,570	80.2

The R_H and the estimated molecular weight (MW) of the assemblies with R_H <15 nm are shown. The molecule numbers (N_{MW}) in the assemblies were calculated using 19.573 kDa for one rP172 molecule. Based on data published in Du et al. [2005].

lated as 3.5 nm using a molecular weight of 18,697 Da and a partial specific volume of 0.731 cm^3/g (the average partial specific volume from 13 structure-known globular proteins) [Harpaz et al., 1994]. The 'tail' of the C terminus (-TKREEVD) (fig. 2, red thread) is highly hydrophilic and has net negative charges (calculated isoelectric point = 4.87; http://us.expasy.org/tools/pi_tool.html) over a wide range of pH. Its length can theoretically vary between 1 and 2 nm (assuming an α-helix or a β-strand conformation). The circular dichroism study has suggested that the C terminus of amelogenin is in a random coil conformation [Goto et al., 1993]. Modeled as a hard sphere for the whole molecule, the apparent radius would be 2.25–2.75 nm.

In our most recent study, we have performed a systematic analysis of the size distribution of amelogenin assemblies and their intermediate subunits using a highly sensitive DynaPro MSX/TC light scattering instrument, with a size detection range of 1 nm to 1 μm [Du et al., 2005]. A highly purified pig recombinant amelogenin rP172 was used in three different solution conditions: 60% acetonitrile (a relatively hydrophobic solvent), acetate buffer (pH 5.5), and distilled water (pH 6.5) (table 1). It was found that typical nanospheres of R_H = 13–27 nm were the most stable assembling form in either buffer or water. Small particles with R_H less than 10 nm were detected in short measurement intervals indicating the presence of subunits prior to nanosphere formation [Fincham et al., 1998]. Measurements in 60% aqueous acetonitrile and at low protein concentration (approximately 20 μg/ml) have revealed the presence of monomers and discrete oligomers such as dimers, trimers, and hexamers. These were defined as the basic subunits of typical R_H = 13–27 nm nanospheres. The size distribution of the recombinant mouse amelogenin rM179 nanospheres appeared to be smaller when evaluated by small-angle X-ray scattering compared with those evaluated by DLS. These observations have supported the proposed model of a dense hydrophobic core with a flexible hydrophilic region exposed on the surface of the molecule [Aichmayer et al., 2005].

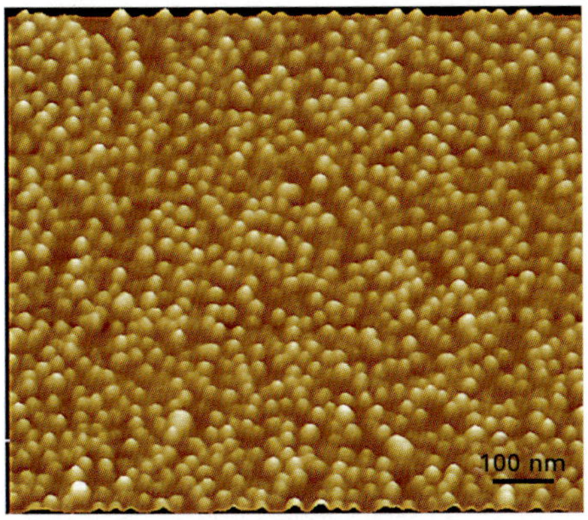

1

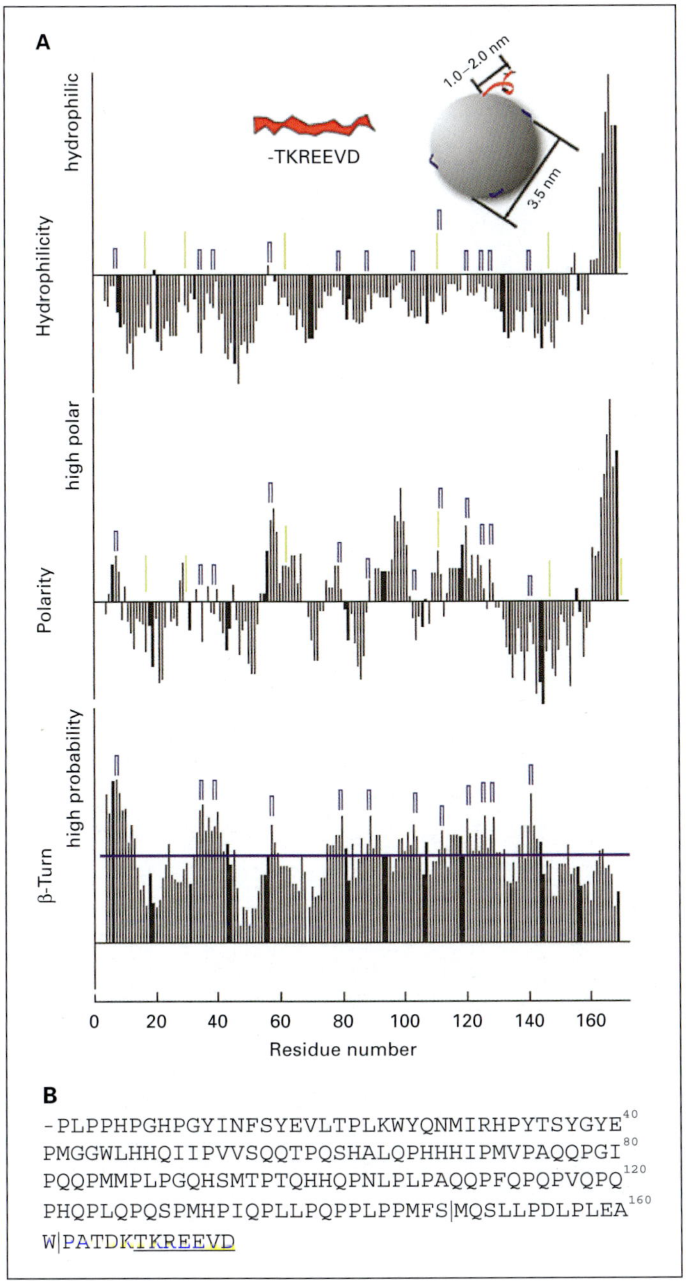

2

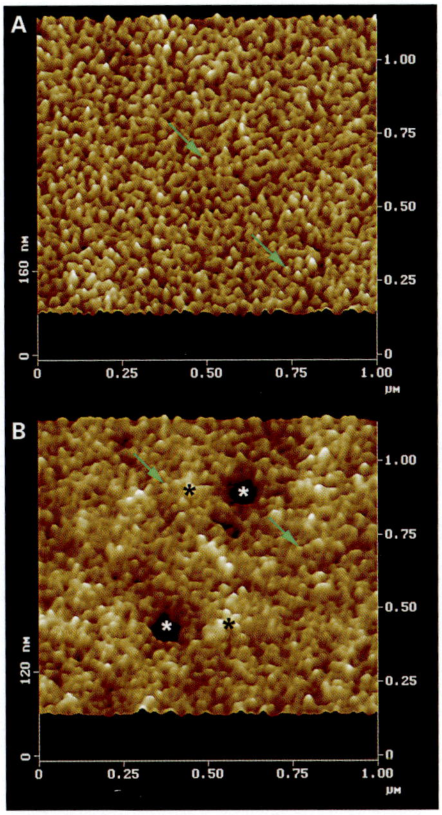

3

Fig. 1. Amelogenin nanospheres made of a recombinant mouse protein (rM179) adsorbed on mica, fixed by Karnovsky fixative, and imaged by AFM in a tapping mode as previously described [Wen et al., 2001].

Fig. 2. Sequence analysis of porcine amelogenin and a proposed model for its folding based on theoretical and experimental data published in literature. **A** Hydrophobicity plot by Hopp and Woods [1981]. The analysis was performed using ProtScale software of the ExPASy (Expert Protein Analysis System) proteomics server from the Swiss Institute of Bioinformatics [Gasteiger et al., 2003]. A linear averaging method with a window of 7 amino acids was used. The blue line on the pattern of the β-turn parameter indicates the average of the whole molecule. The sites with a high probability to form a β-turn are highlighted by the blue turn symbols. **B** Amino acid sequence of recombinant porcine amelogenin. The protein lacks the first methionine and a phosphate group on Ser^{16} position. The in vivo proteolytic cleavage sites resulting in the formation of P148 (S/M) and P161 (F/S) are labeled. The proposed flexible negatively charged 7 amino acids are underlined. Reproduced from Du et al. [2005], with permission.

Fig. 3. Tapping mode AFM images of the clear (**A**) and opaque (**B**) 'gel-like' matrix reconstructed from recombinant mouse amelogenin rM179 as described previously [Wen et al., 2001]. Arrows point to the individual nanosphere assemblies. White and black asterisks denote the cavities and large aggregates, respectively.

Assembly of Amelogenin Nanospheres into Higher-Order Structures

The question as to whether amelogenin nanospheres have a tendency to further assemble into higher-order structures in vitro has motivated us to study the physiochemical properties and structure of reconstituted amelogenin gels [Wen et al., 1999b]. These studies were also designed to explore the reversible temperature-sensitive aggregation properties of amelogenins, originally demonstrated by Nikiforuk and Simmons [1965]. We studied the structure of concentrated solutions of amelogenins (100–300 mg/ml) at two different temperatures, made either from recombinant protein or from an heterogeneous native extract. The 'gel-like' amelogenin preparations that rendered translucent at 4°C and opaque at room temperature were fixed using Karnovsky fixation technique and examined by scanning electron microscopy (SEM) and TEM as well as AFM. These reconstituted amelogenin preparations were composed of spherical structures ranging in size from 20 to 200 nm in diameter. The clear to opaque transition with a raise in temperature appeared to be the result of formation of numerous globular 'voids', presumably as the result of increased hydrophobic interactions between the spherical subunits creating more empty space (fig. 3). The change in size distribution of the spherical structures with temperature has supported the theory that an increase in temperature promotes hydrophobic forces between the nanospheres resulting in the formation of larger subunits.

Although the studies on amelogenin 'gel-like' preparations have provided some explanation on their physiochemical properties and the presence of nanosphere subunits, observation of highly ordered structures with defined orientation of the nanospheres within the 'gel-like' matrix was still lacking. Organized alignment of the nanospheres was achieved following our recent attempt to crystallize amelogenin [Du et al., 2005]. By applying the classical technique of hanging drop for solvent evaporation, and using the full-length recombinant porcine amelogenin rP172, we obtained elongated fibrous structures that we named 'microribbons' [Du et al., 2005]. The microribbons were hundreds of microns in length, tens of microns in width, and a few microns in thickness (fig. 4).

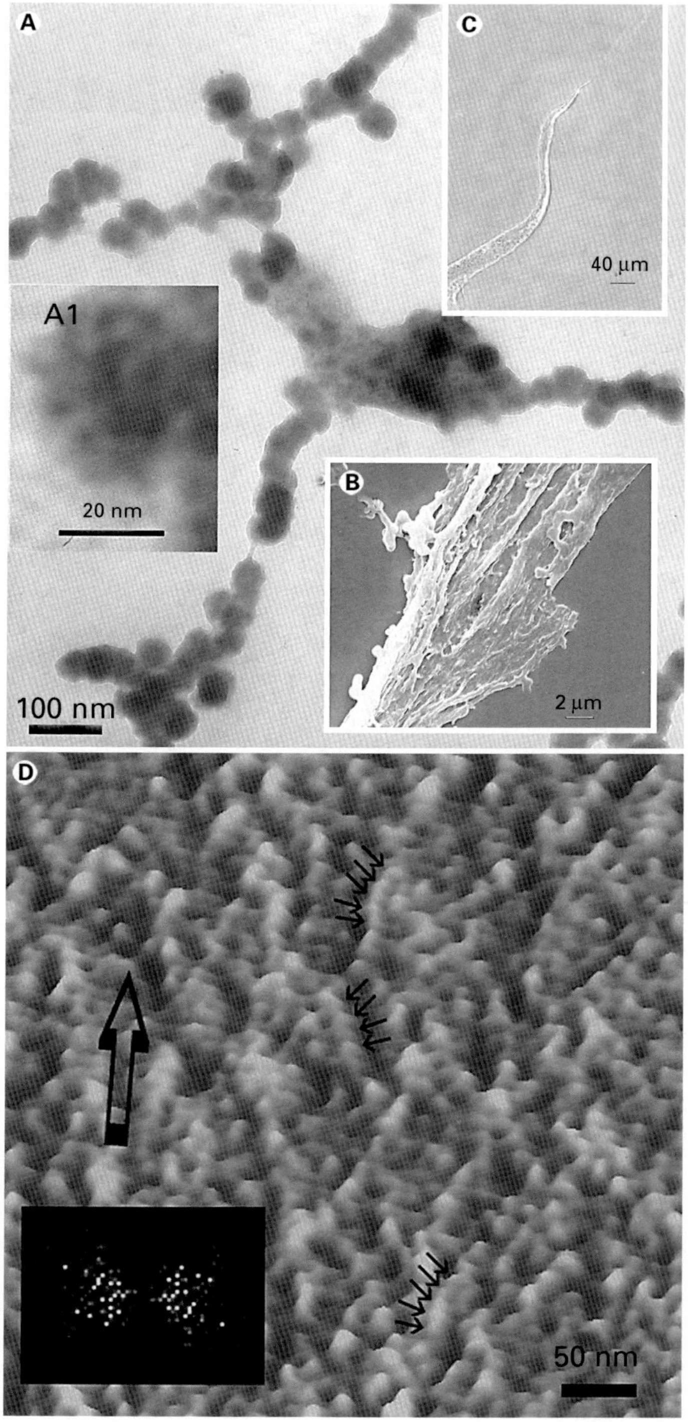

Fig. 4. TEM micrograph showing the assembly of amelogenin nanospheres into chains during microribbon assembly (**A**). SEM of bundles of nanosphere chains prior to the microribbon formation (**B**). Optical micrograph of an amelogenin microribbon (**C**). AFM in tapping mode of the surface of an amelogenin microribbon showing the periodical pattern of arrays of nanospheres aligned approximately along the long axis of the ribbon (block arrow) (**D**). Inset in **D**: the anisotropic pattern of Fourier transform spectra demonstrating the highly ordered alignment of the nanosphere chains. **A**, **D** Reproduced from Du et al. [2005], with permission.

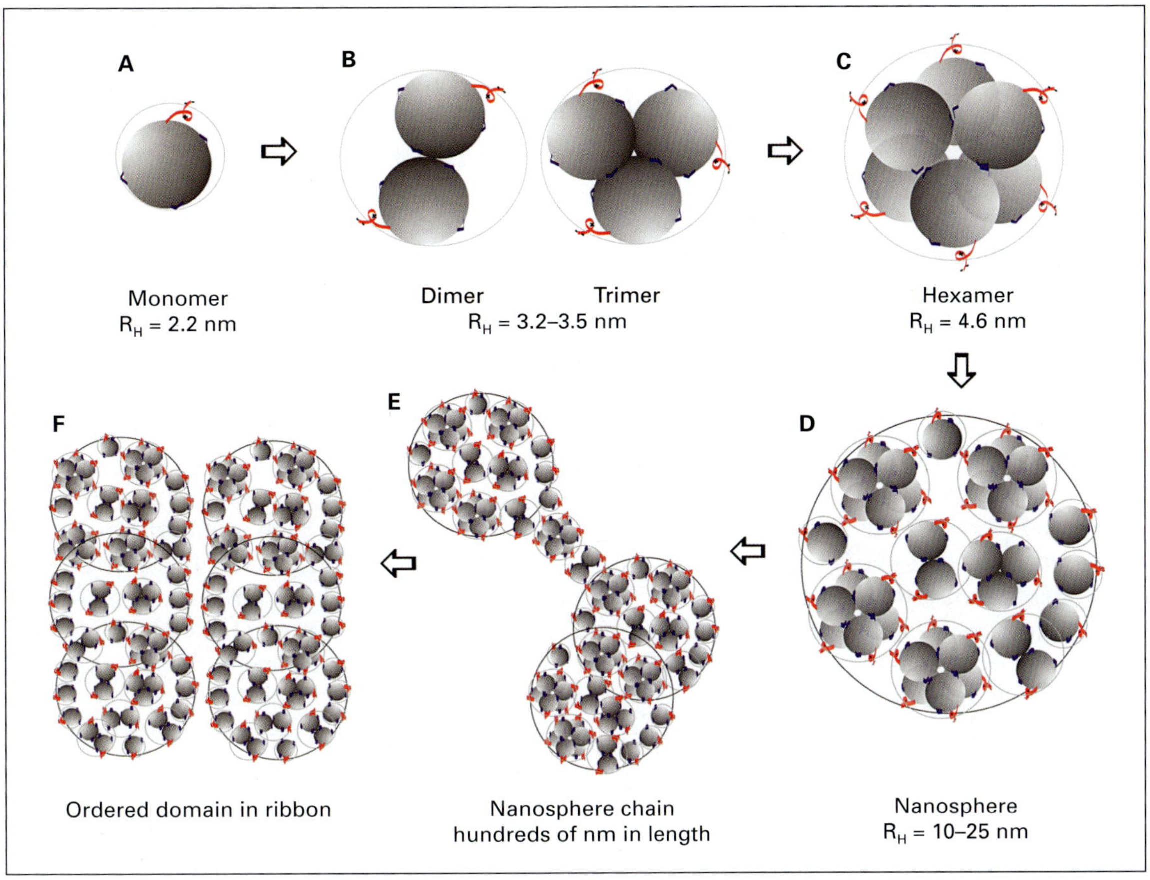

Fig. 5. A schematic model for the step by step assembly of amelogenin molecules from monomers, dimers, trimers, or hexamers to nanospheres and nanochains and eventually microribbons. Reproduced from Du et al. [2005], with permission.

Nanosphere chains were observed under TEM at an intermediate state prior to the formation of microribbons (fig. 4A). Subunits of a few nanometers were detected inside each nanosphere (fig. 4A1). The nanochains then laterally assembled into bundles (fig. 4B) that eventually matured to form the microribbons (fig. 4C). The nanochain structures were also observed on the surface of the microribbons by AFM (fig. 4D). Thc size range of the nanospheres (10–20 nm in diameter) in the microribbon was consistent with the lower limit from DLS measurement in solutions. Those nanochains of more than 100 nm in length were aligned roughly parallel to the long axis of the ribbons.

A schematic presentation of a step by step amelogenin self-assembly starting from a monomer to a microribbon is shown in figure 5. We propose that an amelogenin molecule can fold into a unique globular form that preserves a bipolar nature derived from its primary structure (fig. 2, 5A). The 7-amino-acid length hydrophilic C terminus (-TKREEVD) is relatively flexible and exposed on the surface of the molecule. Oligomerization of amelogenin molecules occurs mainly via hydrophobic interactions (fig. 4A1, 5B–D). Nanosphere structures (R_H = 10–25 nm) are formed through association of monomers and oligomers (fig. 5D). As proposed before, the net negative charges of the hydrophilic C-terminal 7 amino acids (calculated isoelectric point = 4.5) over a wide range of pHs provide the primary repulsive force that stabilizes the nanosphere structures and defines their sizes. Further association of nanospheres results in larger assemblies which were detected to be linear chains of 10–15 nanospheres (fig. 4A, 5E). The bipolar nature of the molecule can facilitate the formation and/or the reorganization of the chain structures. This process can eventually lead to the formation of a ribbon structure (fig. 4C, 5F).

The microribbons did not have a defined X-ray diffraction pattern as it was originally reported [Du et al., 2005].

The defined X-ray diffraction was identified to be the result of cellulose contamination, and this unfortunate finding has been communicated as a letter of correction to the *Science* magazine [Du et al., 2005]. We have further evaluated our data, carrying out new experiments to prepare amelogenin microribbons. We have confirmed the absence of contamination in the formed amelogenin microribbons in situ by Raman microscopy and Fourier transform infrared spectroscopy [Moradian-Oldak et al., in press]. The short linear alignment of nanosphere structures lacking strict periodicity can well explain the weak, or sometimes absence of, diffraction patterns from the microribbons. The microribbons possess birefringence indicating some level of ordered alignment within the microribbons. In view of the observation that the chains of nanospheres are very flexible and of different length, they do not associate in periodic X-ray diffracting structures, but can give the birefringent microribbons. Birefringence have been observed in in vitro preparations of protein extracts from scrapings of the outermost layer of young enamel [Nagasaka, 1994]. These were described by Nagasaka [1994] as 'tiny finger-like rows of short, segmental, birefringent rod-like strings of beads' which were similar to those observed by Fearnhead and Kawasaki [1991].

Assembly of Amelogenin Proteolytic Products

Following its secretion, amelogenin is processed by enamel proteinases in a stepwise and controlled manner [Simmer and Hu, 2002]. At the early stage of enamel formation, the hydrophilic C terminus of amelogenin is removed by enamelysin (MMP-20) producing a product that is stable during the secretory stage [Yamakoshi et al., 1994; Ryu et al., 1999]. This is followed by the removal of the amino-terminal tyrosine-rich amelogenin polypeptide [Fincham et al., 1981]. Enamel structure in enamelysin-null mice is defective supporting the view that proteolytic processing is a pivotal step toward normal enamel formation.

The tendency of amelogenin proteolytic products to aggregate into a semi-ellipsoidal shape in vitro was first demonstrated in negatively stained TEMs of the 21- to 20-kDa proteins isolated from the outermost 3–4 μm scrapings of young porcine enamel [Nagasaka, 1994]. The sample was dissolved in water, at low temperature, in a concentration of 100 mg/ml and sprayed on a TEM grid. A network of 'aggregated units piled up onto one another' resulted in some linear and branched shapes. The size of one unit was reported to be 3 × 5 nm.

We have undertaken studies to investigate the effect of proteolytic activities on the assembly and function of amelogenin protein [Moradian-Oldak et al., 2002, 2003; Sun et al., 2005a, b]. We have used recombinant and native porcine and mouse amelogenins to study amelogenin self-assembly properties in comparison with their isoforms lacking the hydrophilic C terminus [Moradian-Oldak et al., 2002]. Overall, the size distribution of the nanospheres formed by the recombinant porcine amelogenin rP172 was shown to be smaller than these formed by the longer recombinant mouse amelogenin rM179. Removal of the 12 hydrophilic carboxy-terminal residues from rM179 did not decrease the nanosphere size but resulted in the formation of fused nanospheres with their size shifted toward a larger distribution. This observation was supported by comparison between the full-length amelogenins, the recombinant rM179 and native P173 (the '25 kDa') with their processed products recombinant rM166 and native P161 (the '23 kDa') lacking the hydrophilic carboxy terminus. The formation of large precipitates by rM166 above 20°C has also been confirmed in a recent study using small-angle X-ray scattering combined with DLS analysis [Aichmayer et al., 2005]. It is interesting to point out that the 25 C-terminal amino acid cleavage product, at site Ser^{148}/Met, of pig amelogenin P173, known as the '20 kDa' or P148, formed smaller nanospheres. Note that when compared with P161, P148 lacks the following residues: SMQSLLPDLPLEA, which are relatively bulky and mostly hydrophobic.

Recently, a recombinant analogue of the 20-kDa amelogenin proteolytic product named rP148 has been engineered and expressed in *E. coli* [Sun et al., 2005b]. The purified recombinant rP148 lacks the N-terminal Met and ends at Met^{149}. In general, at room temperature, rP148 molecules assemble into monomers, dimers, oligomers, and some nanospheres. Depending on the solution conditions, large aggregates were also observed. When compared with the full-length recombinant porcine amelogenin rP172, recombinant rP148 protein shows different assembly patterns. The recombinant rP172 protein molecules assemble into typical nanospheres with R_H = 10–30 nm, while the majority of rP148 molecules assemble into oligomers with R_H = 3–4 nm. It is not clear whether the approximately 15-nm particles detected in the case of rP148 are similar to the typical nanospheres formed by the full-length amelogenin. However, it is important to notice that distribution of the particle size and their percentage masses depend on protein concentration. In 60% aqueous acetonitrile, the majority of both rP172 and rP148 form small particles with R_H less than 5 nm. While there are more monomers detected for rP148, in the case of rP172, oligomers are formed. The molecules of rP148 showed a higher tendency to aggregate at pH 7.4–8 because of the lack of the hydrophilic C terminus. The absence of the hydrophilic C terminus can have a drastic effect on the configuration of the molecule and hence protein self-assembly. Whether domains within this C terminus are directly involved in protein-protein interaction for self-assembly is not known. Previous studies applying the yeast two-hybrid system strategy have demonstrated that a 16-amino-acid-length region within the C terminus (self-assembly 'B' domain) is critical for protein-protein interaction and proper nanosphere self-assembly. A time-dependent DLS analysis of amelogenin lacking the 'B domain' forms particles that eventually fuse together and collapse [Moradian-Oldak et al., 2000].

Amelogenin as a Temporary Template for Controlled Crystal Growth

The earlier finding that amelogenin can 'slightly' inhibit the seeded crystal growth of apatite in solution has indicated that amelogenin proteins actually interact with apatite crystals [Doi et al., 1984]. The strong adsorption affinity of porcine amelogenin and its proteolytic products on hydroxyapatite crystals were first reported by Aoba et al. [1989] using native amelogenins. It has then been proposed that the 'originally secreted amelogenin may play an active role in amelogenesis'. Later, using a series of pure recombinant and native amelogenins and their isoforms, it was demonstrated that the binding affinity of proteins on the hydroxyapatite is decreased after cleaving the hydrophilic C-terminal segment [Moradian-Oldak et al., 2002]. Following the description of the 'nanospheres', we have considered the interactions of apatite with amelogenin 'nanospheres' as a binding unit as opposed to amelogenin 'monomers'. Bouropoulos and Moradian-Oldak [2003] reported that the adsorption isotherm of amelogenin nanospheres onto hydroxyapatite could be described with a good correlation coefficient ($R^2 = 0.99$) indicating that amelogenin nanospheres can bind to the surface of apatite crystals with defined adsorption sites. Recently, solid-state NMR studies have provided direct evidence for the orientation of the charged C-terminal region of amelogenin protein on the hydroxyapatite surface [Shaw et al., 2004]. In vitro studies on the effect of different amelogenins on the aggregation of hydroxyapatite in solution indicated that the full-length amelogenin caused aggregation of apatite crystals more effectively than the C-terminally cleaved amelogenin [Moradian-Oldak et al., 1998b]. This aggregation effect was interpreted as the 'bridging' of apatite crystals by the preassembled amelogenin nanospheres. Organized bundles of elongated apatite crystals were formed on bioactive glass as well as titanium, in the presence of amelogenin in the mineralization solution [Wen et al., 1999a]. Recently, Beniash et al. [2005] showed that crystallites grown in solution, in the presence of assembled amelogenin, were organized parallel to their c-axial direction. The notion that amelogenin can control the rate and direction of growth of crystals was supported by the recent in vitro study using the fluoroapatite glass ceramic model [Habelitz et al., 2004]. While the presence of the hydrophilic C terminus decreased the affinity of amelogenin to bind to apatite, and inhibited the kinetics of its growth [Moradian-Oldak et al., 1998b], the effect on octacalcium phosphate (OCP) and apatite crystal shape was reported to be independent of the presence of the hydrophilic C-terminal segment [Iijima et al., 2002; Beniash et al., 2005]. It has recently been shown that amelogenins affected the morphology of OCP crystals in a dose-dependent manner, changing crystal morphology from plate-like to more elongated shapes (ribbon-like) [Iijima and Moradian-Oldak, 2004]. The above in vitro studies collectively demonstrate that amelogenin nanospheres interact with synthetic calcium hydroxyapatite and OCP crystal faces in a selective manner and therefore control their morphology and habit. Specific binding of amelogenin nanospheres on side faces of enamel crystals has also been demonstrated by Wallwork et al. [2001].

The above in vitro experimental studies used strategies to examine the effect of amelogenin proteins on crystal growth in solution, in 'gel-like' matrices, and on active surfaces. In our most recent study, we have used amelogenin microribbons as a 'framework' for the growth of crystals. The microribbons were mineralized in a metastable calcium phosphate solution as described previously [Du et al., 2005]. TEM and the corresponding electron diffraction patterns of crystals isolated from these mineralized microribbons confirmed the formation of oriented apatite crystals along their c-axial direction (fig. 6A). AFM images of the surface of a mineralized ribbon have clearly shown the organized alignment of the crystals grown from within these ribbons (fig. 6B). SEM micrographs of apatite crystals grown on the surface of amelogenin microribbons, pretreated with phosvitin revealing the formation of ordered and remarkably oriented crystals, aligned along the long axis of the ribbons (fig. 6C–E). Phosvitin is a highly phosphorylated protein which was used in our experiments as a model for a potent nucleator. We propose that the linear alignment of nanospheres in vitro creates an ideal framework that facilitates the oriented growth of apatite crystals regardless of the presence of an acidic protein such as phosvitin. The oriented nucleation of such crystals in vitro could be promoted through the interactions of the structured amelogenin framework with the highly phosphorylated protein, phosvitin. In the enamel extracellular matrix, this control can be achieved by the coassembly of amelogenin and the nonamelogenin proteins such as the acidic enamelin [Hu and Yamakoshi, 2003; Bouropoulos and Moradian-Oldak, 2004]. Alternatively, the ordered hydrophobic/hydrophilic partitioning of amelogenin molecules could create an oriented array of acidic peptides on a hydrophobic substrate. The control of crystal nucleation and regulation of crystal growth by ordered arrays of acidic functional groups has been elegantly employed in many in vitro model systems and widely implicated in the biomineralization [Addadi and Weiner, 1989; Mann, 1993].

Amelogenin Self-Assembly in vivo

Periodic Structures of the Forming Enamel Organic Matrix

Studies from the early sixties have reported the presence of some relatively periodic structures in developing enamel that might refer to the ultra-structure or architecture of the organic matrix. Watson [1960] originally described enamel 'stippled material' as finely granular material between the distal end of the secretory ameloblast and the mineralization front. Travis and Glimcher [1964] found in the electron microscopic tissue sections that many 'dense lines approximately 48 Å wide' were parallel to each other and 'separated by approximately 120 Å'

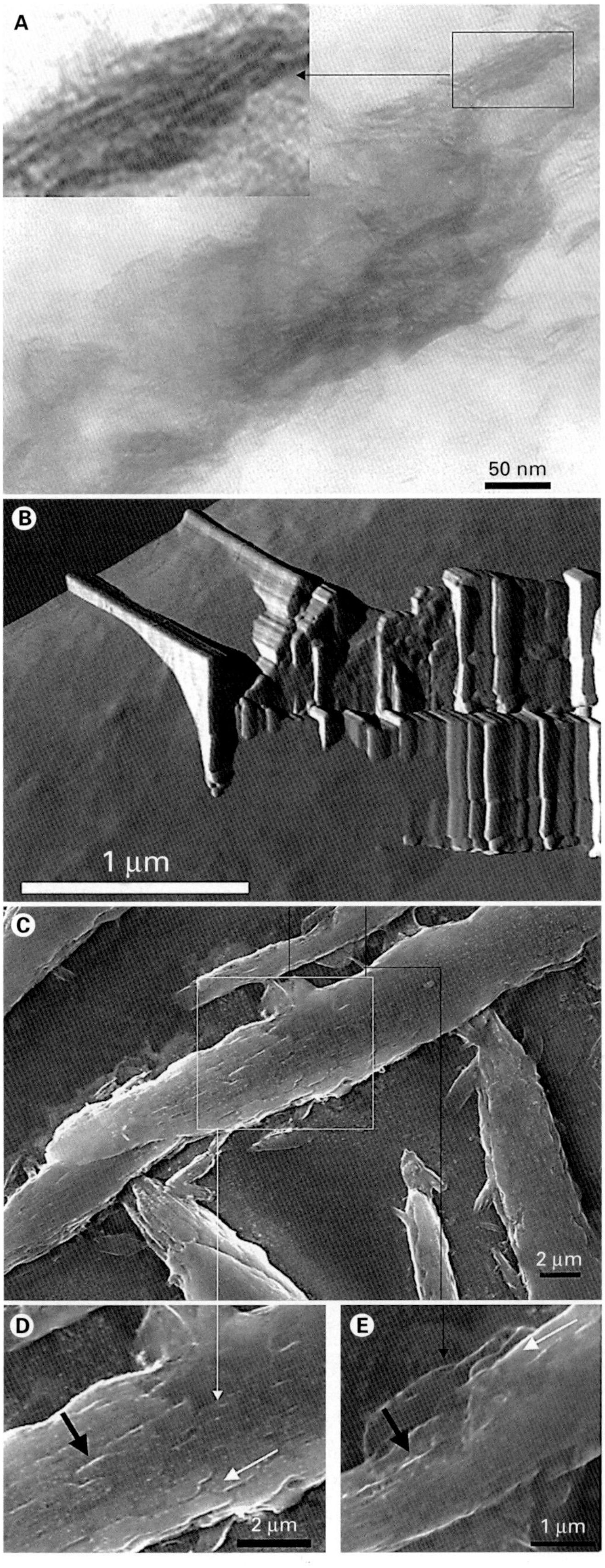

Fig. 6. Oriented growth of apatite crystals on amelogenin microribbons. TEM micrographs of a mineralized microribbon showing the presence of aligned apatite crystals assembled side by side parallel to their c-axis (**A**). Inset in **A**: enlargement of the selected area showing the presence of a row of small assemblies of several nanometers in diameter. The corresponding electron diffraction pattern of a region taken from the edge of a mineralized ribbon has confirmed the oriented alignment of apatite crystals along their c-axial direction [Du et al., 2005]. AFM micrographs in taping mode showing the remarkable orientation and organization of crystals on a microribbon (**B**). SEMs of amelogenin microribbons, mineralized following pretreatment with phosvitin, showing the ordered plate-like crystals along the ribbon axis (**C–E**). Black arrows show the edges of such crystals and white arrows the direction of their orientation. **C–E** Reproduced from Du et al. [2005], with permission.

in a developing embryonic bovine enamel matrix. They interpreted these 'dense lines' as organic matrix filaments. Smales [1975] described a helical structure in which 'the helices varied in overall width from 15 to 30 nm'. Robinson et al. [1981] investigated developing rat incisor enamel using a freeze-fracture technique and indicated that 'the forming region seems to consist largely of spheres 300–500 Å in diameter'. Bai and Warshawsky [1985] found that 'globular particles observed in freeze-fracture replicas of fresh and fixed enamel samples' can be 'removed by 4.0 *M* guanidine extraction'. They concluded that 'amelogenins are the nonstructural, heterodispersed particulate material in the intercrystallite space'.

Two technical questions arise from the observation of periodic structures in the forming enamel after aqueous conventional fixation and TEM. First, the forming enamel that is examined is clearly not in its native structure. Second, the presence of a stippled material detected on sections may be related or unrelated to the nanostructures observed in vitro. In the following sections, we review a comparative study of chemically fixed, dehydrated forming enamel and physically fixed freeze-substituted native enamel.

Possible Differences between Native Enamel and What Is Observed on Resin-Embedded Sections

The forming enamel appears on ultrathin sections as thin flat strips or ribbons. They are more or less parallel and organized in bundles, grouped in enamel rods (or prisms) and in interrod enamel. Between these ribbons, the space is gradually restricted when moving from the most superficial outer zone to deeper enamel. Some electron-dense needle-like structures are located at the edge of these ribbons. They probably represent a part of the native crystals, as demonstrated by the fact that they disappear when the sections are floated on acidic or EDTA solutions prior to examination, the rest being lost during processing of the tissue and the preparation of the sections, despite efforts to minimize this loss.

Observed with the TEM, enamel appears as grouped fibrous or ribbon-like structures, 30–35 nm in thickness, located in the region of outer enamel secretion, which is also the zone of nucleation and elongation of enamel crystallites. This appearance was shown to be dependant on the fixative solution that has been used [Nanci et al., 1983; Bai and Warshawsky, 1985]. Changes are also due to the effects of osmium tetroxide used during postfixation and to the staining agents, namely uranyl acetate and lead citrate. The above comparative analysis demonstrates that the chemical preparation for electron microscopy causes removal of the forming crystallites as well as some matrix components from the enamel section. Therefore, the actual organization of the native forming enamel may substantially differ from what is observed on resin-embedded sections after usual chemical fixation followed by dehydration, resin embedding, and staining of the sections.

The 'Stippled' Material: A Fixation Artifact, a Precursor, or Degradation Material?

Granular or 'stippled' material has been reported to be present in variable amounts between the secretion site of rod and interrod enamel and the surface of Tomes' processes, where membrane infoldings may be the putative secretory sites of secretory ameloblasts [Nanci and Warshawsky, 1984a]. It has been proposed that the stippled material is a breakdown product resulting from poor fixation [Nanci and Warshawsky, 1984b]. However, according to Slavkin et al. [1976], following the intraperitoneal injection of 3H-tryptophan, the stippled material began to be labeled after 30 min, and labeling was gradually reinforced with time up to 24 h. They concluded that the stippled material represents newly secreted precursor enamel proteins. In addition to these diverging views, it was added by Chen and Eisenmann [1984] that in some experimental conditions, there was no relationship between the formation of stippled material and the fixative procedure. Effectively, rats receiving intraperitoneal injections of fluoride in a dose-dependant manner displayed stippled material, whereas in the control rats, the appearance was actually dependant on the fixative solution. This was also the case following strontium administration [Goldberg and Boskey, 1996], after deletion of the N terminus of the amelogenin [Dunglas et al., 2002], or using antisense inhibition of AMEL translation [Diekwisch et al., 1993]. The above observations collectively suggest that the stippled material is not an artifact of fixation. There are two possible interpretations of the presence of stippled material taken as an actual structure in the forming enamel. First, shortly after secretion, granules mostly constituted by assembled amelogenin proteins, associated with the other enamel matrix molecules, may appear as stippled material. Second, the stippled material is a result of amelogenin degradation by enamelysin (MMP-20) [Bartlett and Simmer, 1999]. Expelled from the forming enamel shortly after secretion and assembly, these residues issued from the initial steps of the enamel maturation aggregate before they are reinternalized into the Tomes' processes. This accumulation of partially degraded molecules is exaggerated in the pathological models mentioned above that lead to the formation of stippled material.

With the conventional methods that have been used so far, it is impossible to define more clearly the actual nature of the granular material seen between the Tomes' processes and the zone of enamel growth. In vitro studies support the concept of self-assembly of the native amelogenin molecules, and therefore, the identification of the stippled material as nanospheres. This fits in well with some radioautographic studies. However, in vivo studies do not rule out the possible identification of the stippled material as a degradation product.

Conventional TEM Studies

From observations dealing with conventional fixation of the tissue, previous reports have provided interpretations of the ultrastructure of the forming enamel [Ronnholm, 1962]. Fibrils grouped into rod and interrod structures orientate the formation of crystallites. They are parallel to the long axis of the prism. Cross-bridges have also been described. According to Smales [1975], the figures seen on ultrathin sections are consistent with a double line of electron-dense material with cross-bridges. This author suggests that the organic matrix is organized as a double helix around the forming crystallites with an overall width of 15–30 nm and a pitch varying from 30 to 90 nm. This interpretation of a periodic structure has never been confirmed, despite that an elliptical organization of enamel tubules was also suggested by Jessen [1968]. More substantially, Travis and Glimcher [1964] and Glimcher [1979] have reported tubular structures oriented parallel to the long axis of the prism, 35–50 nm in diameter. Crystals are nucleated and increase in width inside the tubules. They grow until they are about 70 nm wide and 30 nm thick. They may extend throughout the whole thickness of enamel. Originally seen as doublets, oblique sections suggest that they are indeed forming tubules, with cross-bridges suggesting a periodicity. A few investigations were carried out on freeze fracture replicas of conventionally fixed material [Goldberg and Escaig, 1982; Bai and Warshawsky, 1985]. Large and small granules randomly distributed or aligned were observed together with structureless areas. Granules or globular structures were observed, removed by guanidine extraction, and restored by albumin and ovalbumin solutions, and therefore, might result from the assembly of amelogenin molecules [Bai and Warshawsky, 1985] (see section Nanospheres and Their Subunits).

The Forming Enamel after Rapid Freezing and Freeze Substitution

Freeze fracture replicas of unfixed frozen forming enamel were prepared by Robinson et al. [1981]. In the forming enamel, globular structures of 30–50 nm in diameter were present, first randomly arranged and then aligned at a further stage. At later stages of formation, crystallites 50–60 nm wide and 5–6 nm thick were observed. At maturation stage, globular material outlined the surface of crystals, which were no longer seen at later stages of enamel development. This is the first in vivo report exploring the appearance of unfixed enamel and reporting the actual existence of globular structures.

Using the rapid freezing, freeze substitution technique, we examined the unfixed forming enamel both on replicas and on ultrathin sections, trying to relate the structures observed and the progression of enamel formation [Goldberg, 1990]. On replicas that matched well with early stages of enamel formation, globular structures about 5–10 nm in diameter were aligned, forming bands that were closely packed (fig. 7A). A few globules were larger, about 20–30 nm in width. Despite the rapid freezing technique that may pick up events that occur within a few milliseconds, no information was gained on the preorganization of the just secreted proteins. A few random granules were seen in the space between Tomes' processes and the edge of the outer forming enamel, and it seems that the secretion product appearing as globular structures is immediately aligned and contributes to the formation of longitudinal bands (fig. 7A). This suggests either that the secretory material is prepacked inside the cell processes before they are expelled, or that the self-assembly of the molecules occurs concomitantly with secretion, maybe when they are released in the extracellular space [Brookes et al., 2006]. At these very early stages and close to the Tomes' processes, longitudinal ribbons, formed by the longitudinal aggregation of nanospheres (fig. 7B). Some preparations, where the fractured surface formed an angle with the long axis of the ribbons, support that they may well be organized as tubules. Therefore, the appearance seen on the in vivo replica of physically fixed enamel fits in well with the results obtained from in vitro preparations that are arguments in favor of the role of nanospheres in enamel formation (see section Assembly of Amelogenin Nanospheres into Higher-Order Structures).

Soon after, the structure of the ribbons became more complex and two groups of granules are seen. First, at the lateral edges of the ribbons, large globules of about

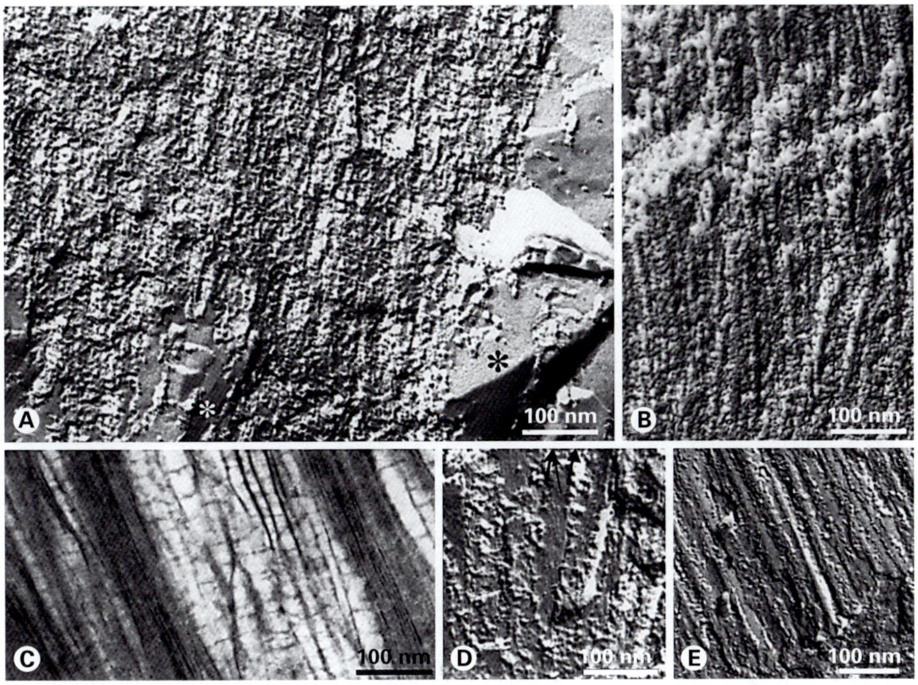

Fig. 7. Rapid freezing, freeze-substituted preparation of forming enamel. **A** Alignments of globular structures are seen near Tomes' processes (asterisks) and the zone of enamel growth. **B** Globules or nanospheres are aligned into longitudinal ribbons in the subjacent enamel. **C** Ultrathin section of forming enamel displays longitudinal ribbons segmented and linked by thin fibrils. **D** In a deeper part of the forming enamel, large globules are aligned from a part of ribbons where 8- to 10-nm-thick 4–5 subunits form a 15–20° angle with the long axis of the ribbon. **E** When mineralization is more advanced, flat structureless ribbons form the surface of crystals. A few granules are located at the edges of the crystals.

10 nm are aligned (fig. 7D). This organization provides a more or less regular periodic pattern. Secondly, the surface occupied by the ribbons seems to be subdivided into 4–5 bands, forming a 15° angle with the long axis of the ribbons, produced by the alignments of tiny granules about 2–3 nm in diameter. Each of the subdivisions was about 10 nm in width (fig. 7D). This observation suggests that the initial organization into simple alignments of granules is further modified during the preparation of crystal formation. Examination at stages that seem to correspond to crystal growth shows that flat structureless ribbons and granules disappear during later stages of maturation (fig. 7E). On ultrathin sections of physically fixed (rapid freezing followed by freeze substitution) forming enamel, longitudinal ribbons were seen. Some electron-dense needle-like structures were located inside the ribbon, near one edge. On a very regular basis, the ribbons seemed to be formed by round or square subunits about 36 nm in height and 27–31 nm in width. This periodic appearance was reinforced by the presence of cross-banding, tiny filaments at right angles to the long axis of the ribbons, providing a ladder-like appearance to this forming enamel (fig. 7C). This pattern was clearly seen in the upper forming zone, but still recognized in the inner part.

Concluding Remarks

Numerous in vitro experimental data has supported the proposed function of amelogenin in controlling the shape, mineral phase, orientation, and organization of growing enamel crystals. The hypothesis that self-assembly of amelogenin protein into nanospheres is a key factor in controlling the oriented and elongated growth of carbonated apatite crystals during enamel formation is also supported by several in vivo experimental evidence. The finding that amelogenin nanospheres in solution and upon slow solvent evaporation have a tendency to assemble into organized microribbons without the presence of cells, crystals, or any other nonamelogenin proteins (i.e. enamelin or ameloblastin) gives us a valuable clue to the function of this extracellular protein and its potential to control crystal orientation and elongation through macromolecular assembly. It is important to mention that we do not suggest that microribbons with dimensions similar to those formed in vitro by protein crystallization techniques are also formed in vivo. However, we do propose that the biological relevance of amelogenin microribbon formation is the tendency of the nanospheres to assemble into elongated chain structures, and similar periodic structures observed earlier in vivo could be the result of such a linear assembly. After reviewing the early literature, it is concluded that both on ultrathin sections and on replicas of physically fixed enamel, a periodic pattern was recognized, which was not seen on chemically fixed (aldehyde) sections. First, this pattern was due to the alignment of globular subunits that merge to form 'ribbons' or 'tubules', and this fits in well with the longitudinal association of nanospheres mentioned in section Assembly of Amelogenin Nanospheres into Higher-Order Structures. Second, thin filaments are clearly seen in the narrow spaces between the ribbons. They are in continuity with interruptions between the globular subunits that do not merge totally at that stage of enamel formation. These filaments are cross-banding the ribbons or tubules. This organization suggests a functional interaction between molecules, presumably amelogenins, as globular structures and nonamelogenins as filaments. Altogether, they play a crucial role in the organization of the extracellular matrix of the forming enamel as a template for crystal nucleation and growth.

Acknowledgments

The authors thank Dr. Chang Du, Dr. Giuseppe Falini, Mrs. Sun Zhi, Dr. Yuwei Fan, and Mr. Christopher Abbott for their technical support, data collection and for contributing to the study of amelogenin assembly and function. This work was supported by NIH-NIDCR grants DE-15332, DE-13414, and DE15644 (to J.M.-O.). The in vivo investigations were carried out with the financial support of the French Ministry of Education and Research to the team EA2496. We thank Dr. Michael Paine and Dr. Thomas Diekwisch for reviewing the manuscript.

References

Addadi, L., E. Beniash, S. Weiner (2002) Assembly and mineralization processes in biomineralization; in Jones War, C.N.R. (ed): Supramolecular Organization and Materials Design. Cambridge, Cambride University Press, pp 1–34.

Addadi, L., S. Weiner (1989) Stereochemical and structural relations between macromolecules and crystals in biomineralization; in Mann, S., J. Webb, R.J.P. Williams (eds): Biomineralization, Chemical and Biochemical Perspectives. New York, Weinheim, pp 133–152.

Aichmayer, B., H.C. Margolis, R. Sigel, Y. Yamakoshi, J.P. Simmer, P. Fratzl (2005) The onset of amelogenin nanosphere aggregation studied by small-angle X-ray scattering and dynamic light scattering. J Struct Biol *151:* 239–249.

Aoba, T., K. Kawano, E.C. Moreno (1990) Molecular conformation of porcine amelogenins and its significance in protein-mineral interaction: ^{1}H-NMR photo-CIDNP study. J Biol Buccale *18:* 189–194.

Aoba, T., E.C. Moreno, M. Kresak, T. Tanabe (1989) Possible roles of partial sequences at N- and C-termini of amelogenin in protein-enamel mineral interaction. J Dent Res *68:* 1331–1336.

Arsenault, A.L., B.W. Robinson (1989) The dentino-enamel junction: a structural and microanalytical study of early mineralization. Calcif Tissue Int *45:* 111–121.

Bai, P., H. Warshawsky (1985) Morphological studies on the distribution of enamel matrix proteins using routine electron microscopy and freeze-fracture replicas in the rat incisor. Anat Rec *212:* 1–16.

Bartlett, J.D., J.P. Simmer (1999) Proteinases in developing dental enamel. Crit Rev Oral Biol Med *10:* 425–441.

Beniash, E., J.P. Simmer, H.C. Margolis (2005) The effect of recombinant mouse amelogenins on the formation and organization of hydroxyapatite crystals in vitro. J Struct Biol *149:* 182–190.

Bonar, L.C., M.J. Glimcher, G.L. Mechanic (1965) The molecular structure of the neutral-soluble proteins of embryonic bovine enamel in the solid state. J Ultrastruct Res *13:* 308–317.

Bouropoulos, N., J. Moradian-Oldak (2003) Analysis of hydroxyapatite surface coverage by amelogenin nanospheres following the Langmuir model for protein adsorption. Calcif Tissue Int *72:* 599–603.

Bouropoulos, N., J. Moradian-Oldak (2004) Induction of apatite by the cooperative effect of amelogenin and the 32-kDa enamelin. J Dent Res *83:* 278–282.

Brookes, S., S.P. Lyngstadaas, C. Robinson, R.C. Shore, J. Kirkham (2006) Intracellular nanosphere subunit assembly as revealed by amelogenin molecular cross-linking studies. Eur J Oral Sci *114(suppl 1):* in press.

Caterina, J.J., Z. Skobe, J. Shi, Y. Ding, J.P. Simmer, H. Birkedal-Hansen, J.D. Bartlett (2002) Enamelysin (matrix metalloproteinase 20)-deficient mice display an amelogenesis imperfecta phenotype. J Biol Chem *277:* 49598–49604.

Chen, S., D.R. Eisenmann (1984) Ultrastructural study of the effects of fixation and fluoride injection on stippled material during amelogenesis in the rat. Arch Oral Biol *29:* 681–686.

Chou, P.Y., G.D. Fasman (1978) Prediction of protein conformation. Adv Enzym *47:* 45.

Cuy, J.L., A.B. Mann, K.J. Livi, M.F. Teaford, T.P. Weihs (2002) Nanoindentation mapping of the mechanical properties of human molar tooth enamel. Arch Oral Biol *47:* 281–291.

Daculsi, G., B. Kerebel (1978) High-resolution electron microscope study of human enamel crystallites: size, shape, and growth. J Ultrastruct Res *65:* 163–172.

Daculsi, G., J. Menanteau, L.M. Kerebel, D. Mitre (1984) Length and shape of enamel crystals. Calcif Tissue Int *36:* 550–555.

Diekwisch, T.G.H., S. David, P. Bringas, V. Santos, H.C. Slavkin (1993) Antisense inhibition of amelogenin translation demonstrates supramolecular controls for enamel OHAPP crystal-growth during embryonic mouse molar development. Development *117:* 471–482.

Doi, Y., E.D. Eanes, H. Shimokawa, J.D. Termine (1984) Inhibition of seeded growth of enamel apatite crystals by amelogenin and enamelin proteins in vitro. J Dent Res *63:* 98–105.

Du, C., G. Falini, S. Fermani, C. Abbott, J. Moradian-Oldak (2005) Supramolecular assembly of amelogenin nanospheres into birefringent microribbons. Science *307:* 1450–1454 [erratum (2005) published in Science *309:* 2166].

Dunglas, C., D. Septier, M.L. Paine, D.H. Zhu, M.L. Snead, M. Goldberg (2002) Ultrastructure of forming enamel in mouse bearing a transgene that disrupts the amelogenin self-assembly domains. Calcif Tissue Int *71:* 155–166.

Eastoe, J.E. (1960) Organic matrix of tooth enamel. Nature *187:* 411–412.

Eastoe, J.E. (1964) The chemical composition of bone and tooth; in Hardwich, J.L., H.R. Held, K.G. König (eds): Advances in Fluoride Research and Dental Caries Prevention. Oxford, Pergamon Press, pp 5–17.

Eastoe, J.E. (1979) Enamel protein chemistry – past, present, and future. J Dental Res *58(B):* 753–763.

Fearnhead, R., K. Kawasaki (1991) On the physical role of amelogenin in the biomineralization of tooth enamel; in Suga, S., H. Nakahara (eds): Mechanisms and Phylogeny of Mineralization in Biological Systems. New York, Springer, pp 79–81.
Fincham, A.G., A.B. Belcourt, J.D. Termine, W.T. Butler, W.C. Cothran (1981) Dental enamel matrix: sequences of two amelogenin polypeptides. Biosci Rep *1:* 771–778.
Fincham, A.G., W. Leung, J. Tan, J. Moradian-Oldak (1998) Does amelogenin nanosphere assembly proceed through intermediary-sized structures? Connect Tissue Res *38:* 237–240; discussion 241–236.
Fincham, A.G., J. Moradian-Oldak (1993) Amelogenin post-translational modifications: carboxy-terminal processing and the phosphorylation of bovine and porcine 'TRAP' and 'LRAP' amelogenins. Biochem Biophys Res Commun *197:* 248–255.
Fincham, A.G., J. Moradian-Oldak, T.G.H. Diekwisch, D.M. Lyaruu, J.T. Wright, P. Bringas, Jr., H.C. Slavkin (1995) Evidence for amelogenin 'nanospheres' as functional components of secretory-stage enamel matrix. J Struct Biol *115:* 50–59.
Fincham, A.G., J. Moradian-Oldak, J.P. Simmer (1999) The structural biology of the developing dental enamel matrix. J Struct Biol *126:* 270–299.
Fincham, A.G., J. Moradian-Oldak, J.P. Simmer, P.E. Sarte, E.C. Lau, T.G.H. Diekwisch, H.C. Slavkin (1994) Self-assembly of a recombinant amelogenin protein generates supramolecular structures. J Struct Biol *112:* 103–109.
Fukumoto, S., T. Kiba, B. Hall, N. Iehara, T. Nakamura, G. Longenecker, P.H. Krebsbach, A. Nanci, A.B. Kulkarni, Y. Yamada (2004) Ameloblastin is a cell adhesion molecule required for maintaining the differentiation state of ameloblasts. J Cell Biol *167:* 973–983.
Gasteiger, E., A. Gattiker, C. Hoogland, I. Ivanyi, R.D. Appel, A. Bairoch (2003) ExPASy: the proteomics server for in-depth protein knowledge and analysis. Nucleic Acids Res *31:* 3784–3788.
Geller, J.H. (1958) Metabolic significance of collagen in tooth structure. J Dent Res *37:* 276–279.
Gibson, C.W., Z.A. Yuan, B. Hall, G. Longenecker, E. Chen, T. Thyagarajan, T. Sreenath, J.T. Wright, S. Decker, R. Piddington, G. Harrison, A.B. Kulkarni (2001) Amelogenin-deficient mice display an amelogenesis imperfecta phenotype. J Biol Chem *276:* 31871–31875.
Glimcher, M.J. (1979) Phosphopeptides of enamel matrix. J Dent Res *58(B):* 790–806.
Goldberg, M. (1990) Cell biology of tooth enamel formation. Functional electron microscopic. Monogr Oral Sci *14:* 1–199.
Goldberg, M., A.L. Boskey (1996) Lipids and biomineralizations. Prog Histochem Cytochem *31:* 1–187.
Goldberg, M., F. Escaig (1982) Appearance of freeze-fractured rat incisor enamel during the forming stage. Arch Oral Biol *27:* 971–973.
Goto, Y., E. Kogure, T. Takagi, S. Aimoto, T. Aoba (1993) Molecular conformation of porcine amelogenin in solution: three folding units at the N-terminal, central, and C-terminal regions. J Biochem (Tokyo) *113:* 55–60.
Grantham, R. (1974) Amino acid difference formula to help explain protein evolution. Science *185:* 862–864.
Habelitz, S., A. Kullar, S.J. Marshall, P.K. DenBesten, M. Balooch, G.W. Marshall, W. Li (2004) Amelogenin-guided crystal growth on fluoroapatite glass-ceramics. J Dent Res *83:* 698–702.
Habelitz, S., S.J. Marshall, G.W. Marshall, Jr., M. Balooch (2001) Mechanical properties of human dental enamel on the nanometre scale. Arch Oral Biol *46:* 173–183.
Harpaz, Y., M. Gerstein, C. Chothia (1994) Volume changes on protein folding. Structure *2:* 641–649.
Hopp, T.P., K.R. Woods (1981) Prediction of protein antigenic determinants from amino acid sequences. Proc Natl Acad Sci USA *78:* 3824–3828.
Hu, J.C., Y. Yamakoshi (2003) Enamelin and autosomal-dominant amelogenesis imperfecta. Crit Rev Oral Biol Med *14:* 387–398.
Iijima, M., J. Moradian-Oldak (2004) Interactions of amelogenins with octacalcium phosphate crystal faces are dose dependent. Calcif Tissue Int *74:* 522–531.
Iijima, M., Y. Moriwaki, H.B. Wen, A.G. Fincham, J. Moradian-Oldak (2002) Elongated growth of octacalcium phosphate crystals in recombinant amelogenin gels under controlled ionic flow. J Dent Res *81:* 69–73.
Jessen, H. (1968) Elliptical tubules as unit structure of forming enamel matrix in the rat. Arch Oral Biol *13:* 351–352.
Katz, E.P., G.L. Mechanic, M.J. Glimcher (1965) The ultracentrifugal and free zone electrophoretic characterization of the neutral soluble proteins of embryonic bovine enamel. Biochim Biophys Acta *107:* 471–484.
Katz, E.P., J. Seyer, P.T. Levine, M.J. Glimcher (1969) The comparative biochemistry of the organic matrix of developing enamel. 2. Ultracentrifugal and electrophoretic characterization of proteins soluble at neutral pH. Arch Oral Biol *14:* 533–539.
Krebsbach, P.H., S.K. Lee, Y. Matsuki, C. Kozac, K.M. Yamada, Y. Yamada (1996) Full-length sequence, localization, and chromosome mapping of ameloblastin: a novel tooth-specific gene. J Biol Chem *271:* 4431–4435.
Lagerstrom-Fermer, M., U. Landegren (1995) Understanding enamel formation from mutations causing x-linked amelogenesis imperfecta. Conn Tissue Res *32:* 241–246.
Lau, E.C., H.C. Slavkin, M.L. Snead (1990) Analysis of human enamel genes: insights into genetic disorders of enamel. Cleft Palate J *27:* 121–130.
Leytin, V., T. Arad, S. Matlis, L. Daphni, Z. Mao, B. Shay, S. Weiner, D. Deutsch (1998) Cryotransmission electron microscopy and atomic force microscopy of the recombinant human amelogenin protein, self assembled into nanospheres; in Workshop on the Structure and Development of Dental Enamel. Oslo, University of Oslo, Norway.
Lowenstam, H.A., S. Weiner (1989) On Biomineralization. New York, Oxford University Press.
Lyngstadaas, S.P., S. Risnes, B.S. Sproat, P.S. Thrane, H.P. Prydz (1995) A synthetic, chemically modified ribozyme eliminates amelogenin, the major translation product in developing mouse enamel in vivo. EMBO J *14:* 5224–5229.
Mann, S. (1993) Molecular tectonics in biomineralization and biomimetic materials chemistry. Nature *365:* 499–505.
Masuya, H., K. Shimizu, H. Sezutsu, Y. Sakuraba, J. Nagano, A. Shimizu, N. Fujimoto, A. Kawai, I. Miura, H. Kaneda, K. Kobayashi, J. Ishijima, T. Maeda, Y. Gondo, T. Noda, S. Wakana, T. Shiroishi (2005) Enamelin (Enam) is essential for amelogenesis: ENU-induced mouse mutants as models for different clinical subtypes of human amelogenesis imperfecta (AI). Hum Mol Genet *14:* 575–583.
Mechanic, G.L., E.P. Katz, M.J. Glimcher (1967) The Sephadex gel filtration characteristics of the neutral soluble proteins of embryonic bovine enamel. Biochim Biophys Acta *133:* 97–113.
Moradian-Oldak, J., N. Bouropoulos, L. Wang, N. Gharakhanian (2002) Analysis of self-assembly and apatite binding properties of amelogenin proteins lacking the hydrophilic C-terminal. Matrix Biol *21:* 197–205.
Moradian-Oldak, J., C. Du, G. Falini (2006) On the formation of amelogenin microribbons. Eur J Oral Sci *114(suppl 1):* in press.
Moradian-Oldak, J., C. Gergely, N. Bouropoulos, F.J.G. Cuisinier (2004) Adsorption of amelogenin nanospheres onto charged surfaces: a model for tooth enamel re-construction; in Aizenberg, J., W.J. Landis, C. Orme, R. Wang (eds): Material Reserach Society. San Francisco, Material Research Society, pp 63–68.
Moradian-Oldak, J., M. Iijima, N. Bouropoulos, H.B. Wen (2003) Assembly of amelogenin proteolytic products and control of octacalcium phosphate crystal morphology. Connect Tissue Res *44(suppl 1):* 58–64.
Moradian-Oldak, J., I. Jimenez, D. Maltby, A.G. Fincham (2001) Controlled proteolysis of amelogenins reveals exposure of both carboxy- and amino-terminal regions. Biopolymers *58:* 606–616.
Moradian-Oldak, J., W. Leung, A.G. Fincham (1998a) Temperature and pH-dependent supramolecular self-assembly of amelogenin molecules: a dynamic light-scattering analysis. J Struct Biol *122:* 320–327.

Moradian-Oldak, J., M.L. Paine, Y.P. Lei, A.G. Fincham, M.L. Snead (2000) Self-assembly properties of recombinant engineered amelogenin proteins analyzed by dynamic light scattering and atomic force microscopy. J Struct Biol *131:* 27–37.

Moradian-Oldak, J., P.J. Simmer, E.C. Lau, P.E. Sarte, H.C. Slavkin, A.G. Fincham (1994) Detection of monodisperse aggregates of a recombinant amelogenin by dynamic light scattering. Biopolymers *34:* 1339–1347.

Moradian-Oldak, J., J. Tan, A.G. Fincham (1998b) Interaction of amelogenin with hydroxyapatite crystals: an adherence effect through amelogenin molecular self-association. Biopolymers *46:* 225–238.

Nagasaka, S. (1994) Electron microscopy of biochemically characterized, newly secreted tooth enamel proteins. Arch Oral Biol *39:* 105–110.

Nanci, A., P. Bai, H. Warshawsky (1983) The effect of osmium postfixation and uranyl and lead staining on the ultrastructure of young enamel in the rat incisor. Anat Rec *207:* 1–16.

Nanci, A., H. Warshawsky (1984a) Characterization of putative secretory sites on ameloblasts of the rat incisor. Am J Anat *171:* 163–189.

Nanci, A., H. Warshawsky (1984b) Relationship between the quality of fixation and the presence of stippled material in newly formed enamel of the rat incisor. Anat Rec *208:* 15–31.

Nikiforuk, G., N.S. Simmons (1965) Purification and properties of protein from embryonic bovine enamel. J Dent Res *44(suppl):* 1119–1122.

Paine, M.L., M.L. Snead (1997) Protein interactions during assembly of the enamel organic extracellular matrix. J Bone Min Res *12:* 221–227.

Paine, M.L., H.J. Wang, W. Luo, P.H. Krebsbach, M.L. Snead (2003) A transgenic animal model resembling amelogenesis imperfecta related to ameloblastin over-expression. J Biol Chem *278:* 19447–19452.

Paine, M.L., S.N. White, W. Luo, H. Fong, M. Sarikaya, M.L. Snead (2001) Regulated gene expression dictates enamel structure and tooth function. Matrix Biol *20:* 273–292.

Paine, M.L., D.H. Zhu, W. Luo, P.J. Bringas, M. Goldberg, S.N. White, Y.P. Lei, M. Sarikaya, H.K. Fong, M.L. Snead (2000) Enamel biomineralization defects result from alterations to amelogenin self-assembly. J Struct Biol *132:* 191–200.

Papagerakis, P., J.M. Ibarra, N. Inozentseva, P. DenBesten, M. MacDougall (2005) Mouse amelogenin exons 8 and 9: sequence analysis and protein distribution. J Dent Res *84:* 613–617.

Ravindranath, R.M., J. Moradian-Oldak, A.G. Fincham (1999) Tyrosyl motif in amelogenins binds N-acetyl-D-glucosamine. J Biol Chem *274:* 2464–2471.

Renugopalakrishnan, V., N. Pattabiraman, M. Prabhakaran, E. Strawich, M.J. Glimcher (1989) Tooth enamel protein, amelogenin, has a probable beta-spiral internal channel, Gln112-Leu138, within a single polypeptide chain: preliminary molecular mechanics and dynamics studies. Biopolymers *28:* 297–303.

Robinson, C., S.J. Brookes, R.C. Shore, J. Kirkham (1998) The developing enamel matrix: nature and function. Eur J Oral Sci *106(suppl 1):* 282–291.

Robinson, C., P. Fuchs, D. Deutsch, J.A. Weatherell (1978) Four chemically distinct stages in developing enamel from bovine incisor teeth. Caries Res *12:* 1–11.

Robinson, C., P. Fuchs, J.A. Weatherell (1981) The appearance of developing rat incisor enamel using freeze-fracture technique. J Crystal Growth *53:* 160–165.

Ronnholm, E., III (1962) The structure of the organic stroma of human enamel during amelogenesis. J Ultrastruct Res *6:* 368–389.

Ryu, O.H., A.G. Fincham, C.C. Hu, C. Zhang, Q. Qian, J.D. Bartlett, J.P. Simmer (1999) Characterization of recombinant pig enamelysin activity and cleavage of recombinant pig and mouse amelogenins. J Dent Res *78:* 743–750.

Shaw, W.J., A.A. Campbell, M.L. Paine, M.L. Snead (2004) The C-terminus of the amelogenin, LRAP, is orientated next to the hydroxyapatite surface. J Biol Chem *279:* 40263–40266.

Simmer, J.P., A.G. Fincham (1995) Molecular mechanisms of dental enamel formation. Crit Rev Oral Biol Med *6:* 84–108.

Simmer, J.P., J.C. Hu (2002) Expression, structure, and function of enamel proteinases. Connect Tissue Res *43:* 441–449.

Simmer, J.P., E.C. Lau, C.C. Hu, T. Aoba, M. Lacey, D. Nelson, M. Zeichner-David, M.L. Snead, H.C. Slavkin, A.G. Fincham (1994) Isolation and characterization of a mouse amelogenin expressed in *Eschericia coli.* Calcif Tissue Int *54:* 312–319.

Slavkin, H.C., W. Mino, P. Bringas, Jr. (1976) The biosynthesis and secretion of precursor enamel protein by ameloblasts as visualized by autoradiography after tryptophan administration. Anat Rec *185:* 289–312.

Smales, F.C. (1975) Structural subunit in prisms of immature rat enamel. Nature *258:* 772–774.

Smith, C. (1998) Cellular and chemical events during enamel maturation. Crit Rev Oral Biol Med *9:* 128–161.

Smith, C.E., J.R. Pompura, S. Borenstein, A. Fazel, A. Nanci (1989) Degradation and loss of matrix proteins from developing enamel. Anat Rec *224:* 292–316.

Snead, M.L., E.C. Lau, M. Zeichner-David, A.G. Fincham, S.L. Woo, H.C. Slavkin (1985) DNA sequence for cloned cDNA for murine amelogenin reveal the amino acid sequence for enamel-specific protein. Biochem Biophys Res Commun *129:* 812–818.

Stack, M.V. (1954) Organic constituents of enamel. J Am Dent Assoc *48:* 297–306.

Stack, M.V. (1956) The carbohydrate content of human dental enamel. J Dent Res *35:* 966.

Sun, Z., C. Abbott, J. Moradian-Oldak (2005a) Control of amelogenin assembly and dis-assembly by enamelysin (MMP-20); in The 8th International Conference on Chemistry and Biology of Mineralized Tissue. Banff, University of Toronto Press.

Sun, Z., M.M. Ahsan, H. Wang, C. Du, C. Abbott, J. Moradian-Oldak (2005b) Assembly and processing of an engineered amelogenin proteolytic product (rP148). Eur J Oral Sci *114(suppl 1):* in press.

Termine, J.D., D.A. Torchia, K.M. Conn (1979) Enamel matrix: structural proteins. J Dent Res *58:* 773–781.

Toyosawa, S., C. O'Huigin, F. Figueroa, H. Tichy, J. Klein (1998) Identification and characterization of amelogenin genes in monotremes, reptiles, and amphibians. Proc Natl Acad Sci USA *95:* 13056–13061.

Travis, D.F., M.J. Glimcher (1964) The structure and organization of, and the relationship between the organic matrix and the inorganic crystals of embryonic bovine enamel. J Cell Biol *23:* 447–497.

Uchida, T., C. Murakami, N. Dohi, K. Wakida, T. Satoda, O. Takahashi (1997) Synthesis, secretion, degradation, and fate of ameloblastin during the matrix formation stage of the rat incisor as shown by immunocytochemistry and immunochemistry using region-specific antibodies. J Histochem Cytochem *45:* 1329–1340.

Wallwork, M.L., J. Kirkham, J. Zhang, A. Smith, S. Brookes, R.C. Shore, S.R. Wood, O. Ryu, C. Robinson (2001) Binding of matrix proteins to developing enamel crystals: an atomic force microscope study. Langmuir *17:* 2508–2513.

Warshawsky, H. (1989) Organization of crystals in enamel. Anat Rec *224:* 242–262.

Watson, M.L. (1960) The extracellular nature of enamel in the rat. J Biophys Biochem Cytol *7:* 489–492.

Wen, H.B., A.G. Fincham, J. Moradian-Oldak (2001) Progressive accretion of amelogenin molecules during nanospheres assembly revealed by atomic force microscopy. Matrix Biol *20:* 387–395.

Wen, H.B., J. Moradian-Oldak, A.G. Fincham (1999a) Modulation of apatite crystal growth on Bioglass by recombinant amelogenin. Biomaterials *20:* 1717–1725.

Wen, H.B., J. Moradian-Oldak, W. Leung, P. Bringas, Jr., A.G. Fincham (1999b) Microstructures of an amelogenin gel matrix. J Struct Biol *126:* 42–51.

Yamakoshi, Y., T. Tanabe, M. Fukae, M. Shimizu (1994) Porcine amelogenins. Calcif Tissue Int *54:* 69–75.

Cells Tissues Organs

Cells Tissues Organs 2005;181:219–231
DOI: 10.1159/000091383

Proteomics and Genetics of Dental Enamel

Jan C.-C. Hu Yasuo Yamakoshi Fumiko Yamakoshi Paul H. Krebsbach
James P. Simmer

University of Michigan Dental Research Lab, Ann Arbor, Mich., USA

Key Words

Amelogenin · Ameloblastin · Enamelin · Matrix metalloproteinase 20 · Kallikrein 4 · Dentin sialophosphoprotein gene

Abstract

The initiation of enamel crystals at the dentino-enamel junction is associated with the expression of dentin sialophosphoprotein (*DSPP,* a gene normally linked with dentin formation), three 'structural' enamel proteins – amelogenin *(AMELX),* enamelin *(ENAM),* and ameloblastin *(AMBN)* – and a matrix metalloproteinase, enamelysin *(MMP20).* Enamel formation proceeds with the steady elongation of the enamel crystals at a mineralization front just beneath the ameloblast distal membrane, where these proteins are secreted. As the crystal ribbons lengthen, enamelysin processes the secreted proteins. Some of the cleavage products accumulate in the matrix, others are reabsorbed back into the ameloblast. Once crystal elongation is complete and the enamel layer reaches its final thickness, kallikrein 4 (KLK4) facilitates the breakdown and reabsorption of accumulated enamel matrix proteins. The importance of the extracellular matrix proteins to proper tooth development is best illustrated by the dramatic dental phenotypes observed in the targeted knockouts of enamel matrix genes in mice *(Dspp, Amelx, Ambn, Mmp20)* and in human kindreds with defined mutations in the genes *(DSPP, AMELX, ENAM, MMP20, KLK4)* encoding these matrix proteins. However, ablation studies alone cannot give specific mechanistic information on how enamel matrix proteins combine to catalyze the formation of enamel crystals. The best approach for determining the molecular mechanism of dental enamel formation is to reconstitute the matrix and synthesize enamel crystals in vitro. Here, we report refinements to the procedures used to isolate por-

Abbreviations used in this paper

AMBN	ameloblastin gene
AMELX	amelogenin gene
DEJ	dentino-enamel junction
DGI	dentinogenesis imperfecta
DGP	dentin glycoprotein
DPP	dentin phosphoprotein
DSP	dentin sialoprotein
DSPP	dentin sialophosphoprotein
ENAM	enamelin gene
KLK4	kallikrein 4
KLK4	kallikrein 4 gene
MMP	matrix metalloproteinase
MMP20	enamelysin gene
RP-HPLC	reversed-phase high-performance liquid chromatography
TFA	trifluoroacetic acid

KARGER

Fax +41 61 306 12 34
E-Mail karger@karger.ch
www.karger.com

Accessible online at:
www.karger.com/cto

James P. Simmer, DDS, PhD
Department of Biological and Material Sciences
University of Michigan Dental Research Lab
1210 Eisenhower Place, Ann Arbor, MI 48108 (USA)
Tel. +1 734 975 9318, Fax +1 734 975 9329, E-Mail jsimmer@umich.edu

cine enamel and dentin proteins, recent advances in the characterization of enamel matrix protein posttranslational modifications, and summarize the results of human genetic studies that associate specific mutations in the genes encoding matrix proteins with a range of dental phenotypes.

Introduction

Tooth formation initiates with the expression of signaling molecules at selected sites along the oral epithelium covering the maxillary and mandibular prominences during embryonic development. The signals are received by underlying cells, which had previously migrated to their positions from the cranial neural crest. These 'ectomesenchymal' cells respond to the epithelial signals by expressing a host of transcription factors (including MSX1 and PAX9) that drive subsequent differentiation [Tucker and Sharpe, 2004]. They also induce regulated signaling pathway molecules (including AXIN2) that alter expression in the overlying epithelium [Lammi et al., 2004]. The coordinated network of reciprocal communications that orchestrate tooth formation is astoundingly complex and is often summarized by the expression 'epithelial-mesenchymal interactions'. Genetic defects that interfere with normal development at the earliest stage of odontogenesis tend to arrest tooth development and cause familial tooth agenesis [Satokata and Maas, 1994; Vastardis et al., 1996; Peters et al., 1998; Nieminen et al., 2001; Lammi et al., 2004].

Tooth development proceeds through the bud, cap, bell, crown formation and root formation stages, which reflect the morphological appearances of developing tooth organ sections under light microscopy [Nanci, 2003]. Dental enamel formation, or amelogenesis, initiates on the surface of freshly mineralized dentin in the late bell stage and continues from that time onward to tooth eruption. The molecular dynamics of amelogenesis involve genes expressing matrix proteins that are secreted into a controlled extracellular environment where they assemble into the supramolecular complexes that catalyze, shape, and organize crystals of calcium hydroxyapatite. Protein turnover and degradation are essential parts of the process. The mechanism of enamel biomineralization is unknown, but significant advances have been made in identifying the molecular participants, determining their structures, and characterizing the enamel defects that occur in their absence.

Rather than speculate on the molecular mechanisms of dental enamel formation, which has been done before [Simmer and Fincham, 1995; Fincham and Simmer, 1997; Fincham et al., 1999], we describe recent research results that are leading us toward a mechanistic understanding, which is not yet realized. We believe that the best way to demonstrate how proteins catalyze the formation of enamel crystals is to reconstitute the enamel matrix, starting with the dentino-enamel junction (DEJ), and to grow enamel crystals in vitro. Using the porcine animal model, which offers the advantages of having large developing teeth that can be obtained from commercial and research slaughterhouses, great progress has been made in the identification, isolation, and characterization of extracellular matrix molecules involved in amelogenesis. Proof of the importance of these enamel matrix proteins in dental enamel formation comes from the dental phenotypes displayed by knockout mice and human kindreds suffering from inherited dental malformations caused by defined mutation in the genes encoding extracellular matrix proteins.

Isolation of Enamel Proteins from Developing Teeth

We have refined and expanded the nondissociative, pH-based extraction methods previously used to isolate and characterize amelogenin *(AMELX)* [Fukae et al., 1979, 1980; Fukae and Shimizu, 1983; Yamakoshi et al., 1989, 1994], enamelin *(ENAM)* [Tanabe et al., 1990; Uchida et al., 1991a; Yamakoshi, 1995; Fukae et al., 1996; Yamakoshi et al., 1998], ameloblastin *(AMBN)* [Uchida et al., 1995; Yamakoshi et al., 2001], enamelysin *(MMP20)* [Yamada et al., 2003], and kallikrein 4 *(KLK4)* [Tanabe, 1984; Simmer et al., 1998] to isolate enamel matrix proteins, and dissociative extraction methods to isolate dentin sialophosphoprotein (DSPP)-derived proteins [Yamakoshi et al., 2005a, b]. Intact amelogenin, KLK4, matrix metalloproteinase (MMP)-20 and three DSPP-derived cleavage products – dentin sialoprotein (DSP), dentin glycoprotein (DGP), and dentin phosphoprotein (DPP) – can be isolated in sufficient quantities from developing pig teeth for most structural and functional analyses. Selected ameloblastin and enamelin cleavage products have been isolated and characterized, but the intact proteins, while detectable in enamel extracts, are too scarce to be isolated and studied.

The combination of low expression levels and rapid proteolysis makes the isolation of uncleaved enamelin and ameloblastin from developing teeth impractical. The obvious alternative is to use recombinant enamel proteins. Recombinant proteins offer advantages in quantity and in their ease of labeling and introducing specific substitutions. However, making recombinant enamel proteins is difficult because they all have posttranslational modifications, and these modifications are often extensive. Recombinant proteins are most easily expressed in *Escherichia coli,* but bacteria synthesize unmodified proteins that are of limited usefulness for functional studies. Often, recombinant expression in eukaryotic cells does not necessarily result in the same pattern of posttranslational modifications as occurs in developing teeth. Expression of amelogenin in insect cells using the baculovirus system, for instance, generated an unphosphorylated recombinant protein [Ryu et al., 2004]. The enzymes that catalyze the addition of posttranslational modifications are not ubiquitous, so the cells used to generate recombinant enamel proteins should be as closely related to ameloblasts as possible and the recombinant proteins themselves need to be isolated and characterized to verify that they structurally match those secreted during normal tooth development. This, of course, requires that the posttranslational modifications that occur in vivo be known.

Enamel Protein Functions

While the enamel extracellular matrix has never been reconstituted, and true enamel crystals have never been grown in vitro, confidence that enamel extracellular matrix proteins are critical for proper dental enamel crystal formation is strong and comes from examining enamel formed in their absence. Knockout mice have been generated for DSPP [Sreenath et al., 2003], amelogenin [Gibson et al., 2001], ameloblastin [Fukumoto et al., 2004], and enamelysin [Caterina et al., 2002], each of which displayed obvious dental phenotypes. In humans, specific gene mutations in *DSPP, AMELX, ENAM, MMP20,* and *KLK4* have been characterized in kindreds with dental phenotypes. These studies clearly demonstrate that the six extracellular matrix proteins featured in this report are essential for normal enamel formation. Less clear are the precise functional roles played by each matrix component. In ablation studies, it is always necessary to keep in mind that the observed phenotypes reflect not only the absence of the normal protein product (primary effects), but also secondary effects that occur because of the host response to the primary defects. In a complex process like amelogenesis where ameloblasts attach to and sample (by endocytosis) the mineralizing matrix they generate, secondary effects are likely to be considerable. Partly because of the inherent ambiguity of using knockout models and genotype-phenotype correlations to define the functional roles of enamel matrix proteins, reconstitution studies are essential to unlock the mechanism of enamel biomineralization.

Current Research

At the present time, we are nearing a point where all or most of the critical genes encoding enamel extracellular matrix constituents have been identified. We will be more confident of this conviction when candidate gene approaches used to identify mutations underlying inherited dental malformations are consistently successful (they are not at the present time) [Kim et al., in press]. The enamel matrix of developing porcine teeth continues to be surveyed, and no new proteins, except those derived from serum contamination, have been identified in recent analyses. Differential display polymerase chain reaction was recently used to identify a gene expressed by maturation stage ameloblasts, amelotin *(AMTN)* [Iwasaki et al., 2005]. The major focus of protein analyses has turned to characterization of the structural properties of the matrix proteins, especially in terms of their posttranslational modifications and protein-protein interactions, to engineer the expression of recombinant proteins that are structurally identical to in vivo products, and to identify and correlate mutations in the genes encoding human enamel matrix proteins to the type of mineralization defects that arise.

Materials and Methods

All experimental procedures involving the use of animals were reviewed and approved by the Institutional Animal Care and Use Program at the University of Michigan.

Extraction of Enamel and Dentin from Developing Pig Teeth

Tooth germs of permanent molars were surgically extracted with a hammer and chisel from the upper and lower jaws of 6-month-old pigs, within minutes of each animal's termination at the Michigan State University Meat Laboratory (East Lansing, Mich., USA). The enamel organ epithelia and dental pulp tissue are removed and the hard tissue is quickly frozen on dry ice. As much dental enamel as possible is removed by scraping with a curette. The remaining hard tissue is ground to a powder using a jaw crusher and used for the isolation of dentin proteins.

Dividing Enamel Proteins into Four Extracts Based upon Differential Solubility

The soft enamel scrapings are sequentially extracted into four fractions based upon solubility: (1) neutral extract, (2) alkaline extract, (3) acid extract, and (4) residual insoluble material. The neutral extraction is obtained by homogenizing the enamel shavings in Sörensen buffer, which is made by mixing Na_2HPO_4 and KH_2PO_4 to achieve a final phosphate concentration of 50 m*M* and a pH of

7.4. Material not soluble in the neutral extract is obtained by centrifugation. The pellet is resuspended in carbonate buffer, which is made by mixing bicarbonate $NaHCO_3$ and carbonate Na_2CO_3 to achieve a final concentration of 50 m*M* and a pH of 10.8. The neutral and alkaline extracts include the following proteinase inhibitors: 5 m*M* 1,10-phenanthroline (Sigma, St. Louis, Mo., USA) and Protease Inhibitor Cocktail Set III (Novagen, Madison, Wisc., USA). Material not soluble in the alkaline extract is pelleted by centrifugation, resuspended in 0.5 *M* acetic acid, and homogenized. Centrifugation separates the acid extract from residual insoluble material.

Further Fractionation of the Neutral Extract

The neutral enamel extract is separated into four fractions by successive ammonium sulfate precipitations at 40 and then 65% saturation. The 40–65% saturation pellet is divided into acid-soluble and acid-insoluble fractions by resuspending in 0.5 *M* acetic acid, with insoluble material being separated by centrifugation. The supernatant is desalted using a YM-3 membrane (Amicon, Beverly, Mass., USA). The ammonium sulfate fractions are further purified by C18 reversed-phase high-performance liquid chromatography (RP-HPLC). Samples are dissolved in 0.1% trifluoroacetic acid (TFA) and injected onto a C18 reversed-phase column (TSK-gel ODS-120T, 7.5 mm × 30 cm; Tosoh, Tokyo, Japan). The column is eluted with a shallow gradient (typically 40–60% buffer B in 40 min) at a flow rate of 1.0 ml/min. Buffer A is 0.1% TFA; buffer B is 0.1% TFA in 80% aqueous acetonitrile.

Further Fractionation of the Alkaline Extract

The alkaline enamel extract is applied to a Q Sepharose Fast Flow column (ion exchange column, 1.6 × 20 cm; Amersham Pharmacia, Uppsala, Sweden) and eluted with a linear gradient (0–25% buffer B). Buffer A is 50 m*M* Tris-HCl/6 *M* urea; buffer B is buffer A/1 *M* NaCl. Individual chromatographic peaks are applied to a Sephadex G-100 column (size exclusion column, 2.6 × 100 cm; Amersham Pharmacia), equilibrated with carbonate buffer containing protease inhibitors, and run at a flow rate of 0.4 ml/min at 4°C. Individual chromatographic peaks are finally separated by RP-HPLC.

Extraction of Dentin Proteins from the Dentin Powder

All extraction steps are carried out at 4°C or on ice. Protease Inhibitor Cocktail Set III (1 m*M* AEBSF, 0.8 μ*M* aprotinin, 50 μ*M* bestatin, 15 μ*M* E-64, 20 μ*M* leupeptin, and 10 μ*M* pepstatin; Calbiochem) and 1 m*M* 1,10-phenanthroline (Sigma) are included in each buffer during the extraction. Each extraction of dentin powder is repeated three times. The power is resuspended in Milli-Q water, homogenized and then centrifuged at 7,000 *g* to separate dissolved (W extract) from suspended material. The pellet is resuspended in 50 m*M* Tris-HCl/4 *M* guanidine buffer (pH 7.4) (G extract), homogenized and centrifuged. The pellet is dissolved in 50 m*M* Tris-HCl/4 *M* guanidine/0.5 *M* EDTA buffer (pH 7.4) (E extract) and centrifuged. The G and E extracts are desalted and concentrated using a Spectra/Por 3 (Spectrum Laboratories Inc., Rancho Dominguez, Calif., USA) with a YM-3 membrane (Amicon), and then lyophilized and stored at –80°C.

Isolation and DSPP-Derived Proteins

The lyophilized guanidine/EDTA (E) extract is dissolved in 10 ml of 50 m*M* Tris-HCl/6 *M* urea buffer (pH 7.4) and fractionated by an anion exchange chromatography with a Q Sepharose Fast Flow column (1.6 × 20 cm; Amersham Pharmacia). The column is first equilibrated with 50 mM Tris-HCl/6 *M* urea buffer (pH 7.4) and eluted with a linear NaCl gradient (0–0.5 *M*) containing 50 m*M* Tris-HCl/6 *M* urea buffer (pH 7.4). Both DSP and DPP elute in the third peak, which is concentrated with a YM-3 membrane, and further fractionated by hydroxyapatite affinity HPLC using a Beckman System Gold HPLC system equipped with a Bio-Scale CHT5 ceramic hydroxyapatite, type I column (column volume 5 ml; Bio-Rad, Hercules, Calif., USA). The column is equilibrated with 10 m*M* sodium phosphate buffer (pH 6.8) and eluted with a linear gradient of 1.0 *M* sodium phosphate buffer (pH 6.8). DPP elutes in the last peak as a pure protein. DGP and DSP elute in the second peak, which is concentrated and separated by size exclusion chromatography with a Superdex 200 column (1.6 × 60 cm; Amersham Biosciences) equilibrated with 50 m*M* Tris-HCl/4 *M* guanidine buffer (pH 7.4). DSP and DGP elute in the first and third peaks, respectively. Both fractions are dialyzed and further fractionated by RP-HPLC using a Discovery C18 column (10 mm ID × 25 cm; Supelco, Bellefonte, Pa., USA).

Results and Discussion

Flow diagrams for the fractionation of enamel and dentin proteins are shown in figure 1. Chromatograms of the enamel fractionations along with SDS-PAGE and amelogenin Western analyses have been previously published [Yamakoshi et al., 2004]. The following is a brief summary of the posttranslational modifications identified in extracellular matrix proteins secreted by the ameloblasts, and the phenotypes observed when expression of these proteins is defective.

Amelogenin

The major amelogenin isoform secreted into the porcine enamel matrix has 173 amino acids (P173). Its only posttranslational modification is the phosphorylation of Ser^{16} [Fincham and Moradian-Oldak, 1993]. Amelogenin is processed by enamelysin (MMP-20) starting near its C terminus. The major cleavage products that accumulate in the matrix are P1–162, P1–148, P1–43, P1–45, P46–148, P1–62, and P63–148. The sites of amelogenin posttranslational modifications are shown in figure 2. P173 is found in the alkaline extract and can be isolated to homogeneity by sequential ion exchange (Q2) and RP-HPLC (R2) [Yamakoshi et al., 2004]. Recombinant porcine amelogenin (P172) expressed in bacteria has been used in many studies, but lacks the N-terminal methionine and is not phosphorylated [Ryu et al., 1999]. Amelogenin assembles into spheres, about 20 nm in diameter, that appear to separate and support the growing enamel ribbons during the secretory stage [Fincham et al., 1994].

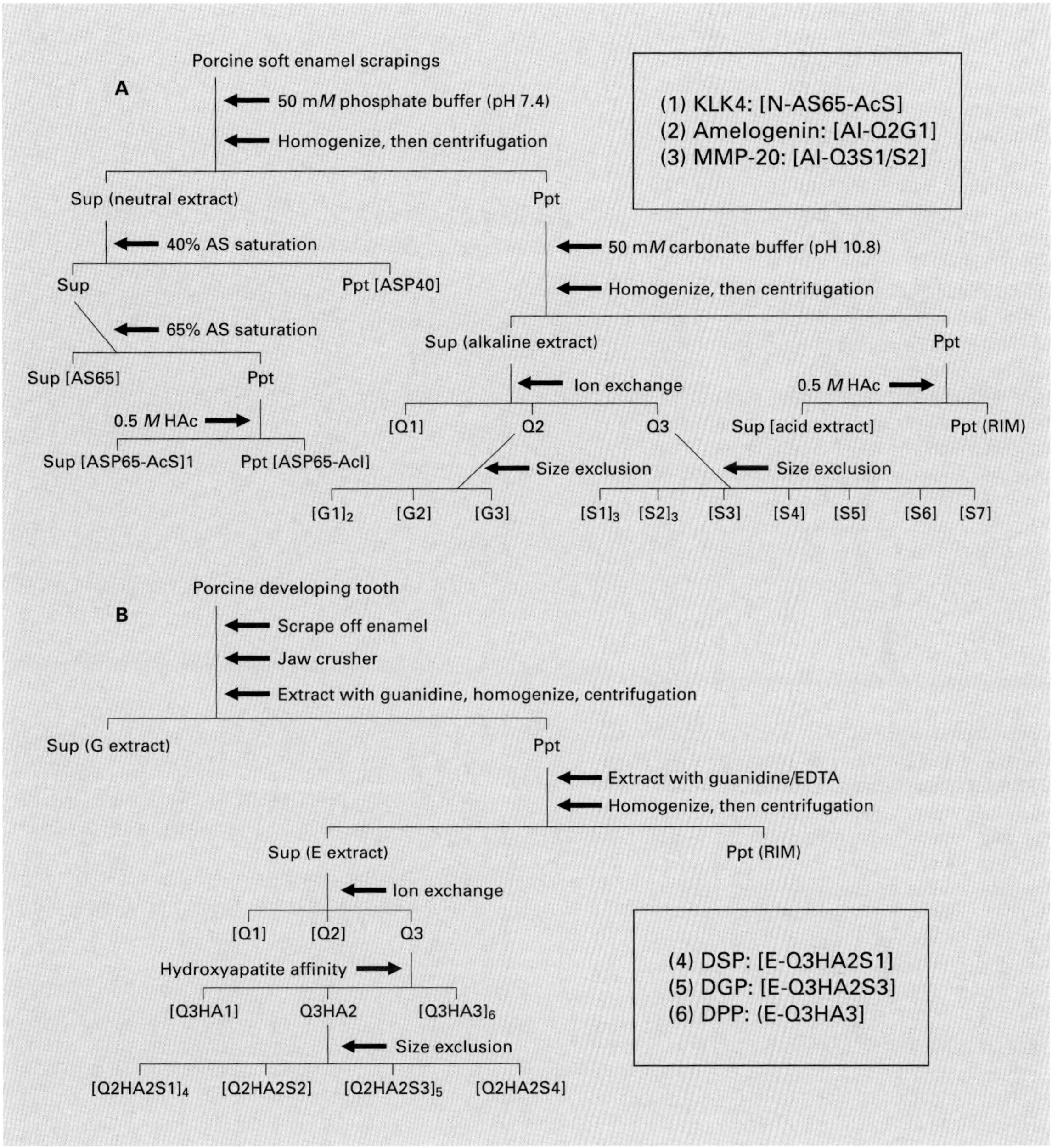

Fig. 1. Isolation of porcine enamel and dentin proteins. Flow diagram showing the extraction of enamel (**A**) and dentin proteins (**B**). Fractions that are subsequently fractionated by C18 RP-HPLC are enclosed in brackets. Enamel proteins are extracted from enamel scrapings using neutral, basic, and acidic buffers, which separate enamel proteins into four unequal fractions: neutral (N), alkaline (AL), acid (Ac), and residual insoluble material (RIM). Successive ammonium sulfate precipitations divide the neutral enamel extract into five fractions: (1) ammonium sulfate precipitate (ASP) at 40% saturation (ASP40); (2) 40–65% ammonium sulfate precipitate that is soluble in acid (ASP65-AcS); (3) 40–65% ammonium sulfate precipitate that is insoluble in acid (ASP65-AcI); (4) 65% ammonium sulfate soluble (ASS65); (5) the 40–65% ammonium sulfate soluble that is acid insoluble (ASS65-AcI). The neutral insoluble material that is extracted with carbonate buffer (alkaline extract) is injected onto a Q Sepharose column, which produces three fractions: Q1, Q2, and Q3 by ion exchange. Fraction Q2 is injected onto a Sephadex G-100 column, dividing it into three fractions (G1, G2, and G3) by size exclusion. Fraction Q3 is injected onto a Superdex 200 column, which divides it into seven fractions (S1–S7). Subscripted numbers indicate fractions containing full-length enamel proteins (1–3) or DSPP derivates (4–6) that are listed in the boxes on the top and bottom right.

Fig. 2. Primary structures of porcine amelogenin, ameloblastin, and KLK4. **A** The major porcine amelogenin isoform (NM_213800) has 173 amino acids with the phosphorylation of Ser^{16} (1) being its only posttranslational modification. Amelogenin is processed by enamelysin to generate cleavage products that accumulate in the developing enamel matrix. The major cleavage sites are after Gly^{43} (a), Trp^{45} (b), His^{62} (c), Phe^{148} (d), and Trp^{162} (e). The major ameloblastin isoform (U43404) has 395 amino acids. A second 380-amino-acid ameloblastin isoform, due to alternative splicing, lacks the segment from Tyr^{73} to Gln^{87} (underlined). **B** Ameloblastin posttranslational modifications are not completely characterized. Known posttranslational modifications include the hydroxylation of Pro^{11} (1), phosphorylation of Ser^{17} (2), Pro^{324} (3), and an O-linked, unsulfated, sialic acid-containing glycosylation on Thr^{361} (4). Porcine ameloblastin cleavage products show that ameloblastin is cleaved after Asn^{31} (a), Gln^{130} (b), Arg^{170} (c), Gly^{300} (d), Arg^{319} (e), and Ser^{374} (f). Two serines are in the appropriate context for phosphorylation (Ser^{209} and Ser^{210}, bold), but have not been characterized. **C** The porcine KLK4 (NM_213802) zymogen, or proprotein, has 225 amino acids and is activated by cleavage of the propeptide after His^6 (a). KLK4 is highly and variably glycosylated and appears to have attachments at all three potential N-linked glycosylation sites: Asn^{108}, Asn^{142}, and Asn^{186} (underlined). KLK4 has 12 cysteines involved in the following six disulfide bridges: Cys^{13}:Cys^{140} (1:6), Cys^{32}:Cys^{47} (2:3), Cys^{115}:Cys^{212} (4:12), Cys^{122}:Cys^{185} (5:10), Cys^{151}:Cys^{165} (7:8), and Cys^{175}:Cys^{200} (9:11).

A

Amelogenin

```
               *1                          ↓a
MPLPPHPGHPGYINFSYEVLTPLKWYQNMIRHPYTSYGYEPMGG  44
↓b               ↓c
WLHHQIIPVVSQQTPQSHALQPHHHIPMVPAQQPGIPQQPMMPL  88
PGQHSMTPTQHHQPNLPLPAQQPFQPQPVQPQPHQPLQPQSPMH 132
               ↓d          ↓e
PIQPLLPQPPLPPMFSMQSLLPDLPLEAWPATDKTKREEVD    173
```

B

Ameloblastin

```
          *1    *2             ↓a
VPAFPRQPGTPGVASLSLETMRQLGSLQGLNMLSQYSRFGFGKS  44
FNSLWMHGLLPPHSSFQWMRPREHETQQYEYSLPVHPPPLPSQP  88
                                          ↓b
SLQPQQPGQKPFLQPTVVTSIQNPVQKGVPQPPIYQGHPPLQQV 132
                                      ↓c
EGPMVQQQVAPSEKPPEAELPGLDFADPQDPSMFPIARLISQGP 176
VPQDKPSPLYPGMFYMSYGANQLNSPARLGILSSEEMAGGRGGP 220
LAYGAMFPGFGGMRPNLGGMPPNSAKGGDFTLEFDSPAAGTKGP 264
                                    ↓d
EKGEGGAEGSPVAEANTADPESPALFSEVASGVLGGLLANPKGK 308
           ↓e  *3                  ↓f
IPNLARGPAGRSRGPPGVTPADADPLMTPGLADAYETYGADETT 352
        *4
TLGLQEEMTMDSTATPYSEHTSMPGNKAQQPQIKRDAWRFQEP  395
```

C

Kallikrein 4

```
      ↓a     *1                *2
FINGGHIINGEDCNPHSQPWQAALFLEDDFFCGGVLVHPQWVLSAA  45
 *3
HCFQNSYTIGLGLHNLEPEQEPGSQMMEASLSIQHPEYNEPSMAND  90
                            *4       *5
LMLIKLKESVSLSDTVRNISVVSQCPTPGDSCLVSGWGRLASGRLP 135
    *6       *7              *8         *9
QVLQCVNISVASEEVCKARYGPVYHPSMFCAGGGQDQKDSCHGDSG 180
    *10           *11              *12
GPLICNGSLQGLVSFGQAQCGQPNVPGVYTNLCKFTDWIQTTIQAS 225
```

Amelogenin null mice display major enamel defects. Enamel crystals fail to elongate during the secretory stage, but a disorganized, weaker mineral layer precipitates beneath maturation stage ameloblasts [Gibson et al., 2001]. As of this writing, 14 different defects in AMELX have been characterized in families suffering from X-linked amelogenesis imperfecta. The designations of these mutations, based upon their predicted effect on the amelogenin protein, are p.0 [Lagerstrom et al., 1991], p.W4S and p.M1T [Kim et al., 2004a], p.W4X [Sekiguchi et al., 2001b], p.H129fs187 [Sekiguchi et al., 2001a], p.I5-A8delinsT [Lagerstrom-Fermer et al., 1995], p.T51I, p.P158fs187, and p.E191X [Lench and Winter, 1995], p.P52fsX53 [Aldred et al., 1992; Lench et al., 1994], p.P70T [Collier et al., 1997; Hart et al., 2000; Ravassipour et al., 2000], p.H77L [Hart et al., 2002], p.Y141fs187 [Greene et al., 2002], and p.L181fs187 [Kindelan et al., 2000; Hart et al., 2002]. Different phenotypic patterns appear to correlate with mutations affecting three regions of the amelogenin protein [Wright et al., 2003]. In general, females show alternating vertical bands of normal and thinner enamel. Males have virtually no enamel.

Growing literature suggests that amelogenin and particular isoforms of amelogenin formed by alternative splicing serve critical signaling functions during the development of odontogenic and other tissues. However,

Enamelin

*1
MPMQMPRMPGFSSKSEEMMRYGHFNFMNAPHMAHLGTLYGNGMQL 45

PQFFPQYQMPMWPQPPPNKKHPQKPSASKQQSKTDPAPESQKPNQ 90

↓a
PQPKTPTPKQPLNEPSPTPTQPEEETQTPQAFPPFGNGLFPYQQP 135

*2 *3
LWHVPHRIPPGYGRPPTSNEEGGNPYFGFFGYHGFGGRPPYYSEE 180

*4 *5
MFEQDFEKPKEKDPPKTETPATEPSVNTTVPETNSTQPNAPNPRG 225

*6 ↓b
NDTSPTGTSGQGPNPRSNPTGQNGPAV**N**VSGQGVPRSQSPWGPRQ 270

TIIHENYPNPNIRGFPARRQWRPPGPAMGHRRNGPFYRNQQIQRG 315

PRWNSFTLEGKQAVRPGYPTYRRVYGSTARSNPPNYAGNSANLRR 360

KPEGPNKNPMVTNVAPPGPKHGTVDQNENIQNPREKQVSQKERTV 405

VPTRDPSGPWRNSQDYGI**N**KSNYKLPQPEDNMLVPNFNSIDQREN 450

↓c
SYYPRGESKRAPNSDGQTQTQIIPKGIVLEPRRIPYESETNQPEL 495

*7
KHSAYQPVYTEGIPSPAKEHFPAGRNTWNQQEISPPFKEDPGRQE 540

EHLPHLSHGSRVHVYYPDYNPYDPRENSPYLRSNTWYERDDSPNT 585

↓d
MGQPENPHYPMNTPDPKETIPYNEEDPIDPTGDEHFPGQSRWDME 630

↓e
ELSFKEDPTVRHYEGEQYTSNQPKEYLPYSLDNPSKPREDFLYGE 675

FYPWNPEENFPSYNTAPTVSSPVESRGYYANNAVGQEESTMFPSW 720

SSWDPRTQAQGQKEGRPYLNRNFWDQSTNLYKTPTSSPHQKENQP 765

YS**N**NSPAGLQKNPTWHEGENLNYGMQITRLNSPERDHLAFPDLIP 810

PDYPGGQKESHVFHLSQRGP**CC**AGGSMWPKNNPLALQDYTQSFGL 855

APGENPDTSIGYAEDSHIKYARQTVSPTSIVPGQR**N**SSEKILPGE 900

SQNPSPFKDDVSTLRRSTP**C**SVKSQLSQRGIMPLPEANSLQSKNT 945

P**C**LTSDLGGDGNNVLEQIFEGNQLNERTVDLTPEQLVFGTPDKEP 990

RPEGIPNEMQG**N**ESERQQQRQSSILQLP**C**FGSKLANYHTSSIGTP 1035

SSLGRQDSFDGDPIMPTETPNSLAGLATGAQFQNINVDPLNEDEH 1080

TPFDSLQIGTNPQDQVQD**C**LLLQA 1104

Fig. 3. Primary structure of porcine enamelin. Porcine enamelin (U52196) is the largest enamel protein, with 1,104 amino acids. Known enamelin posttranslational modifications include the phosphorylation of Ser^{15} (1), Ser^{153} (2), and Ser^{178} (3), glycosylation of Asn^{207} (4), Asn^{214} (5), and Asn^{226} (6), and the hydroxylation of Pro^{509} (7). Additionally, there are five asparagines that are in the appropriate context for glycosylation and five cysteines that might participate in disulfide bridges (bold), but have not been characterized. Enamelin is the most rapidly degraded enamel protein, with only the 32-kDa enamelin (Leu^{136}-Arg^{241}) accumulating in abundance. The 32-kDa enamelin is generated by cleavages at arrows a and b. A 25-kDa cleavage product (G^{476}-Trp^{637}) is generated by cleavages at arrows c and d. The N terminus of a 34-kDa enamelin is generated by a cleavage at arrow e.

the authors of this report are impressed by the normal development of all tissues except enamel in the amelogenin knockout and in human kindreds with *AMELX* mutations, and doubt the significance of functions attributed to amelogenin outside of enamel formation.

Ameloblastin

There are two porcine ameloblastin isoforms with 380 and 395 amino acids [Hu et al., 1997]. The P395 is the more abundant form and differs from the P380 by the inclusion of a 15-amino-acid segment (Tyr^{73}-Gln^{87}). The sites of ameloblastin posttranslational modifications are shown in figure 2. Ameloblastin is a bipolar molecule; its N-terminal side is basic, while the C-terminal side is acidic. The two modified residues on the N-terminal side are the hydroxylation of Pro^{11} and the phosphorylation of Ser^{17}. The ameloblastin N terminus is represented by three main cleavage products in enamel extracts: the 17 kDa (V^{1}–Arg^{170}), the 15 kDa (V^{1}–Gln^{130}), and the 13 kDa (Met^{29}–Gln^{130}), which concentrate in the sheath space during the secretory stage [Uchida et al., 1991b, 1995]. The acidic C-terminal side has a sulfated, unsialylated, O-linked glycosylation at Thr^{361}, while Pro^{324} is hydroxylated [Yamakoshi et al., 2001]. Several glycosylated cleavage products that concentrate near the enamel surface among the rod crystallites and are extracted from

A

Dentin sialoprotein

```
IPVPQIKPLERHAIDKSVNLNLLAKSKAPVQDELNANDTTKG   42
SGIPMHDHDIGRQQDTKDGYKGERNGSEWADVGGNSSSARPM   84
LANKEENTEDPNGDAGQPEPYGHDGLHGRGDSSPANGLRGQV  126
                            *1
SILDNTGTANGSHVNGVTDKNSKNEDVGNASQSENATVVPED  168
                     *2
RYQVAGSNNSIGHEDEINGNFCRNGGDVSETTPPGEGEINGN  210
                           *3          *4
EETGVTSGGSGAGNREFAGLDNSDGSPSGNGADEEEDKGSGD  252
DEGEETGNGERTADTSKGQENPSHGEEEAEEEDDDHSLGQNS  294
ISSEDEGPGHKEAAHATDGDNTSKSEEDSDNIPGESRSQRIE  336
DTQKPNQRETKAVANGVTAISEPLAIGKSQDKGIEIAAPR    376
```

B

Dentin glycoprotein

```
     *1
SGNRSNITKEAGKVSEDRESKGQHGMIVGKGSVKTQGEADI 416
                    *2*3*4   *5
MQRPGPKSEPGNKPGPSKTHSDSNSEGYDSYEFDGKSMQG  456
```

Fig. 4. Primary structures of DSP and DGP. **A** Dentin sialoprotein (NM_213777) is highly modified following translation, but most of these modifications remain uncharacterized. Asn^{155} (1) is glycosylated, Cys^{190} (2) participates in an intermolecular disulfide bridge, and Ser^{238} (3) and Ser^{250} (4) are glycosaminoglycan attachment sites. The posttranslational status of seven predicted N-linked and three predicted O-linked glycosylations (bold) remain untested. **B** Dentin glycoprotein, which extends from Ser^{377} to Gly^{456}, has exactly five posttranslational modifications: N382 (1) is glycosylated, and Ser^{437} (2), Ser^{439} (3), Ser^{441} (4), and Ser^{446} (5) are phosphorylated. The only known DSPP proteolytic cleavages (after Arg^{376} and Gly^{456}) separate the molecule into three domains.

enamel shavings with neutral buffer are derived from the C terminus. These cleavage products have been previously described as the 29- and 27-kDa calcium-binding proteins (Leu^{301}–Pro^{395}), the 15- and 13-kDa stains-all-positive proteins (Ser^{320}–Pro^{395} and Ser^{320}–Ser^{374}) [Fukae and Tanabe, 1987; Murakami et al., 1997; Yamakoshi et al., 2001], and a 9-kDa piece from the C terminus starting at Tyr^{343} [Yamakoshi et al., in press].

Ameloblastin knockout mice (*Ambn–/–*) do not form an enamel layer [Fukumoto et al., 2004]. No mutations in human *AMBN* have yet been linked to amelogenesis imperfecta, presumably because its pattern of inheritance is autosomal recessive and therefore occurs only rarely.

Enamelin

Enamelin is the largest enamel protein, with 1,104 amino acids (fig. 3). Most of the protein is rapidly degraded or reabsorbed following its secretion and has not been well characterized [Hu and Yamakoshi, 2003]. The 186-kDa secreted protein is processed from its C terminus to generate 155-, 145-, and 89-kDa (Met^{1}–Trp^{627}) N-terminal cleavage products. One highly modified cleavage product, known as the 32-kDa enamelin (Leu^{136}–Arg^{241}), accumulates among the rod crystallites throughout the entire thickness of secretory stage enamel [Tanabe et al., 1990; Uchida et al., 1991a]. This 106-amino-acid domain contains two phosphoserines and three N-linked glycosylations [Yamakoshi, 1995, 1998]. The sites of enamelin posttranslational modifications are shown in figure 3. Enamelin contains five cysteine residues in its C-terminal domain, and the interesting possibility of intra- or intermolecular disulfide bridges has not yet been explored.

To date, seven different disease-causing mutations have been identified in *ENAM:* p.K53X [Mardh et al., 2002], p.M71-Q157 [Kim et al., 2005b], p.A158-Q178del [Rajpar et al., 2001], p.N197fsX277 [Kida et al., 2002; Hart et al., 2003a; Kim et al., 2005b], p.V340-M341insSQYQYCV [Ozdemir et al., 2005a], and p.P422fsX448 [Hart et al., 2003b; Ozdemir et al., 2005a]. The dental phenotype can be as minor as circumscribed enamel pits on the buccal surfaces of the anterior teeth and occlusal surfaces of posterior teeth, but more typically, the enamel is thinner than normal, with horizontal banding especially near to the cemento-enamel junction. The enamel phenotype is very severe, approaching agenesis, when both *ENAM* alleles are defective.

Enamelysin (MMP-20) and KLK4

MMP-20 and KLK4 are proteolytic enzymes that are critical for proper dental enamel formation. Both enzymes were first isolated from porcine enamel extracts, and their cDNAs were cloned from a porcine enamel organ epithelia-derived cDNA library [Bartlett et al., 1996;

Simmer et al., 1998]. Computer modeling shows that MMP-20 has a structure typical of MMPs [Ryu et al., 2000]. Its only posttranslational modification is a disulfide bridge connecting the first and last residues of its hemopexin domain, and nicking of the polypeptide backbone within this domain causes the protein to migrate as a doublet at 45 and 41 kDa on SDS-PAGE [Yamada et al., 2003]. MMP-20 segregates into the Q3 fraction of the alkaline extract. There are a number of good reviews about MMP-20 [Bartlett and Simmer, 1999; Simmer and Hu, 2002; Bartlett, 2004]. The enamelin (–/–) knockout mouse has hypomineralized thin enamel that tends to delaminate from the underlying dentin [Caterina et al., 2002].

KLK4 is a serine proteinase that was originally designated as enamel matrix serine proteinase 1 [Simmer, 2004]. A computer model of porcine KLK4 shows that it contains six disulfide bridges in common with other serine proteinases, and that its three predicted N-linked glycosylation sites localize to the back of the protein, away from the active site [Scully et al., 1998]. The locations of these modifications are shown in figure 2. KLK4 migrates as a smear between 32 and 36 kDa on SDS-PAGE and zymograms. Studies of recombinant and native forms of KLK4 suggest that the protein in the enamel matrix is heterogeneous and can be glycosylated at 1, 2, or all 3 sites, and that glycosylation is required for activity [Ryu et al., 2002]. KLK4 is isolated from the neutral enamel extract in the acid soluble portion of the 65% ammonium sulfide precipitate (AS65-AcS). It has been reported that KLK4 is unique among the KLKs in being transported into the nucleus, rather than being secreted. However, the interpretation of these findings has been strongly challenged [Simmer and Bartlett, 2004]. Mutations in both alleles of *KLK4* and *MMP20* result in pigmented hypomaturation forms of amelogenesis imperfecta [Hart et al., 2004; Kim et al., 2005c; Ozdemir et al., 2005b].

DSPP Derivatives

Porcine DSPP is a chimeric protein that is expressed by ameloblasts in the 'presecretory' stage, as well as by odontoblasts [Begue-Kirn et al., 1998]. While critical for proper dentin formation, DSPP may also be important during the earliest part of enamel formation, at the DEJ. Protein analyses in rat led to the isolation and characterization of the first DSPP cDNAs [Ritchie et al., 1994; Ritchie and Wang, 1996]. Subsequent molecular biology studies turned up a variety of DSPP cDNAs that varied by having deletions of various lengths from the highly redundant DPP coding region, which has generated a confusing nomenclature that includes the designations DMP2 and DMP3 [George et al., 1999]. The rat DSPP genomic sequence does not have the requisite splice junctions (GT…AG) for alternative RNA splicing to explain the existence of these deletions. Recent studies from pig indicate that these deletions are likely artifacts caused by errors in reverse transcription and/or polymerase chain reaction [Yamakoshi et al., 2003]. In the pig, DSPP is cleaved into three stable structural/functional domains: DSP, DGP, and DPP [Yamakoshi et al., 2005b].

Porcine DSP (I^1–R^{376}) is the N-terminal cleavage product of DSPP and has 376 amino acids. There are nine putative N-glycosylation sites in the DSP primary sequence (fig. 4). Among these, only one glycosylation (Asn^{155}) has been verified, and glycosylation of the other sites have not been ruled out. DSP has large glycosaminoglycan chains, comprised of chondroitin 6-sulfate chains, attached to Ser^{238} and Ser^{250} [Yamakoshi et al., 2005a]. Disulfide bonds connect Cys^{190} from two different DSP molecules to form covalent dimers. The release of carbohydrate attachments by procedures specific for O-linked gylcosylations suggests that DSP has at least one O-linked attachment, which is presumed to occur at any of the three predicted sites, i.e. Thr^{199}, Thr^{213}, and Thr^{264}. DSP shows affinity for hyaluronic acid, suggesting that it might contribute to large proteoglycan structures in vivo.

Porcine dentin glycoprotein is comprised of the 81 amino acids (Ser^{377}–Gly^{457}) between the DSP and DPP proteins. DGP is glycosylated at Asn^{382} and has four phosphoserines (Ser^{437}, Ser^{439}, Ser^{441}, and Ser^{446}). Any of five different complex biantennary structures, both sialidated and unsialidated, can be attached to Asn^{282} [Yamakoshi et al., 2005b]. Porcine DPP is largely uncharacterized. Although DPP is easily purified [Kuboki et al., 1979], its high degree of phosphorylation and redundant amino acid sequence make it particularly difficult to study. The first 38 amino acids of bovine DPP have been characterized, and all 19 serines in this region were phosphorylated [Huq et al., 2000]. At the present time, after completion of the human genome project, the DNA sequence of the coding region for human DPP remains uncertain, as the genomic (NC_000004) and cDNA (NM_014208) reference sequences show major differences.

As of this writing, nine different mutations in *DSPP* have been reported in kindreds with inherited dentin defects: p.Y6D [Rajpar et al., 2002], p.A15V [Malmgren et al., 2004], p.P17T [Xiao et al., 2001], IVS2–3C→G [Kim et al., 2004b], p.V18F [Xiao et al., 2001; Kim et al.,

2005a], pQ45X [Zhang et al., 2001], IVS3+1G→A [Xiao et al., 2001], p.R68W [Malmgren et al., 2004], and pdel1160–1171/p.ins1198–1199 [Dong et al., 2005]. Historically, inherited dentin defects have been classified as either dentin dysplasia types I and II, or dentinogenesis imperfecta (DGI) types I, II, or III [Shields et al., 1973]. DGI type I is now universally designated as osteogenesis imperfecta with dentinogenesis imperfecta and is caused by mutations in either of the type I collagen genes [O'Connell and Marini, 1999], although rare cases have been characterized where the bony defects are within normal limits [Pallos et al., 2001]. The *Dspp* (–/–) mouse shows a dental phenotype resembling DGI type II, which is the most common human phenotype [Sreenath et al., 2002]. Mutations in the *DSPP* gene have been shown to cause dentin dysplasia type II, DGI type II, and DGI type III. Although there are several other potential candidate genes for these disorders, only DSPP mutations have been found in the kindreds yet characterized. The recent genetic results suggest that the current classical scheme might have overemphasized minor phenotypic differences and split a single disease entity into several designations.

Human genetic studies and mouse knockout studies have conclusively demonstrated that all of the genes encoding the major extracellular matrix proteins are critical for normal tooth development. However, these studies cannot provide specific information about how matrix components work together to catalyze the deposition of dental enamel. Our long-term strategy for determining the molecular mechanisms of dental enamel formation involves reconstituting the enamel extracellular matrix, starting at the DEJ. Comprehensive purification procedures have been developed that allow for the isolation of full-length amelogenin, MMP-20, KLK4, and the DSPP derivatives DSP, DGP and DPP from developing pig teeth, while only specific enamelin and ameloblastin cleavage products that accumulate during amelogenesis can be isolated from in vivo sources. All proteins in the enamel extracellular matrix have posttranslational modifications, but the structures and positions of these modifications have only been determined for amelogenin, MMP-20, and DGP. Continued genetic analyses will determine if the full range of critical extracellular components have been identified, while continued protein and molecular biology studies will provide us with the protein reagents necessary to synthesize enamel in vitro. Significant progress has already been made, and we look forward to the day when the ameloblast can be replaced by the scientist and enamel crystals are synthesized in vitro, both to understand the mechanism and to develop materials that can better restore lost or damaged dental structures.

Acknowledgements

We thank Mr. Tom Forton, Manager of the Michigan State University Meat Laboratory, and members of the Michigan State University Department of Animal Science for their kind assistance in obtaining fresh developing molars from pigs slaughtered at their facility. This investigation was supported by USPHS Research Grants DE12769, DE15846, and DE11301 from the National Institute of Dental and Craniofacial Research, National Institutes of Health, Bethesda, Md., USA.

References

Aldred, M.J., P.J. Crawford, E. Roberts, N.S. Thomas (1992) Identification of a nonsense mutation in the amelogenin gene (AMELX) in a family with X-linked amelogenesis imperfecta (AIH1). Hum Genet *90:* 413–416.

Bartlett, J.C. (2004) Enamelysin; in Barrett, A., N. Rawlings, J. Woessner (eds): Handbook of Proteolytic Enzymes. London, Academic Press.

Bartlett, J.D., J.P. Simmer (1999) Proteinases in developing dental enamel. Crit Rev Oral Biol Med *10:* 425–441.

Bartlett, J.D., J.P. Simmer, J. Xue, H.C. Margolis, E.C. Moreno (1996) Molecular cloning and mRNA tissue distribution of a novel matrix metalloproteinase isolated from porcine enamel organ. Gene *183:* 123–128.

Begue-Kirn, C., P.H. Krebsbach, J.D. Bartlett, W.T. Butler (1998) Dentin sialoprotein, dentin phosphoprotein, enamelysin and ameloblastin: tooth-specific molecules that are distinctively expressed during murine dental differentiations. Eur J Oral Sci *106:* 963–970.

Caterina, J.J., Z. Skobe, J. Shi, Y. Ding, J.P. Simmer, H. Birkedal-Hansen, J.D. Bartlett (2002) Enamelysin (matrix metalloproteinase 20)-deficient mice display an amelogenesis imperfecta phenotype. J Biol Chem *277:* 49598–49604.

Collier, P.M., J.J. Sauk, S.J. Rosenbloom, Z.A. Yuan, C.W. Gibson (1997) An amelogenin gene defect associated with human X-linked amelogenesis imperfecta. Arch Oral Biol *42:* 235–242.

Dong, J., T. Gu, L. Jeffords, M. MacDougall (2005) Dentin phosphoprotein compound mutation in dentin sialophosphoprotein causes dentinogenesis imperfecta type III. Am J Med Genet A *132:* 305–309.

Fincham, A.G., J. Moradian-Oldak (1993) Amelogenin post-translational modifications: carboxy-terminal processing and the phosphorylation of bovine and porcine 'TRAP' and 'LRAP' amelogenins. Biochem Biophys Res Commun *197:* 248–255.

Fincham, A.G., J. Moradian-Oldak, J.P. Simmer (1999) The structural biology of the developing dental enamel matrix. J Struct Biol *126:* 270–299.

Fincham, A.G., J. Moradian-Oldak, J.P. Simmer, P. Sarte, E.C. Lau, T. Diekwisch, H.C. Slavkin (1994) Self-assembly of a recombinant amelogenin protein generates supramolecular structures. J Struct Biol *112:* 103–109.

Fincham, A.G., J.P. Simmer (1997) Amelogenin proteins of developing dental enamel. Ciba Found Symp *205:* 118–130; discussion 130–134.

Fukae, M., H. Ijiri, T. Tanabe, M. Shimizu (1979) Partial amino acid sequences of two proteins in developing porcine enamel. J Dent Res *58:* 1000–1001.

Fukae, M., M. Shimizu (1983) Amino acid sequence of the main component of porcine enamel proteins. Jpn J Oral Biol *25:* 29.

Fukae, M., T. Tanabe (1987) ^{45}Ca-labeled proteins found in porcine developing dental enamel at an early stage of development. Adv Dent Res *1:* 261–266.

Fukae, M., T. Tanabe, H. Ijiri, M. Shimizu (1980) Studies on porcine enamel proteins: a possible original enamel protein. Tsurumi U Dent J *6:* 87–94.

Fukae, M., T. Tanabe, C. Murakami, N. Dohi, T. Uchida, M. Shimizu (1996) Primary structure of the porcine 89-kDa enamelin. Adv Dent Res *10:* 111–118.

Fukumoto, S., T. Kiba, B. Hall, N. Iehara, T. Nakamura, G. Longenecker, P.H. Krebsbach, A. Nanci, A.B. Kulkarni, Y. Yamada (2004) Ameloblastin is a cell adhesion molecule required for maintaining the differentiation state of ameloblasts. J Cell Biol *167:* 973–983.

George, A., R.S.R. Srinivasan, K. Liu, A. Veis (1999) Rat dentin matrix protein 3 is a compound protein of rat dentin sialoprotein and phosphophoryn. Connect Tissue Res *40:* 49–57.

Gibson, C.W., Z.A. Yuan, B. Hall, G. Longenecker, E. Chen, T. Thyagarajan, T. Sreenath, J.T. Wright, S. Decker, R. Piddington, G. Harrison, A.B. Kulkarni (2001) Amelogenin-deficient mice display an amelogenesis imperfecta phenotype. J Biol Chem *276:* 31871–31875.

Greene, S.R., Z.A. Yuan, J.T. Wright, H. Amjad, W.R. Abrams, J.A. Buchanan, D.I. Trachtenberg, C.W. Gibson (2002) A new frameshift mutation encoding a truncated amelogenin leads to X-linked amelogenesis imperfecta. Arch Oral Biol *47:* 211–217.

Hart, P.S., M.J. Aldred, P.J. Crawford, N.J. Wright, T.C. Hart, J.T. Wright (2002) Amelogenesis imperfecta phenotype-genotype correlations with two amelogenin gene mutations. Arch Oral Biol *47:* 261–265.

Hart, S., T. Hart, C. Gibson, J.T. Wright (2000) Mutational analysis of X-linked amelogenesis imperfecta in multiple families. Arch Oral Biol *45:* 79–86.

Hart, T.C., P.S. Hart, M.C. Gorry, M.D. Michalec, O.H. Ryu, C. Uygur, D. Ozdemir, S. Firatli, G. Aren, E. Firatli (2003b) Novel ENAM mutation responsible for autosomal recessive amelogenesis imperfecta and localised enamel defects. J Med Genet *40:* 900–906.

Hart, P.S., T.C. Hart, M.D. Michalec, O.H. Ryu, D. Simmons, S. Hong, J.T. Wright (2004) Mutation in kallikrein 4 causes autosomal recessive hypomaturation amelogenesis imperfecta. J Med Genet *41:* 545–549.

Hart, P.S., M.D. Michalec, W.K. Seow, T.C. Hart, J.T. Wright (2003a) Identification of the enamelin (g.8344delG) mutation in a new kindred and presentation of a standardized ENAM nomenclature. Arch Oral Biol *48:* 589–596.

Hu, C.C., M. Fukae, T. Uchida, Q. Qian, C.H. Zhang, O.H. Ryu, T. Tanabe, Y. Yamakoshi, C. Murakami, N. Dohi, M. Shimizu, J.P. Simmer (1997) Sheathlin: cloning, cDNA/polypeptide sequences, and immunolocalization of porcine enamel sheath proteins. J Dent Res *76:* 648–657.

Hu, J.C., Y. Yamakoshi (2003) Enamelin and autosomal-dominant amelogenesis imperfecta. Crit Rev Oral Biol Med *14:* 387–398.

Huq, N.L., K.J. Cross, G.H. Talbo, P.F. Riley, A. Loganathan, M.A. Crossley, J.W. Perich, E.C. Reynolds (2000) N-terminal sequence analysis of bovine dentin phosphophoryn after conversion of phosphoseryl to S-propylcysteinyl residues. J Dent Res *79:* 1914–1919.

Iwasaki, K., E. Bajenova, E. Somogyi-Ganss, M. Miller, V. Nguyen, H. Nourkeyhani, Y. Gao, M. Wendel, B. Ganss (2005) Amelotin – a novel secreted, ameloblast-specific protein. J Dent Res *84:* 1127–1132.

Kida, M., T. Ariga, T. Shirakawa, H. Oguchi, Y. Sakiyama (2002) Autosomal-dominant hypoplastic form of amelogenesis imperfecta caused by an enamelin gene mutation at the exon-intron boundary. J Dent Res *81:* 738–742.

Kim, J.W., J.C. Hu, J.I. Lee, S.K. Moon, Y.J. Kim, K.T. Jang, S.H. Lee, C.C. Kim, S.H. Hahn, J.P. Simmer (2005a) Mutational hot spot in the DSPP gene causing dentinogenesis imperfecta type II. Hum Genet *116:* 186–191.

Kim, J.W., B.P.J. Lin, J.P. Simmer, J.C.C. Hu (in press) Mutational analysis of candidate genes in 24 amelogenesis imperfecta families. Eur J Oral Sci.

Kim, J.W., S.H. Nam, K.T. Jang, S.H. Lee, C.C. Kim, S.H. Hahn, J.C. Hu, J.P. Simmer (2004b) A novel splice acceptor mutation in the DSPP gene causing dentinogenesis imperfecta type II. Hum Genet *115:* 248–254.

Kim, J.W., F. Seymen, B.P. Lin, B. Kiziltan, K. Gencay, J.P. Simmer, J.C. Hu (2005b) ENAM mutations in autosomal-dominant amelogenesis imperfecta. J Dent Res *84:* 278–282.

Kim, J.W., J.P. Simmer, T.C. Hart, P.S. Hart, M.D. Ramaswami, J.D. Bartlett, J.C. Hu (2005c) MMP-20 mutation in autosomal recessive pigmented hypomaturation amelogenesis imperfecta. J Med Genet *42:* 271–275.

Kim, J.W., J.P. Simmer, Y.Y. Hu, B.P.L. Lin, C. Boyd, J.T. Wright, C.J.M. Yamada, S.K. Rayes, R.J. Feigal, J.C.C. Hu (2004a) Amelogenin p.M1T and p.W4S mutations underlying hypoplastic X-linked amelogenesis imperfecta. J Dent Res *83:* 378–383.

Kindelan, S.A., A.H. Brook, L. Gangemi, N. Lench, F.S. Wong, J. Fearne, Z. Jackson, G. Foster, B.M. Stringer (2000) Detection of a novel mutation in X-linked amelogenesis imperfecta. J Dent Res *79:* 1978–1982.

Kuboki, Y., R. Fujisawa, K. Aoyama, S. Sasaki (1979) Calcium-specific precipitation of dentin phosphoprotein: a new method of purification and the significance for the mechanism of calcification. J Dent Res *58:* 1926–1932.

Lagerstrom, M., N. Dahl, Y. Nakahori, Y. Nakagome, B. Backman, U. Landegren, U. Pettersson (1991) A deletion in the amelogenin gene (AMG) causes X-linked amelogenesis imperfecta (AIH1). Genomics *10:* 971–975.

Lagerstrom-Fermer, M., M. Nilsson, B. Backman, E. Salido, L. Shapiro, U. Pettersson, U. Landegren (1995) Amelogenin signal peptide mutation: correlation between mutations in the amelogenin gene (AMGX) and manifestations of X-linked amelogenesis imperfecta. Genomics *26:* 159–162.

Lammi, L., S. Arte, M. Somer, H. Jarvinen, P. Lahermo, I. Thesleff, S. Pirinen, P. Nieminen (2004) Mutations in AXIN2 cause familial tooth agenesis and predispose to colorectal cancer. Am J Hum Genet *74:* 1043–1050.

Lench, N.J., A.H. Brook, G.B. Winter (1994) SSCP detection of a nonsense mutation in exon 5 of the amelogenin gene (AMGX) causing X-linked amelogenesis imperfecta (AIH1). Hum Mol Genet *3:* 827–828.

Lench, N.J., G.B. Winter (1995) Characterisation of molecular defects in X-linked amelogenesis imperfecta (AIH1). Hum Mutat *5:* 251–259.

Malmgren, B., S. Lindskog, A. Elgadi, S. Norgren (2004) Clinical, histopathologic, and genetic investigation in two large families with dentinogenesis imperfecta type II. Hum Genet *114:* 491–498.

Mardh, C.K., B. Backman, G. Holmgren, J.C. Hu, J.P. Simmer, K. Forsman-Semb (2002) A nonsense mutation in the enamelin gene causes local hypoplastic autosomal dominant amelogenesis imperfecta (AIH2). Hum Mol Genet *11:* 1069–1074.

Murakami, C., N. Dohi, M. Fukae, T. Tanabe, Y. Yamakoshi, K. Wakida, T. Satoda, O. Takahashi, M. Shimizu, O.H. Ryu, J.P. Simmer, T. Uchida (1997) Immunochemical and immunohistochemical study of 27 and 29 kDa calcium binding proteins and related proteins in the porcine tooth germ. Histochem Cell Biol *107:* 485–494.

Nanci, A. (ed) (2003) Ten Cate's Oral Histology: Development, Structure, and Function, ed 6. St. Louis Mosby.

Nieminen, P., S. Arte, D. Tanner, L. Paulin, S. Alaluusua, I. Thesleff, S. Pirinen (2001) Identification of a nonsense mutation in the PAX9 gene in molar oligodontia. Eur J Hum Genet *9:* 743–746.

O'Connell, A.C., J.C. Marini (1999) Evaluation of oral problems in an osteogenesis imperfecta population. Oral Surg Oral Med Oral Pathol Oral Radiol Endod *87:* 189–196.

Ozdemir, D., P.S. Hart, E. Firatli, G. Aren, O.H. Ryu, T.C. Hart (2005a) Phenotype of ENAM mutations is dosage-dependent. J Dent Res *84:* 1036–1041.
Ozdemir, D., P.S. Hart, O.H. Ryu, S.J. Choi, M. Ozdemir-Karatas, E. Firatli, N. Piesco, T.C. Hart (2005b) MMP20 active-site mutation in hypomaturation amelogenesis imperfecta. J Dent Res *84:* 1031–1035.
Pallos, D., P.S. Hart, J.R. Cortelli, S. Vian, J.T. Wright, J. Korkko, D. Brunoni, T.C. Hart (2001) Novel COL1A1 mutation (G559C) [correction of G599C] associated with mild osteogenesis imperfecta and dentinogenesis imperfecta. Arch Oral Biol *46:* 459–470.
Peters, H., A. Neubuser, K. Kratochwil, R. Balling (1998) Pax9-deficient mice lack pharyngeal pouch derivatives and teeth and exhibit craniofacial and limb abnormalities. Genes Dev *12:* 2735–2747.
Rajpar, M.H., K. Harley, C. Laing, R.M. Davies, M.J. Dixon (2001) Mutation of the gene encoding the enamel-specific protein, enamelin, causes autosomal-dominant amelogenesis imperfecta. Hum Mol Genet *10:* 1673–1677.
Rajpar, M.H., M.J. Koch, R.M. Davies, K.T. Mellody, C.M. Kielty, M.J. Dixon (2002) Mutation of the signal peptide region of the bicistronic gene DSPP affects translocation to the endoplasmic reticulum and results in defective dentine biomineralization. Hum Mol Genet *11:* 2559–2565.
Ravassipour, D.B., P.S. Hart, T.C. Hart, A.V. Ritter, M. Yamauchi, C. Gibson, J.T. Wright (2000) Unique enamel phenotype associated with amelogenin gene (AMELX) codon 41 point mutation. J Dent Res *79:* 1476–1481.
Ritchie, H.H., H. Hou, A. Veis, W.T. Butler (1994) Cloning and sequence determination of rat dentin sialoprotein, a novel dentin protein. J Biol Chem *269:* 3698–3702.
Ritchie, H.H., L.H. Wang (1996) Sequence determination of an extremely acidic rat dentin phosphoprotein. J Biol Chem *271:* 21695–21698.
Ryu, O.H., A.G. Fincham, C.C. Hu, C. Zhang, Q. Qian, J.D. Bartlett, J.P. Simmer (1999) Characterization of recombinant pig enamelysin activity and cleavage of recombinant pig and mouse amelogenins. J Dent Res *78:* 743–750.
Ryu, O.H., D. Hsiung, C.C. Hu, X. Sun, X. Cao, J.D. Bartlett, J.P. Simmer (2000) The structure and function of enamelysin (MMP-20); in Goldberg, M., A. Boskey, C. Robinson (eds): Chemistry and Biology of Mineralized Tissues: Proceedings of the Sixth International Conference, 1998, Vittel, France. Rosemont, American Academy of Orthopaedic Surgeons, pp 363–367.
Ryu, O., J.C. Hu, Y. Yamakoshi, J.L. Villemain, X. Cao, C. Zhang, J.D. Bartlett, J.P. Simmer (2002) Porcine kallikrein-4 activation, glycosylation, activity, and expression in prokaryotic and eukaryotic hosts. Eur J Oral Sci *110:* 358–365.
Ryu, O.H., J.L. Villemain, X. Cao, C.H. Zhang, J.C.C. Hu, J.P. Simmer (2004) Characterization of recombinant pig amelogenin expressed from a baculovirus/insect cell system; in Kobayashi, I., H. Ozawa (eds): Biomineralization: Formation, Diversity, Evolution and Application. Proceedings of the 8th International Symposium on Biomineralization, Niigata, Sept 25–28, 2001. Hadano, Tokai University Press, pp 343–347.
Satokata, I., R. Maas (1994) Msx1 deficient mice exhibit cleft palate and abnormalities of craniofacial and tooth development. Nat Genet *6:* 348–356.
Scully, J.L., J.D. Bartlett, M.G. Chaparian, M. Fukae, T. Uchida, J. Xue, C.C. Hu, J.P. Simmer (1998) Enamel matrix serine proteinase 1: stage-specific expression and molecular modeling. Connect Tissue Res *39:* 111–122; discussion 141–149.
Sekiguchi, H., S. Alaluusua, K. Minaguchi, M. Yakushiji (2001a) A new mutation in the amelogenin gene causes X-linked amelogenesis imperfecta. J Dent Res *80:* 617.
Sekiguchi, H., M. Kiyoshi, M. Yakushiji (2001b) DNA diagnosis of X-linked amelogenesis imperfecta using PCR detection method of the human amelogenin gene. Dent Jpn *37:* 109–112.
Shields, E.D., D. Bixler, A.M. el-Kafrawy (1973) A proposed classification for heritable human dentine defects with a description of a new entity. Arch Oral Biol *18:* 543–553.
Simmer, J. (2004) Prostase; in Barrett, A., N. Rawlings, J. Woessner (eds): Handbook of Proteolytic Enzymes. London, Academic Press.
Simmer, J.P., J.D. Bartlett (2004) Kallikrein 4 is a secreted protein. Cancer Res *64:* 8481–8482; author reply 8482–8483.
Simmer, J.P., A.G. Fincham (1995) Molecular mechanisms of dental enamel formation. Crit Rev Oral Biol Med *6:* 84–108.
Simmer, J.P., M. Fukae, T. Tanabe, Y. Yamakoshi, T. Uchida, J. Xue, H.C. Margolis, M. Shimizu, B.C. DeHart, C.C. Hu, J.D. Bartlett (1998) Purification, characterization, and cloning of enamel matrix serine proteinase 1. J Dent Res *77:* 377–386.
Simmer, J.P., J.C. Hu (2002) Expression, structure, and function of enamel proteinases. Connect Tissue Res *43:* 441–449.
Sreenath, T., B. Hall, G. Longenecker, T. Thyagarajan, R.N. D'Souza, S. Hong, J.T. Wright, M. MacDougall, A.B. Kulkarni (2002) Targeted disruption of the mouse dentin sialophosphoprotein gene (abstract 3889). IADR.
Sreenath, T., T. Thyagarajan, B. Hall, G. Longenecker, R. D'Souza, S. Hong, J.T. Wright, M. MacDougall, J. Sauk, A.B. Kulkarni (2003) Dentin sialophosphoprotein knockout mouse teeth display widened predentin zone and develop defective dentin mineralization similar to human dentinogenesis imperfecta type III. J Biol Chem *278:* 24874–24880.
Tanabe, T. (1984) Purification and characterization of proteolytic enzymes in porcine immature enamel. Tsurumi U Dent J *10:* 443–452.
Tanabe, T., T. Aoba, E.C. Moreno, M. Fukae, M. Shimizu (1990) Properties of phosphorylated 32 kd nonamelogenin proteins isolated from porcine secretory enamel. Calcif Tissue Int *46:* 205–215.
Tucker, A., P. Sharpe (2004) The cutting-edge of mammalian development; how the embryo makes teeth. Nat Rev Genet *5:* 499–508.
Uchida, T., M. Fukae, T. Tanabe, Y. Yamakoshi, T. Satoda, C. Murakami, O. Takahashi, M. Shimizu (1995) Immunochemical and immunocytochemical study of a 15 kDa non-amelogenin and related proteins in the porcine immature enamel: proposal of a new group of enamel proteins sheath proteins. Biomed Res *16:* 131–140.
Uchida, T., T. Tanabe, M. Fukae, M. Shimizu (1991a) Immunocytochemical and immunochemical detection of a 32 kDa nonamelogenin and related proteins in porcine tooth germs. Arch Histol Cytol *54:* 527–538.
Uchida, T., T. Tanabe, M. Fukae, M. Shimizu, M. Yamada, K. Miake, S. Kobayashi (1991b) Immunochemical and immunohistochemical studies, using antisera against porcine 25 kDa amelogenin, 89 kDa enamelin and the 13–17 kDa nonamelogenins, on immature enamel of the pig and rat. Histochem *96:* 129–138.
Vastardis, H., N. Karimbux, S.W. Guthua, J.G. Seidman, C.E. Seidman (1996) A human MSX1 homeodomain missense mutation causes selective tooth agenesis. Nat Genet *13:* 417–421.
Wright, J.T., P.S. Hart, M.J. Aldred, K. Seow, P.J. Crawford, S.P. Hong, C.W. Gibson, T.C. Hart (2003) Relationship of phenotype and genotype in X-linked amelogenesis imperfecta. Connect Tissue Res *44(suppl 1):* 72–78.
Xiao, S., C. Yu, X. Chou, W. Yuan, Y. Wang, L. Bu, G. Fu, M. Qian, J. Yang, Y. Shi, L. Hu, B. Han, Z. Wang, W. Huang, J. Liu, Z. Chen, G. Zhao, X. Kong (2001) Dentinogenesis imperfecta 1 with or without progressive hearing loss is associated with distinct mutations in DSPP. Nat Genet *27:* 201–204.
Yamada, Y., Y. Yamakoshi, R. Gerlach, C. Hu, K. Matsumoto, M. Fukae, S. Oida, J. Bartlett, J. Simmer (2003) Purification and characterization of enamelysin from secretory stage pig enamel. Arch Comp Biol Tooth Enam *8:* 21–25.
Yamakoshi, Y. (1995) Carbohydrate moieties of porcine 32 kDa enamelin. Calcif Tissue Int *56:* 323–330.
Yamakoshi, Y., J.C. Hu, M. Fukae, T. Iwata, J.W. Kim, H. Zhang, J.P. Simmer (2005a) Porcine dentin sialoprotein is a proteoglycan with glycosaminoglycan chains containing chondroitin 6-sulfate. J Biol Chem *280:* 1552–1560.
Yamakoshi, Y., J.C. Hu, M. Fukae, H. Zhang, J.P. Simmer (2005b) Dentin glycoprotein: the protein in the middle of the dentin sialophosphoprotein chimera. J Biol Chem *280:* 17472–17479.

Yamakoshi, Y., J.C. Hu, S. Liu, C. Zhang, S. Oida, M. Fukae, J.P. Simmer (2003) Characterization of porcine dentin sialoprotein (DSP) and dentin sialophosphoprotein (DSPP) cDNA clones. Eur J Oral Sci *111:* 60–67.
Yamakoshi, Y., J.C.C. Hu, O.H. Ryu, T. Tanabe, S. Oida, M. Fukae, J.P. Simmer (2004) A comprehensive strategy for purifying pig enamel proteins; in Kobayashi, I., H. Ozawa (eds): Biomineralization: Formation, Diversity, Evolution and Application. Proceedings of the 8th International Symposium on Biomineralization, Niigata, Sept 25–28, 2001. Hadano, Tokai University Press, pp 326–332.
Yamakoshi, Y., F.H. Pinheiro, T. Tanabe, M. Fukae, M. Shimizu (1998) Sites of asparagine-linked oligosaccharides in porcine 32 kDa enamelin. Connect Tissue Res *39:* 39–46; discussion 63–67.
Yamakoshi, Y., T. Tanabe, M. Fukae, M. Shimizu (1989) Amino acid sequence of porcine 25 kDa amelogenin; in Fearnhead, R.W. (ed): Tooth Enamel V. Tokyo, Florence Publishers, pp 314–321.
Yamakoshi, Y., T. Tanabe, M. Fukae, M. Shimizu (1994) Porcine amelogenins. Calcif Tissue Int *54:* 69–75.
Yamakoshi, Y., T. Tanabe, S. Oida, C.C. Hu, J.P. Simmer, M. Fukae (2001) Calcium binding of enamel proteins and their derivatives with emphasis on the calcium-binding domain of porcine sheathlin. Arch Oral Biol *46:* 1005–1014.
Yamakoshi, Y., H. Zhang, J.C.C. Hu, T. Iwata, J.P. Simmer (in press) Proteomic analysis of enamel matrix using two-dimensional protein fractionation. Eur J Oral Sci.
Zhang, X., J. Zhao, C. Li, S. Gao, C. Qiu, P. Liu, G. Wu, B. Qiang, W.H. Lo, Y. Shen (2001) DSPP mutation in dentinogenesis imperfecta Shields type II. Nat Genet *27:* 151–152.

Cells
Tissues
Organs

Cells Tissues Organs 2005;181:232–240
DOI: 10.1159/000091384

Role of Phosphophoryn in Dentin Mineralization

Anne George   Jianjun Hao

Department of Oral Biology, University of Illinois, Chicago, Ill., USA

Key Words
Dentin mineralization · Phosphophoryn · Type I collagen fibrillogenesis · Extracellular matrix

Abstract
Mineral deposition is essential for the development of hard tissues like bone and teeth. In matrix-mediated mechanisms responsible for dentin formation, type I collagen defines the framework for mineral deposition and by itself is not sufficient to support nucleation of hydroxyapatite. However, in the presence of non-collagenous proteins, nucleation sites have been identified within the hole regions of the fibrils, and at these sites, mineral crystals can grow and propagate. Non-collagenous proteins constitute 5–10% of the total extracellular matrix proteins. They are embedded within the mineral deposits, suggesting a possible interaction with the mineral phase. During dentin formation, phosphophoryn (PP), an abundant macromolecule in the extracellular matrix, can initiate mineral deposition in localized regions by matrix-mediated mineralization mechanism. In our work, we have demonstrated that PP, due to its highly phosphorylated post-translational modification, can bind calcium ions with high affinity and at the same time aggregate collagen fibrils at the mineralization front. Molecular modeling has further demonstrated that the spacing of the carboxyl and phosphate groups present on PP might be essential for dictating the crystal orientation relative to the collagen substrate. Thus, PP may provide the interface linkage between mineral crystal and collagen fibrils.

Introduction

Biomineralization, the biogenic formation of mineral deposits, is one of the most widespread processes in nature. For this reason, biomineralization merits particular attention since many biominerals are deposited in a highly controlled manner to produce crystals which are uniformly sized and crystallographically unique [Lowenstam and Weiner, 1989]. All aspects of this mineral deposition are important, but our attention has been focused on the processes in eukaryotes, where the mineral deposition at

Abbreviations used in this paper

AFM	atomic force microscopy
DMP2	dentin matrix protein 2
DR	dummie residue
PBS	phosphate-buffered saline
PP	phosphophoryn
SAXS	small angle X-ray scattering

KARGER
Fax +41 61 306 12 34
E-Mail karger@karger.ch
www.karger.com

Accessible online at:
www.karger.com/cto

Anne George, PhD
Department of Oral Biology
801 S. Paulina
Chicago, IL 60612 (USA)
Tel. +1 312 492 8821, Fax +1 312 996 6044, E-Mail anneg@uic.edu

extracellular sites is clearly mediated and regulated by proteins and other components which the cells secrete to form the matrix. A basic strategic plan for matrix-mediated mineralization is that the cells first form the structural components of the extracellular matrix and then deliver regulatory macromolecules which modify the properties of the matrix and lead to the location and stereospecific nucleation of mineral crystal [Veis, 1988].

Dentin is a mineralized collagenous tissue formed by matrix-mediated mechanisms [George et al., 1998]. Three significant components of the mineralized dentin are collagen fibrils, which define the space and do not support mineralization directly, a variety of mineral interactive proteins, and platy crystals of carbonated apatite [He and George, 2004]. The crystals grow in the collagen fibrils in parallel arrays with their crystallographic c-axes, coaligned with the long axes of the fibrils [Landis et al., 1996]. These mineralized collagen fibrils serve as basic building blocks in all types of bone and dentin.

A key interactive protein of the dentin matrix is an acidic Asp-Ser-rich variety known as phosphophoryn (PP). The molecule is called thus as it is considered to be a 'phosphate carrier' [Dimuzio and Veis, 1978]. PPs have been considered to be the archetype of macromolecules which might regulate the biomineralization process. A very important structural feature is the presence of $(DSS)_n$ (Asp-Ser-Ser) repeats interspersed throughout the molecule with the SD (Ser-Asp) domains predominant at the C-terminal end of the molecule [Sabsay et al., 1991]. Conformational analysis suggested that the phosphorylated form of the DS*S* (S* represents phosphorylated serine) repeat sequences assume a unique structure with well-defined ridges of phosphates and carboxylates available for counter ion binding [George et al., 1996]. The principal modification is that most of the serine groups in both the DSS and SD domains are phosphorylated. Phosphorylation of all potential serines results in a highly negatively charged molecule and is a virtual sink for the binding of calcium ions [Veis et al., 1997].

The structure and orientation of the phosphate motifs on either side of the backbone would be a key factor for oriented crystal nucleation. Published reports demonstrate that with bovine dentin PP at high concentrations (0.45 mg/ml), one Ca^{2+} is bound for every aspartyl and phosphoseryl residue. At lower bovine dentin PP (approximately 0.05 mg/ml), only one third of the amount of Ca^{2+} is bound at the same ionic strength [Lee and Veis, 1980]. These data suggest that at a low concentration, the molecule folded back on itself, creating partially ordered, internally bridged structures, whereas at higher concentrations, intermolecular calcium-mediated aggregates formed. Recognition between PP and the hydroxyapatite surface on a certain plane may result in oriented crystal growth [Addadi et al., 1992]. As the protein backbone is flexible, binding of calcium ions results in more rigid β-sheet structures and serves as templates for oriented crystal nucleation and growth.

Another function attributed to PP is its collagen-binding capacity. A significant fraction of PP is cross-linked to dentin collagen in vivo [Dahl et al., 1998]. Results demonstrate that a single PP molecule can interact with and effectively cross-link two or more collagen molecules and that such cross-linking does lead to the formation of molecularly staggered collagen-PP aggregates, even at acid pH [Dahl and Veis, 2003]. When native PP was immobilized on agarose beads [Saito et al., 2000] or on collagen fibrils by in vivo or in vitro cross-linking, it induced apatite formation from metastable calcium phosphate solutions that do not spontaneously precipitate.

Thus, PP exhibits multifunctional roles. The post-translational modification of PP is important to its function, namely assisting in the specific localization of mineral on the collagen fibril and ordered nucleation and growth of hydroxyapatite. In this manuscript, we demonstrate that PP can fulfill these functions effectively only when the serines are phosphorylated.

Materials and Methods

Expression of Recombinant Protein

The 244-residue carboxyl-terminal domain of rat PP, predominantly containing aspartic acid serine repeats, has been cloned, and the corresponding protein has been expressed recombinantly in *Escherichia coli*. This portion of PP, named dentin matrix protein 2 (DMP2), is not phosphorylated by bacteria, and thus, provided a means to study the function of the phosphate groups.

Effect of PP and Recombinant DMP2 on Type I Collagen Fibrillogenesis

Lathyritic rat skin collagen was prepared as previously described [Veis, 1988]. To reconstitute type I collagen fibrils in vitro, 100 µl of 1 mg/ml type I collagen in 0.01 *M* acetic acid, 4°C, was mixed with 900 µl of 1 µ*M* protein in 9.3 m*M* Na_2HPO_4, 5.83 m*M* KH_2PO_4, 150 m*M* NaCl, pH 7.04. The mixture was warmed to 37°C and the kinetics of fibrillogenesis monitored at 313 nm.

Atomic Force Microscopy

Following fibrillogenesis, 10 µl of the collagen fibril suspension was adsorbed onto a freshly peeled mica surface for 10 min. After washing with water, the sample was air dried and collagen fibrils were imaged by atomic force microcopy (AFM) in tapping mode using silicon probes (Olympus). A multimode Nanoscope III AFM (Digital instruments) operating with a D-scanner was used.

Small Angle X-Ray Scattering Measurements

Solution X-ray scattering experiments were carried out at the Advanced Photon Source, Argonne National Laboratory, on Beam Line 15ID-D. A sample detector distance of 563 mm (short range) was used to cover the range of scattering vector Q from 0.0187 to 0.807 $Å^{-1}$, where $Q = (4\pi \sin\theta)/\lambda$; 2θ is the scattering angle, and λ is the wavelength of the X-ray. Samples were mounted in 1.5-mm quartz microcapillaries. Five successive 10-second exposures were recorded for each droplet. Each protein sample exposure was preceded by recording the buffer scattering. The scattering profiles of the five successive shots were averaged and the buffer scattering profile was subtracted. For Kratky plots, the scattering data were plotted as $I(Q) \cdot Q^2$ versus Q. Protein samples were placed in 10 m*M* HEPES, 165 m*M* NaCl, pH 7.4. Samples were run in the presence and absence of 5 m*M* $CaCl_2$.

Native PP and recombinant DMP2 (rDMP2) used in the experiment had a concentration of 5 mg/ml.

Ab initio Modeling

Low-resolution models were generated by the ab initio program Gasbor using small angle X-ray scattering (SAXS) data, as previously published [He et al., 2005]. Gasbor searches a chain-compatible spatial resolution of an exact number of dummy residues (DRs) corresponding to the $C\alpha$ atoms of protein amino acids and uses simulated annealing to build a locally 'chain-compatible' DR model inside the same search volume [Svergun et al., 2001]. The DR modeling is able to better account for the internal structure and generally provides more detailed models than those given by the shape determination algorithms. For each protein with and without calcium, results from at least ten separate runs were averaged by the package Damaver [Volkov et al., 2003] to construct the average model representing the general structural features of all the reconstructions.

Structure Analysis of Model Peptides

Polypeptide structure was modeled by energy minimization using the Discover CVFF repetitive build program (Biosym software) on a Silicon Graphics R-4000, X/Z graphics workstation. Molecular modeling was performed by the energy minimization protocol Discover CVFF force field and automatic set parameters for 10,000 iterations until the system energy converged at –207 kcal/mol. The CVFF repetitive build program is a generalized force field with parameters specifically designed to minimize polypeptide conformations and is part of the Insight II 950 molecule modeling system from Biosym/MSI (San Diego, Calif., USA) on a Silicon Graphics R-4000, X/Z graphics workstation. The global energy minimum corresponding to the overall favored conformation was obtained. The potential electrostatic repulsions of the charged phosphate and carboxylate groups were taken into account along with the other backbone and side chain interactions [George et al.,1996].

Immunohistochemical Localization of PP

Developing heads were collected from postnatal day 5 mice. The specimens were fixed in 4% paraformaldehyde solution at 4°C and then demineralized in buffered 10% EDTA for 7 days at 4°C. After the initial processing, they were embedded in paraffin and serial sections (5 μm thick), cut, and mounted on charged, treated slides. The paraffin sections were deparaffinized in xylene, rehydrated, and rinsed three times (5 min each) in phosphate-buffered saline (PBS; pH 7.4) prior to quenching of endogenous peroxidase activity (3% H_2O_2 in PBS at room temperature for 10 min). The sections were rinsed three times (5 min each) in PBS and then blocked with 10% normal goat serum for 45 min at room temperature. The sections were again rinsed in PBS solution and incubated with primary antibody 1:2,000 dilution against PP (overnight at 4°C). The C-terminal end of PP was expressed recombinantly (DMP2) and used for the production of PP-specific polyclonal antibody. A negative control was included by using an equal concentration of rabbit preimmune serum as primary antibody. Following incubation with the primary antibody, the tissue sections were rinsed three times (15 min each) in PBS and then incubated with a biotinylated rabbit anti-goat immunoglobulin (1:500) for 60 min at room temperature.

Amplification of the antigen-antibody complex was achieved using avidin-biotin peroxidase (ABC kit; Vector Laboratories, Burlingame, Calif., USA) for 60 min at room temperature. The color reaction was precipitated using 3,3′-diaminobenzidine tetrahydrochloride (Vector Laboratories) for 1–5 min at room temperature. The tissue sections were then counterstained with hematoxylin.

Results

SAXS Experiments

SAXS has become a powerful tool to determine the molecular size, shape and conformational changes for a protein molecule in solution [Semisotnov et al., 1996]. In particular, the Kratky plot of $I(Q) \cdot Q^2$ versus Q has a characteristic and distinctly different shape for globular folded molecules and extended chain or random coil molecules of the same molecular mass. In the Kratky plot, a maximum in $I(Q) \cdot Q^2$ versus Q is indicative of a globular protein or densely folded structure, whereas a plateau at moderate Q (the scattering vector) indicates a random coil-like conformation [Semisotnov et al., 1996; Doniach, 2001; Vachette et al., 2003]. For a compact, globular structure, the peak intensity or the integral around the peak can be indicative of the compactness of the protein molecule [Kataoka and Goto, 1996]. As shown in figure 1a, the conformation of rDMP2 seems to be an example of an extended, essentially random chain structure both in the presence and absence of added 5 m*M* Ca^{2+} ion. The value of $I(Q) \cdot Q^2$ under both conditions exhibited a near zero slope plateau over a wide range of scattering vector (fig. 1a). The Kratky plot of phosphorylated PP yielded virtually the same result as the rDMP2 in the absence of calcium ion, yielding a plateau typical of an unfolded structure, as shown in figure 1b. However, upon addition of 5 m*M* $CaCl_2$, a prominent peak was observed at Q = 0.05 $Å^{-1}$, indicating a conformational change to a more compact structure. This substantial compaction was essentially observed instantaneously upon adding the calcium ion. Since the profile remained constant, i.e. reflecting a static rather than dynamic state, it seems likely that

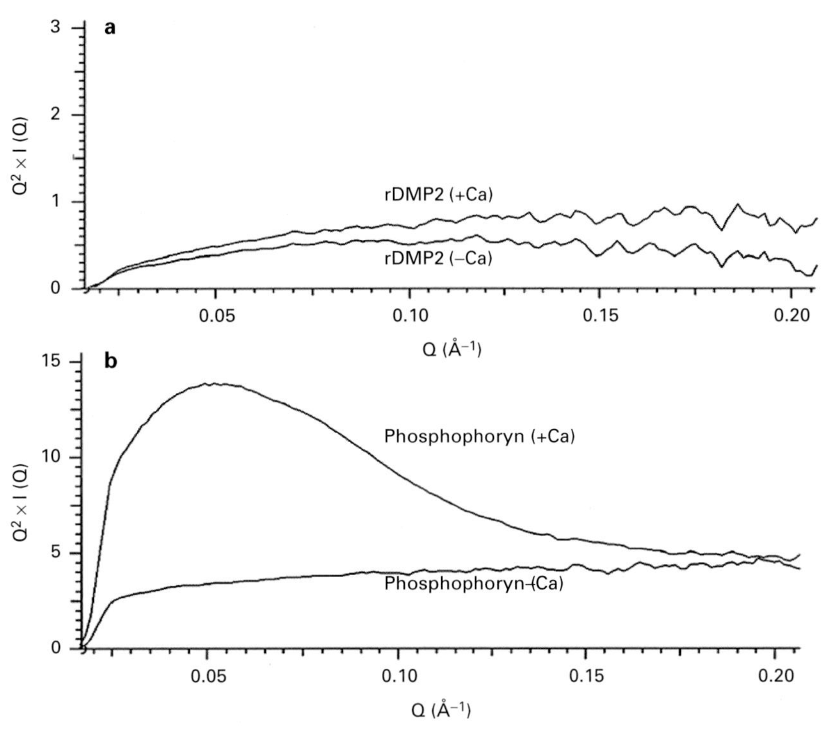

Fig. 1. Analysis of PP and rDMP2 conformations by SAXS. Kratky plots of rDMP2 and PP were determined in the presence and absence of Ca^{2+} ions. The plots of rDMP2 in the presence and absence of calcium showed a similar plateau, indicating its unfolded structure (**a**). In the absence of calcium, PP showed a similar unfolded structure. However, a prominent peak in the presence of Ca^{2+} ion suggested the formation of a more compact globular PP-Ca structure (**b**).

in the presence of Ca^{2+} ion, the PP conformation is a mixture of folded and less folded Ca^{2+}-induced domains.

Ab initio Modeling of PP

To gain further insight into the molecular shape and self-assembly of PP in the presence of calcium, low-resolution protein structures were generated by the ab initio program Gasbor, which depicts protein models through the assembly of DRs and uses simulated annealing to build a locally 'chain-compatible' DR model inside the same search volume [Svergun et al., 2001]. DR models are able to depict the internal structure better and in more detail than those determined by the shape determination algorithms [Koch et al., 2003]. Typical ab initio models of the partial constructs after repetitive ab initio runs for each protein scattering file are displayed in figure 2. From the low-resolution models, it appears that PP adopts an elongated structure, but upon calcium binding assumes a compact globular structure.

Molecular Modeling

Results from molecular modeling (fig. 3) show that ionic ridges are formed along the peptide backbone. Within the DSSDSS domains, pairs of phosphates are shown along the same edge of the extended chain separated by a single amino acid residue. The phosphates in each pair are separated by 5.1 Å, but the pairs are separated along the same edge by about 18 Å. $(SD)_m$ sequences are quite different. They have two well-defined ionic ridges with all of the phosphates on one edge and carboxylates on the opposite sides of the chain, presenting very different ionic distributions than that along the DSS repeats.

Such an arrangement might be essential for oriented crystal nucleation.

Characterization of Collagen-Binding Properties of PP and rDMP2

The ability of PP to interact with type I collagen fibrils and molecules in solution is well documented [Cocking-Johnson and Sauk, 1983; Dahl et al., 1998; Dahl and Veis, 2003]. However, similar to the effects of some proteoglycans, native, phosphorylated PP reduced the rate of thermally induced in vitro fibrillogenesis [Hunter et al., 1996] by extending the lag phase but not the ultimate development of turbidity. In the present study, 1 μM PP did significantly retard type I collagen fibrillogenesis (fig. 4), but in the time period examined, there was no obvious growth phase observed at 313 nm.

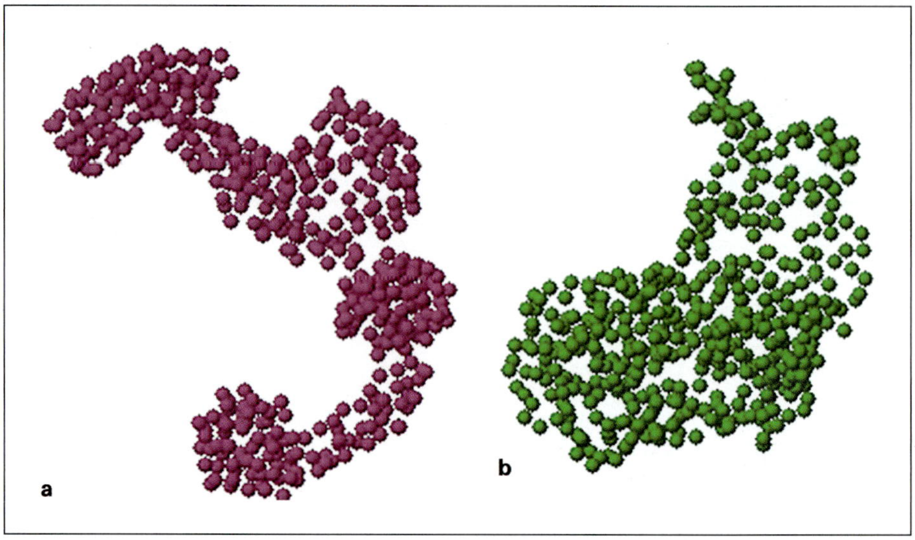

Fig. 2. Structural analysis of DMP2 as deduced from SAXS experiments. Low-resolution structural models were determined using the Gasbor program. **a** Model generated in the absence of calcium. **b** Model generated in the presence of calcium.

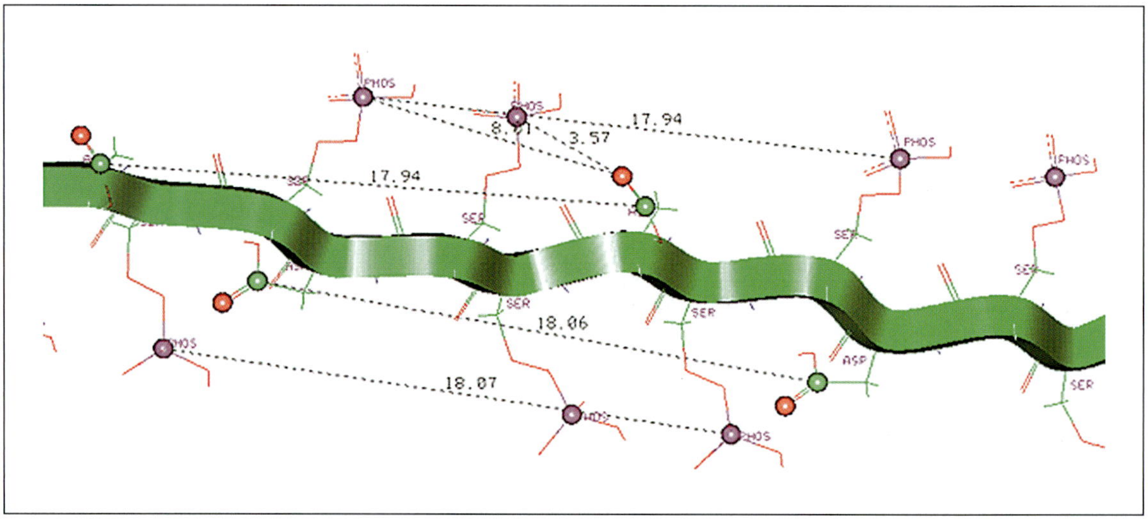

Fig. 3. Polypeptide structure was modeled by energy minimization using the Discover CVFF repetitive build program (Biosym software) on a Silicon Graphics R-4000, X/Z graphics workstation. The energy-minimized structure of a proposed fully phosphorylated DSS domain of DMP2 in the absence of counter ion binding is depicted. The backbone is puckered and the relative dispositions of the phosphate and carboxyl groups to the backbone are observed.

Surprisingly, 1 μ*M* rDMP2 significantly reduced the lag phase and accelerated the growth phase (fig. 4) to a final turbidity higher in the presence of 1 μ*M* rDMP2 as compared with the control collagen.

Characterization of the Reconstituted Collagen Fibrils by AFM

The reconstituted type I collagen fibrils were imaged by AFM. The reconstituted collagen fibrils in the control and in the presence of rDMP2 showed the characteristic periodicity of 67 nm (fig. 5). However, the diameter of the collagen fibrils assembled in the presence of rDMP2 was much greater (fig. 5b) than the diameters seen in the controls. In the presence of PP, unusual aggregates of collagen fibrils with directional orientation were observed (fig. 5c), but with no evidence for any D-periodicity. In the very dense deposits observed in the presence of PP, it appears that one layer of parallel fibrils aligned on top

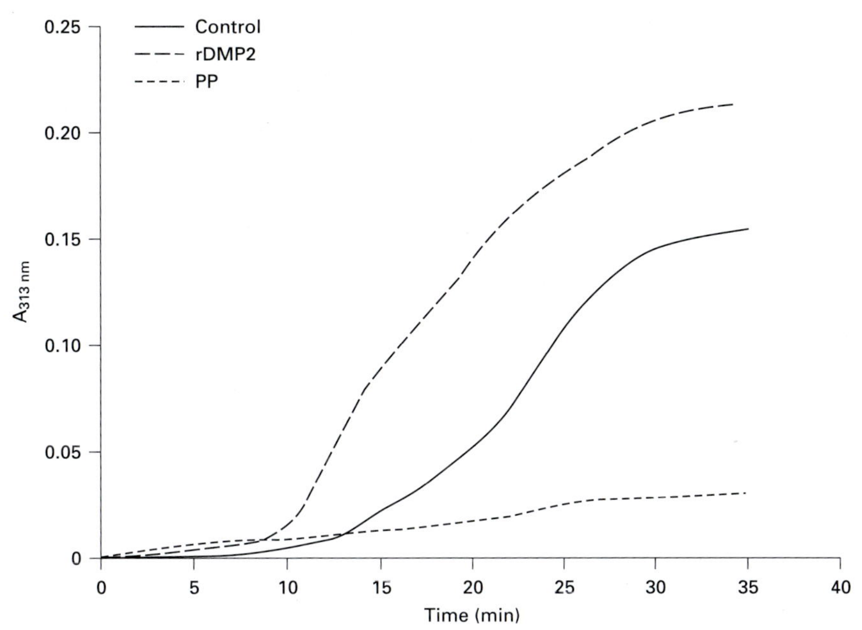

Fig. 4. Collagen-binding properties of rDMP2 and PP. Both rDMP2 and PP exhibited profound influence on the kinetics of type I collagen fibrillogenesis. While rDMP2 accelerated collagen fibrillogenesis, PP was found to retard this process.

of another sublayer of parallel fibrils, in a nearly orthogonal orientation.

Immunohistochemical Localization of PP

Immunohistochemical techniques demonstrate that PP is localized directly at the mineralization front. Within the odontoblast cells, the protein was localized only within fully polarized columnar cells and there was no evidence for the presence of protein in presecretory odontoblasts (fig. 6). Weak expression of PP was detected in the surrounding alveolar bone as well as in the ameloblasts. Expression of PP in the ameloblasts has been reported recently [Paine et al., 2005]. The preimmune serum which was used as a control did not show any reaction (data not shown).

Discussion

Postmitotic odontoblasts remain active for the life of the tooth and secrete primary and secondary dentin. One of the transcripts synthesized by polarized odontoblasts is dentin sialophosphoprotein. The dentin sialophosphoprotein gene which encodes two dentin proteins namely dentin sialoprotein and dentin phosphoprotein is considered a marker for terminally differentiated odontoblasts [Feng et al.,1998]. The major non-collagenous proteins present in all mammalian dentin extracts are members of a closely related family of proteins called the PPs. These proteins are strongly expressed in the odontoblasts and found in small amounts in the osteoblasts [Rahima and Veis, 1998]. Immunohistochemical analysis demonstrates their localization in the odontoblasts and at the mineralization front. Rabie and Veis [1995] have demonstrated that the packaging and the secretory pathways are different for both collagen and PP. However, their very unusual composition, extensive phosphorylation and tissue-specific heterogeneity have made their characterization a difficult task.

The interactions of PP within the extracellular matrix are twofold. Traub et al. [1992] have shown that the PP appears to bind to the collagen fibril preferentially at the e-band in the gap zone. The second interaction is the PP-crystal interaction. Addadi et al. [1992] have shown that the PPs preferentially bind to the (100) face of hydroxyapatite crystals and to the (010) face of octacalcium phosphate. This dual interaction of PP with collagen and crystal may be an important function of PP, assisting in the specific localization of mineral on fibrillar collagen.

The binding of calcium to PP could be clearly visualized by the computer-generated models for polypeptides of PP. Models of the DSS domains indicated that the most probable conformation was a ribbon-like, twisting, trans-extended chain structure with repetitive arrays of

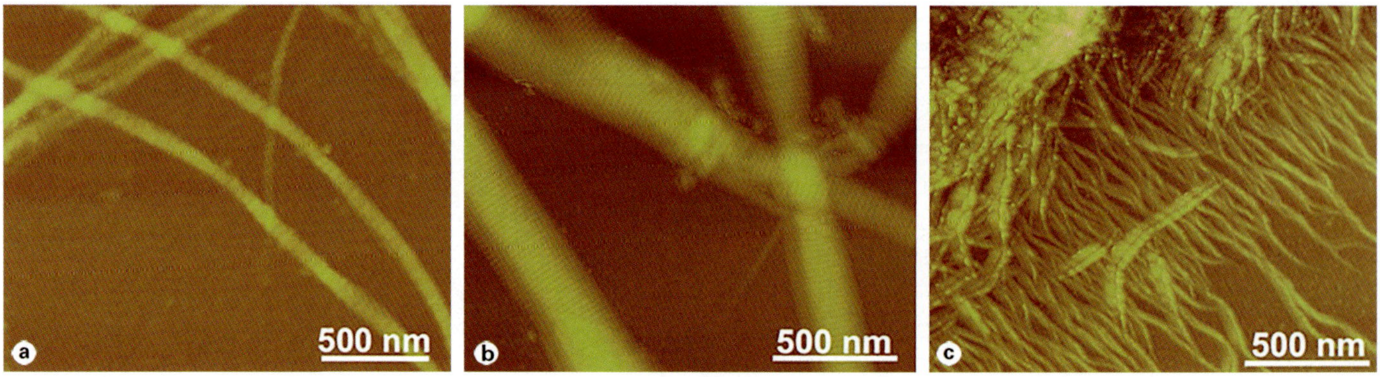

Fig. 5. Influence of rDMP2 and PP on type I collagen assembly as tracked by AFM imaging. Collagen fibrillogenesis was carried out in the presence of rDMP2 and PP. **a** Control collagen alone. **b** Collagen + rDMP2. Note the increased diameter of the reconstituted collagen fibrils. **c** Collagen + PP. Note the aggregation of the fibers. The assembly pattern of type I collagen was different in each case.

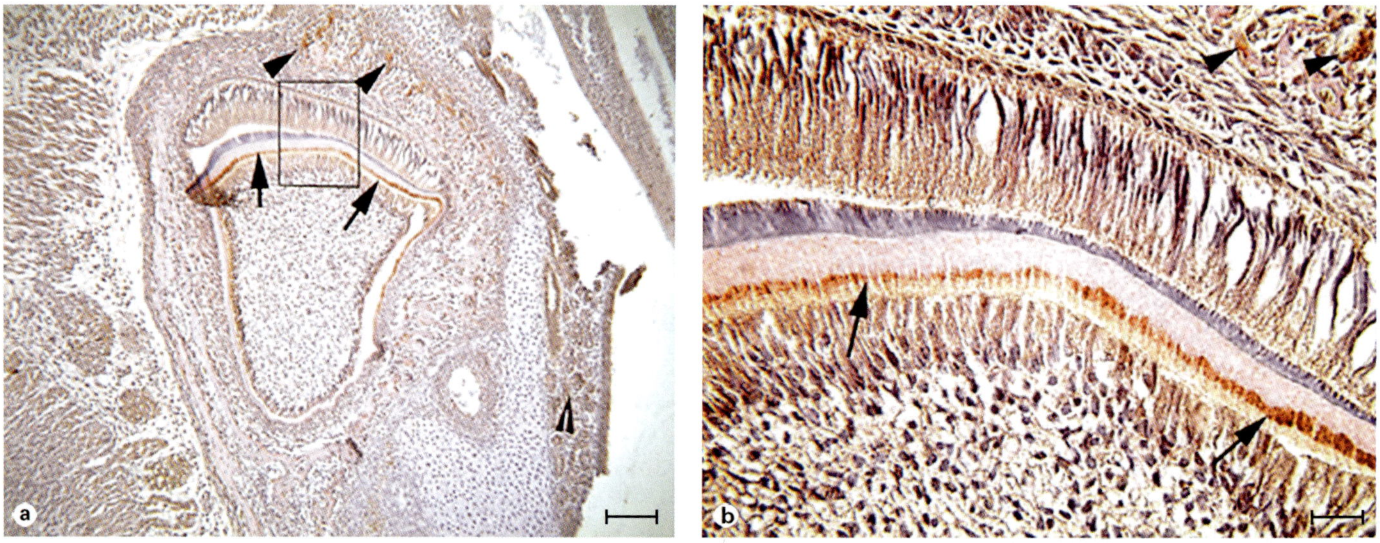

Fig. 6. Localization of PP in 5-day-old mouse incisor. PP was localized at the mineralization front and in the odontoblast cells. Arrows point to the mineralization front in dentin and the surrounding bone matrix. Arrowheads denote alveolar bone. Scale bars = 200 μm (**a**), 20 μm (**b**).

carboxylate and phosphate groups on both edges of the chain. Such a specific structured and spatial arrangement creates areas of high negative charge density and therefore could function efficiently for interaction with Ca^{2+}. The steric arrangement thus created could enhance the possibility of calcium ion bridging between parallel chains or interaction with a hydroxyapatite surface array of Ca^{2+} ions. The presence of charged groups on PP makes them good mediators of interaction with the charged crystal surfaces. Our earlier theoretical study of the possible structures within the most highly phosphorylated $(\text{-DS*S*-})_n$ domains of PP [George et al., 1998] indicated that the most probable conformation was a uniquely ribbon-like, twisting, trans-extended chain structure with repetitive arrays of carboxylate and phosphate groups on both edges of the chain. Such a specific structured spatial arrangement could function efficiently for interaction with Ca^{2+} and could enhance the possibility of calcium-ion bridging between parallel chains, or interaction with a hydroxyapatite surface array of Ca ions. At low PP concentrations, a single chain of PP could be folded by intrachain Ca^{2+} bridges, while at higher PP concentrations, Ca^{2+} ion could enhance intermolecular bridging. The addition of even millimolar concentrations of Ca^{2+} to PP was sufficient to convert PP in dilute solution from a random structure to an ordered β-sheet-like conformation [Lee and Veis, 1980; Stetler-Stevenson and Veis, 1987]. The formation of collagen fibril assembly was particularly interesting in the presence of rDMP2 and PP. In the fibrillogenesis experiments, a shortened lag phase, as seen with rDMP2, has been interpreted as indicating that more critical-sized nuclei are developed, leading to rapid growth of thinner and longer fibrils [Dimuzio and Veis, 1978]. If this is the case, then rDMP2 may have two effects: the rDMP2 may enhance the rates of fibril nucleation and growth in the axial direction, developing the 4 D overlaps leading to the 67-nm periodicity, while also enhancing the side-by-side filament association in the packing, leading to large diameter fibrils. On the contrary, the binding of the native, phosphorylated PP to type I collagen fibrils may aggregate the collagen while completely inhibiting the formation of the fibril axial periodicity. The AFM data show that rDMP2 increases the diameter of reconstituted fibrils during in vitro fibrillogenesis, while maintaining the 67-nm banding pattern. Several studies have demonstrated that PP binds specifically to type I collagen molecules [Traub et al., 1992; Dahl et al.,1998]. In fibrils, the PP appears to bind to the region of the e-band within the hole zone, and it has been argued that this might determine the mineralization site. In the physiological situation, the dentin collagen fibrils assemble and form fibrils before the PP is deposited upon them. Binding may modulate the fibril structure to a moderate extent, but, as discussed above, the main effect is to localize the initial crystal deposits. It is unlikely that PP plays any role in the initial fibril formation. However, electron microscopic analyses showed that the banding patterns of collagen fibrils varied in the mineralization front from that in the predentin zone [Beniash et al., 2000].

Immunolocalization data were particularly interesting and suggest multiple functional roles for PP in dentinogenesis. In dentin, the protein was localized at the mineralization front in the matrix. The presence of PP in ameloblasts might suggest other unidentified functions of PP in ameloblast differentiation and synthesis of enamel matrix.

Overall, PP might function as an important macromolecule during dentin formation. Biological fluids are metastable with respect to calcium phosphate, i.e. they are below the saturation needed for spontaneous precipitation but are well above the saturation to support crystal growth after the initial nucleus has formed [Eanes et al., 1965]. Therefore, a driving force is required to overcome the energy barrier of formation for the existence of thermodynamically stable hydroxyapatite crystals. A biological template with epitaxial match to the crystal surface could provide such a driving force. In the case of PP, calcium-mediated self-assembly of extended $(DS^*S^*)_n$/ $(DS^*)_m$ chain (S* represents phosphoserine) forms a periodic polyelectrolyte template presenting a well-spaced array of carboxyl and phosphate groups, with potential epitaxial match to the apatite surface, thereby facilitating apatite crystallization [Dahlin et al., 1998].

Acknowledgements

This work was supported by National Institutes of Health grant DE 13836. We wish to acknowledge the help of Dr. Gen He with the fibrillogenesis experiment and Dr. James Malone with the molecular modeling.

References

Addadi, L., H. Moradian-Oldak, H.I. Furedi-Milhofer, S. Weiner, A. Veis (1992) Stereochemical aspects of crystal regulation in calcium phosphate-associated mineralized tissues; in Slavkin, H., P. Price (eds): Chemistry and Biology of Mineralized Tissues. New York, Excerpta Medica, pp 153–162.

Beniash, E., W. Traub, A. Veis, S. Weiner (2000) A transmission electron microscope study using vitrified ice sections of predentin: structural changes in the dentin collagenous matrix prior to mineralization. J Struct Biol *132:* 212–225.

Cocking-Johnson, D., J.J. Sauk (1983) The interaction of bovine dentin phosphophoryn and collagen during fibrillogenesis of collagen in vitro. Biochim Biophys Acta *742:* 49–53.

Dahl, T., B. Sabsay, A. Veis (1998) Type I collagen-phosphophoryn interactions: specificity of the monomer-monomer binding. J Struct Biol *123:* 162–168.

Dahl, T., A. Veis (2003) Electrostatic interactions lead to the formation of asymmetric collagen-phosphophoryn aggregates. Connect Tissue Res *44(suppl 1):* 206–213.

Dahlin, S., J. Angstrom, A. Linde (1998) Dentin phosphoprotein sequence motifs and molecular modeling: conformational adaptations to mineral crystals. Eur J Oral Sci *106(suppl 1):* 239–248.

Dimuzio, M.T., A. Veis (1978) The biosynthesis of phosphophoryns and dentin collagen in the continuously erupting rat incisor. Calcif Tissue Res *25:* 169–178.

Doniach, S. (2001) Changes in biomolecular conformation seen by small angle X-ray scattering. Chem Rev *101:* 1763–1778.

Eanes, E.D., I.H. Gillessen, A.S. Posner (1965) Intermediate states in the precipitation of hydroxyapatite. Nature *208:* 365–367.

Feng, J.Q., X. Luan, J. Wallace, D. Jing, T. Ohshima, A.B. Kulkarni, R.N. D'Souza, C.A. Kozak, M. Macdougall (1998) Genomic organization, chromosomal mapping, and promoter analysis of the mouse dentin sialophosphoprotein (Dspp) gene, which codes for both dentin sialoprotein and dentin phosphoprotein. J Biol Chem *273:* 9457–9464.

George, A., L. Bannon, B. Sabsay, J.W. Dillon, J. Malone, A. Veis (1996) The carboxyl terminal domain of phosphophoryn contains unique extended triplet amino acid repeat sequences forming ordered carboxyl-phosphate interaction ridges that may be essential in the biomineralization process. J Biol Chem *271:* 32869–32873.

George, A., R. Srinivasan, S. Thotakura, A. Veis (1998) The phosphophoryn gene family: identical domain structures at the carboxyl end. Eur J Oral Sci *106:* 221–226.

He, G., T. Dahl, A. Veis, A. George (2003) Nucleation of apatite crystals in vitro by self-assembled dentin matrix protein 1. Nat Mater *2:* 552–558.

He, G., A. George (2004) Dentin matrix protein 1 immobilized on type I collagen fibrils facilitates apatite deposition in vitro. J Biol Chem *279:* 11649–11656.

He, G., A. Ramachandran, T. Dahl, S. George, D. Shultz, D. Cookson, A. Veis, A. George (2005) Phosphorylation of phosphophoryn is crucial for its function as a mediator of biomineralization. J Biol Chem *280:* 33109–33114.

Hunter, G.K., P.V. Hauschka, A.R. Poole, L.C. Rosenberg, H.A. Goldberg (1996) Nucleation and inhibition of hydroxyapatite formation by mineralized tissue proteins. Biochem J *317:* 59–64.

Kataoka, M., Y. Goto (1996) X-ray solution scattering studies of protein folding. Folding Des *1:* R107–R114.

Koch, M.H., P. Vachette, D.I. Svergun (2003) Small angle scattering: a view on the properties, structures and structural changes of biological macromolecules in solution. Q Rev Biophys *36:* 147–227.

Landis, W.J., K.J. Hodgens, J. Arena, M.J. Song, B.F. McEwen (1996) Structural relations between collagen and mineral in bone as determined by high voltage electron microscopic tomography. Microsc Res Tech *33:* 192–202.

Lee, S.L., A. Veis (1980) Cooperativity in calcium ion binding to repetitive, carboxylate-seryl-phosphate polypeptides and the relationship of this property to dentin mineralization. Int J Pept Protein Res *16:* 231–240.

Lowenstam, H.A., S. Weiner (1989) On Biomineralization. New York, Oxford University Press.

Paine, M.L., W. Luo, H.J. Wang, P. Bringas, Jr., A.Y. Ngan, V.G. Miklus, D.H. Zhu, M. MacDougall, S.N. White, M.L. Snead (2005) Dentin sialoprotein and dentin phosphoprotein overexpression during amelogenesis. J Biol Chem *280:* 31991–31998.

Rabie, A.M., A. Veis (1995) An immunocytochemical study of the routes of secretion of collagen and phosphophoryn from odontoblast. Connect Tissue Res *31:* 197–209.

Rahima, M., A. Veis (1988) Two classes of dentin phosphophoryns, from a wide range of species, contain immunologically cross-reactive epitope regions. Calcif Tissue Int *42:* 104–112.

Sabsay, B., W.G. Stetler-Stevenson, J.H. Lechner, A. Veis (1991) Domain structure and sequence distribution in dentin phosphophoryn. Biochem J *276:* 699–707.

Saito, T., M. Yamauchi, Y. Abiko, K. Matsuda, M.A. Crenshaw (2000) In vitro apatite induction by phosphophoryn immobilized on modified collagen fibrils. J Bone Miner Res *15:* 1615–1619.

Semisotnov, G.V., H. Kihara, N.V. Kotova, K. Kimura, Y. Amemiya, K. Wakabayashi, I.N. Serdyuk, A.A. Timchenko, K. Chiba, K. Nikaido, T. Ikura, K. Kuwajima (1996) Protein globularization during folding. A study by synchrotron small-angle X-ray scattering. J Mol Biol *262:* 559–574.

Stetler-Stevenson, W.G., A. Veis (1983) Bovine dentin phosphophoryn: composition and molecular weight. Biochemistry *22:* 4326–4335.

Stetler-Stevenson, W.G., A. Veis (1986) Type I collagen shows a specific binding affinity for bovine dentin phosphophoryn. Calcif Tissue Int *38:* 135–141.

Stetler-Stevenson, W.G., A. Veis (1987) Bovine dentin phosphophoryn: calcium ion binding properties of a high molecular weight preparation. Calcif Tissue Int *40:* 97–102.

Svergun, D.L., M.V. Petoukhov, M.H.J. Koch (2001) Determination of domain structure of proteins from X-ray solution scattering. Biophys J *80:* 2946–2953.

Traub, W., A. Jodaikin, T. Arad, A. Veis, B. Sabsay (1992) Dentin phosphophoryn binding to collagen fibrils. Matrix *12:* 197–201.

Vachette, P., M.H. Koch, D.I. Svergun (2003) Looking behind the beamstop: X-ray solution scattering studies of structure and conformational changes of biological macromolecules. Methods Enzymol *374:* 584–615.

Veis, A. (1988) Phosphoproteins from teeth and bone. Ciba Found Symp *136:* 161–177.

Veis, A., K. Payne (1988) Collagen fibrillogenesis; in Nimni, M. (ed): Collagen: Chemistry, Biology and Biotechnology. Boca Raton, CRC Press, pp 113–137.

Veis, A., C. Sfeir, C.B. Wu (1997) Phosphorylation of the proteins of the extracellular matrix of mineralized tissues by casein kinase-like activity. Crit Rev Oral Biol Med *8:* 360–379.

Volkov, V.V., D.I. Svergun (2003) Uniqueness of ab initio shape determination in small-angle scattering. J Appl Crystallogr *36:* 860–864.

Cells
Tissues
Organs

Cells Tissues Organs 2005;181:241–247
DOI: 10.1159/000091385

Differential Regulation of Dentin Matrix Protein 1 Expression during Odontogenesis

Yongbo Lu Shubin Zhang Yixia Xie Yuli Pi Jian Q. Feng

Department of Oral Biology, School of Dentistry, University of Missouri-Kansas City, Kansas City, Mo., USA

Key Words
Dentin matrix protein 1 · Transgenic mice · Tooth development

Abstract
Dentin matrix protein 1 (DMP1) is highly expressed in mineralized tooth and bone. Both in vitro and in vivo data show that DMP1 is critical for mineralization and tooth morphogenesis (growth and development). In this study, we studied *Dmp1* gene regulation. The in vitro transient transfection assay identified two important DNA fragments, the 2.4- and 9.6-kb promoter regions. We next generated and analyzed transgenic mice bearing the β-galactosidase (lacZ) reporter gene driven by the 2.4- or 9.6-kb promoter with the complete 4-kb intron 1. The 9.6-kb *Dmp1*-lacZ mice conferred a DMP1 expression pattern in odontoblasts identical to that in the endogenous *Dmp1* gene. This is reflected by lacZ expression in *Dmp1*-lacZ knock-in mice during all stages of odontogenesis. In contrast, the 2.4-kb *Dmp1*-lacZ mice display activity in odontoblast cells only at the early stage of odontogenesis. Thus, we propose that different transcription factors regulate early or later *cis*-regulatory domains of the *Dmp1* promoter, which gives rise to the unique spatial and temporal expression pattern of *Dmp1* gene at different stages of tooth development.

Introduction

Dentin matrix protein 1 (DMP1), an acidic matrix protein, is a member of the SIBLING (small integrin-binding ligand N-linked glycoprotein) family which is the result of duplication and subsequent divergent evolution of a single ancient gene. These proteins often function by bridging two proteins of fixed structures into a biologically active complex, which also includes bone sialoprotein, dentin sialophosphoprotein, osteopontin, and matrix extracellular phosphoglycoprotein [Fisher et al., 2001; Fisher and Fedarko, 2003]. The members of this SIBLING family share some similar genomic structures and biochemical features, such as the presence of relatively large amounts of sialic acid and phosphate and the Arg-Gly-Asp cell attachment motif.

DMP1 was first identified in odontoblasts [George et al., 1994] and later detected in a number of mineralized

Abbreviations used in this paper

DMP1	dentin matrix protein 1
KO	knockout
PBS	phosphate-buffered saline
PCR	polymerase chain reaction
pRL-TK	thymidine kinase promoter-Renilla luciferase
SIBLING	small integrin-binding ligand N-linked glycoprotein

KARGER
Fax +41 61 306 12 34
E-Mail karger@karger.ch
www.karger.com

Accessible online at:
www.karger.com/cto

Jian Q. Feng, MD, PhD
Department of Oral Biology, University of Missouri-Kansas City
650 E. 25th St.
Kansas City, MO 64108 (USA)
Tel. +1 816 235 5824, Fax +1 816 235 5524, E-Mail fengj@umkc.edu

tissue-associated cell types, including osteocytes, osteoblasts, hypertrophic chondrocytes, and cementoblasts [Toyosawa et al., 2001; Feng et al., 2002]. Recently, DMP1 was also detected in many non-mineralized tissues such as brain [Hirst et al., 1997], human lung cancer [Chaplet et al., 2003], tumors causing oncogenic osteomalacia [Toyosawa et al., 2004], kidneys [Terasawa et al., 2004], and salivaries [Ogbureke and Fisher, 2004].

In vitro studies suggest that DMP1 may act as a transcriptional factor [Narayanan et al., 2001, 2003] and that specific fragments of DMP1 may act either as mineral nucleators or inhibitors depending on their size and extent of phosphorylation [He et al., 2003; Tartaix et al., 2004]. Interestingly, although full-length DMP1 has been cloned and sequenced, the corresponding intact protein has not been isolated from mineralized tissues. However, two proteolytic fragments, a 37-kDa N-terminal fragment and a 57-kDa C-terminal fragment, have been isolated from bone and dentin extracts [Qin et al., 2003], suggesting that these may be the bioactive forms in vivo.

To determine the in vivo role of DMP1 in odontogenesis, we have cloned and sequenced the *Dmp1* gene [Feng et al., 2000] and have generated *Dmp1* knockout (KO) mice [Feng et al., 2003]. Our initial studies show that *Dmp1* KO mice develop a profound tooth phenotype characterized by enlarged pulp chambers, increased width of the predentin zone and hypomineralization, suggesting that DMP1 is critical for normal odontogenesis [Ye et al., 2004]. The tooth phenotype of these mice is strikingly similar to that in dentin sialophosphoprotein KO mice [Sreenath et al., 2003] and shares some features of human dentinogenesis imperfecta III. Furthermore, *Dmp1* KO mice display severe defects in the skeleton, responsible for a chondrodysplasia-like phenotype [Ye et al., 2005] and abnormalities of mineralization [Ling et al., 2005].

Because DMP1 is essential for development and mineralization, it is critical to identify the mechanisms underlying the pattern of the temporal and spatial expression of *Dmp1* during tooth development. The purpose of this study was to search for the regulatory elements that control DMP1 spatial and temporal expression during tooth development. With both the in vitro and in vivo promoter study approaches plus *Dmp1*-lacZ knock-in mice where the *Dmp1* gene is replaced with a lacZ (β-galactosidase) reporter gene, we have identified a region between the first intron and the –2.4 kb of the murine *Dmp1* gene that control its expression in early odontogenesis. We have also demonstrated that regions controlling expression of *Dmp1* in the early stage are different from those controlling its expression in the later stage of odontogenesis. This study will advance sciences in future identification of transcriptional factors that are involved in *Dmp1* regulation.

Materials and Methods

Isolation of Bacterial Artificial Chromosome Clones Containing the Dmp1 *Gene*

Bacterial artificial chromosome clones that contained approximately 250 kb *Dmp1* genomic DNA were isolated from a 129 SV mouse genomic library (Strategene, La Jolla, Calif., USA). Three clones were obtained and hosted in bacterium. One of the clones contained the *Dmp1* gene and approximately 11 kb of upstream and 70 kb of downstream flanking sequences, which was used for subcloning the *Dmp1* promoter.

Construction of Dmp1 *Promoter Reporter Constructs*

The *Dmp1* 10-kb *Eco*RI fragment, spanning from –7,892 to 2,207 bp, was released from the bacterial artificial chromosome clone and subcloned into the *Eco*RI site of the pBluescript SK– vector (Stratagene), designated pSK10. The 3′ part of *Dmp1* intron 1 was obtained by polymerase chain reaction (PCR), using the following primers: forward primer: 5′-(+2,023)TAGGGCAGTGACTTCTGAGCA(+2,043)-3′; reverse primer: 5′-(+4,439)GGATGCGATTCCTCTACCTGT(+4,419)-3′, which spans the junction of *Dmp1* intron 1 and exon 2, including 4 bp of intron 1 and the 17-bp noncoding region of exon 2. The amplified 2,216-bp PCR fragment was subsequently cloned into the *Eco*RV site of the pBluescript SK– vector, designated pSK2. The 3′ part of the *Dmp1* 10-kb *Eco*RI fragment has a 181-bp sequence, which overlaps with the 5′ part of the 2,216-bp PCR fragment. The 10-kb *Eco*RI fragment was further released from the pSK10 and religated to the 3′ part of *Dmp1* intron 1 by upstream cloning after cutting the pSK2 with *Eco*RI, giving rise to the 12-kb DMP1 regulatory sequence, designated as pSK12. For cloning purpose, we also cloned the *Dmp1* 12-kb *Swa*I and *Hpa*I fragment, spanning from –9,624 to 1,996 bp, into the *Eco*RV site of the pBluescript vector, designated pSK512. Using pSK12 and pSK512, we generated the following four promoter constructs: (1) –9,624 bp of the 5′ flanking region, exon 1, and 4,439 bp of intron 1 (14 kb); (2) –7,892 to 4,439 bp; (3) –4,975 to 4,439 bp; (4) –2,433 to 4,439 bp. All four constructs were ligated to the pGL3 basic luciferase plasmid (Promega) with the 95-bp exon 1, the 4,326-bp intron 1, and the 17-bp initial noncoding region of exon 2, as well as various lengths of promoter regions. These promoter constructs were confirmed by a combination of restriction enzyme digestions and DNA sequencing.

Cell Culture, Transient Transfection and Luciferase Reporter Assays

The 2T3 cell line, derived from transgenic mice expressing SV40 large T antigen under the control of the osteocalcin promoter (a gift from S.E. Harris, University of Texas Health Science Center, San Antonio, Tex., USA), was maintained in α-MEM, supplemented with 10% FBS, and 100 IU/ml penicillin, 100 μg/ml streptomycin.

Cells were transfected using Lipofectamine Plus reagents (Invitrogen) according to the manufacturer's recommendations. *Dmp1* promoter luciferase reporter constructs (0.2 μg) or pGL3 basic vector cotransfected with 0.015 μg thymidine kinase promoter-Renilla luciferase (pRL-TK) plasmid as an internal control into 2T3 cells. Cells were harvested and lysed 48 hours after transfection in reporter lysis buffer (Promega) and assayed for luciferase activity using a dual luciferase assay system (Promega). All firefly luciferase values were normalized for transfection efficiency against the Renilla luciferase activities from the cotransfected pRL-TK plasmid. Each assay was performed in triplicate. Values are expressed as the ratio of firefly luciferase activity to Renilla luciferase activity.

Generation of Dmp1*-lacZ Transgenic Mice*

For the production of *Dmp1*-lacZ transgenic mice, the double-purified 18-kb *Dmp1* DNA fragment, containing a –9,624-bp promoter sequence, a 95-bp exon 1, a 4,326-bp intron 1, a 17-bp initial noncoding region of exon 2, a nucleus signaling peptide, lacZ reporter gene, and SV40 poly A, was microinjected into fertilized CD1 eggs at a DNA concentration of 3 ng/μl. Surviving eggs were transferred into the oviducts of pseudopregnant CD1-recipient mice to obtain transgenic mice expressing the lacZ gene. Tail DNA was isolated to screen transgenic mice by using PCR analysis (described below). The transgenic lines were maintained on CD1 background. Totally 12 independent lines were obtained and two of them were tested for β-galactosidase staining and showed a similar expression pattern. The 2.4-kb *Dmp1*-lacZ transgenic mice were generated, as reported previously [Yang et al., 2005]. The animal use protocol was reviewed and approved by the Institutional Animal Care and Use Committee of the University of Missouri at Kansas City.

Tail PCR Genotyping

The genotype of embryos or pups was determined by PCR analysis of genomic DNA extracted from tail DNA. For *Dmp1*-LacZ transgenic mice, the forward primer (5′-ACCTGGCTTCTTTTTAACCTG-3′) and the reverse primer (5′-GGCAATATCGCGGCTCAGTTC-3′) were used and given rise to a 364-bp PCR product. For the DMP1-lacZ knock-in mice, the forward primer (5′CTTGACTTCAGGCAAATAGTGACC3′) and the reverse primer (5′-GCGGAATTCGATAGCTTGGCTG-3′) were used and given rise to a PCR product of 280 bp.

Escherichia coli *β-Galactosidase Assay*

Tooth samples were dissected and washed in cold phosphate-buffered salilne (PBS), and fixed in 4% paraformaldehyde on ice for 30 min to 1 h. The samples were then washed three times with PBS for 15–30 min each, cryoprotected in 15% sucrose in PBS at 4°C until they sank to the bottom, and then in 30% sucrose in PBS overnight at 4°C. They were then embedded in Tissue-Tek OCT (Sakura) at –60°C. Blocks were cryosectioned at 10–12 μm, collected onto positively charged slides (Shandon Microscope Slides Superfrost® Plus), and dried for 2–4 h at room temperature. For newborn, postnatal day 3, day 10, and day 30 mice, the tissue samples were decalcified in 10% EDTA, pH 7.2–7.4, at 4°C for 2–7 days after fixation and then processed for frozen section.

β-Galactosidase staining was performed in embryos and pups according to the method described previously [Feng et al., 2003]. Briefly, the slides were shortly washed in PBS and then stained at 37°C overnight (12–16 h) in freshly prepared lacZ staining solution containing 0.02% NP-40, 0.01% sodium deoxycholate, 10 m*M* Tris (pH 8.0), 2 m*M* magnesium chloride, 5 m*M* potassium ferricyanide, 5 m*M* potassium ferrocyanide, and 0.5 mg/ml X-Gal (Gold BioTechnology, Inc.) in PBS, protected from light. When the staining was completed, the slides were washed extensively in PBS, followed by counterstaining with hematoxylin/eosin, mounted with permount, and photographed under light microscope (Nikon).

Results

Analyses of Dmp1 *Promoter Activity in vitro*

To dissect DNA fragments which control *Dmp1* expression, we first examined the promoter activity of the *Dmp1* genomic DNA with various lengths of promoter-luciferase gene constructs – 10-kb luc, 8-kb luc, 5-kb luc, and 2.4-kb luc – in the 2T3 cell, a preosteoblastic cell line (fig. 1A). All these constructs contain 95-bp exon 1, 4,326-bp intron 1, and a 17-bp noncoding region of exon 2. The transient transfection assay showed a sharp increase in luciferase activity from the 10-kb promoter construct compared with the rest of promoter constructs which displayed relative low luciferase activity (fig. 1B). These transient transfection experiments defined the region, between –9,624 and –7,892 bp, as a potential enhancer for *Dmp1* promoter activity. However, when this region was linked to a heterologous minimal β-globin promoter, it did not enhance β-globin promoter activity (data not shown). This suggests that this enhancer is likely specific for *Dmp1* promoter.

The 2.4-kb Murine Dmp1 *Promoter Is Active in Early Odontogenesis*

To identify promoter regions controlling *Dmp1* expression at different developmental stages during odontogenesis, we selected two promoter fragments for generation of lacZ transgenic mice based on the above in vitro data. The short promoter fragment (from –2,433 to 4,439 bp) was generated first and used for other purposes [Yang et al., 2005]. In this study, we analyzed lacZ expression in transgenic mice harboring the 2.4-kb promoter (*Dmp1*-lacZ$^{2.4P}$) compared with the endogenous *Dmp1* expression patter. Here, we used *Dmp1*-lacZ knock-in mice as controls for two reasons: (1) the same lacZ reporter is used for either lacZ transgenic mice or *Dmp1*-lacZ knock-in mice, and (2) in the lacZ knock-in mice, the endogenous *Dmp1* is replaced by lacZ whose expression precisely reflects the endogenous *Dmp1* expression pattern [Feng et al., 2003].

At E15.5, there were no apparent lacZ signals in either the *Dmp1*-lacZ$^{2.4P}$ (fig. 2A, left panels) or *Dmp1*-lacZ knock-in control (fig. 2A, right panels). At E18.5, the lacZ signal was detected in odontoblasts from the first molar

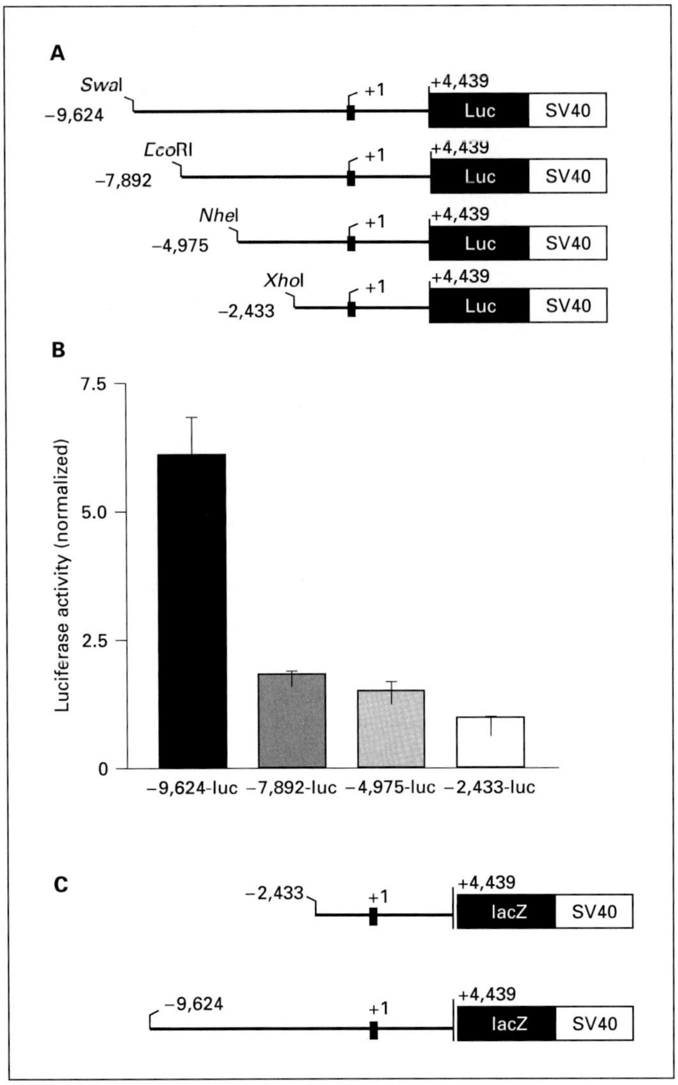

Fig. 1. Schematic presentation of the *Dmp1* promoter fragments used for promoter studies in vitro and in vivo. **A** Diagrams of four *Dmp1* gene regions were fused to the firefly luciferase (Luc) reporter. **B** Values of luciferase driven by four *Dmp1* promoter fragments (−9,624 to 4,439, −7,892 to 4,439, −4,975 to 4,439, and −2,433 to 4,439) were normalized by pRL-TK renilla luciferase activity. Data are expressed as means ± standard errors of three independent experiments. **C** Diagrams of two *Dmp1* gene regions fused to the lacZ reporter. The 2.4-kb lacZ transgene has been reported previously [Yang et al., 2005], and the 9.6-kb lacZ transgene was used for generation of transgenic mice in the present study.

in both embryos (fig. 2B). The same expression pattern was also shown at the neonate stage (fig. 2C). By day 3 after birth, the lacZ signal was stronger with a similar expression pattern in both animals, suggesting that the 2.4-kb *Dmp1* promoter fragment contains controlling domains for *Dmp1* expression during the early stages of odontogenesis (fig. 3A). However, by day 10, the lacZ signal was sharply reduced in the *Dmp1*-lacZ$^{2.4P}$ mice (fig. 3B, arrows, left panels) compared with the *Dmp1*-lacZ knock-in mice (fig. 3B, right panels). By day 30, there were no lacZ signals at all in the *Dmp1*-lacZ$^{2.4P}$ mice (fig. 3C) compared with the *Dmp1*-lacZ knock-in mice (fig. 3C, right panels). Taken together, these results show that the 2.4-kb *Dmp1* promoter fragment contains a basic control domain for *Dmp1* expression at early stages of odontogenesis but not at later developmental stages.

The Dmp1 *Promoter Region between −9.6 and −2.4 kb Contains the Control Domains for* Dmp1 *Expression at Later Odontogenesis*

To further define the DNA regions that are responsible for the *Dmp1* expression in later odontogenesis, we generated transgenic mice harboring the 9.6-kb *Dmp1* promoter-lacZ, containing the intron 1, exon 1, and the 9.6-kb promoter fragment with a total size of approximately 14 kb (*Dmp1*-lacZ$^{9.6P}$) (fig. 1C). This transgenic mouse displayed a similar early expression pattern as in the *Dmp1*-lacZ$^{2.4P}$ and *Dmp1*-lacZ knock-in mice (data not shown). By day 3, there is a very similar expression pattern between the *Dmp1*-lacZ$^{2.4P}$ and *Dmp1*-lacZ$^{9.6P}$ mice (fig. 3A, 4A). However, by days 10 and 30, the *Dmp1*-lacZ$^{9.6P}$ showed a later expression pattern similar to the endogenous *Dmp1*-lacZ knock-in mice (fig. 4B, C); in contrast, the *Dmp1*-lacZ$^{2.4P}$ is largely silent (fig. 3). This suggests that the region between −9.6 and −2.4 kb contains the control domains for *Dmp1* expression in later odontogenesis.

Discussion

In the present study, we compared promoter activity of four *Dmp1*-luc fragments using transient transfection assay. These constructs were designed based on the hypothesis that the major *cis*-regulatory regions specific for *Dmp1* expression in odontoblast cells would be found in one or all of these DNA regions. This in vitro study demonstrates that the 2.4-kb DNA fragment contains a basic promoter activity.

Previously, we showed that the 2.4-kb promoter is highly conservative between the mouse and human [Yang et al., 2005]. Here, we demonstrate that this fragment is sufficient to drive expression of an exogenous reporter gene (lacZ) in the odontoblast layer during embryo and neonate stages using a transgenic approach (fig. 2). This

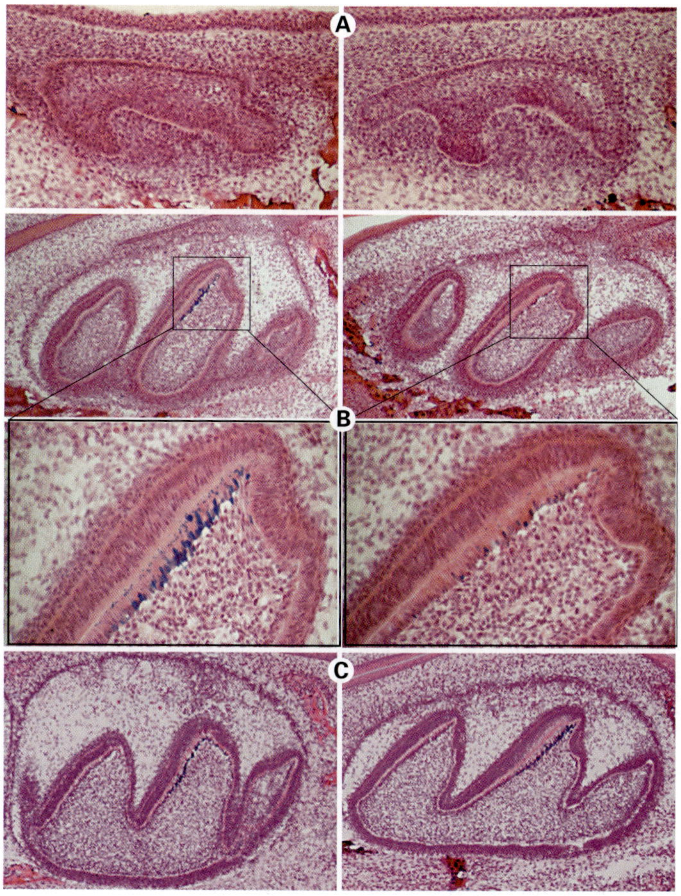

Fig. 2. The *Dmp1*-lac$Z^{2.4P}$ (left panels) shows a similar expression pattern of lacZ in odontoblast cells as in *Dmp1*-lacZ knock-in mice (right panels) during early odontogenesis. Series of frozen sections of the first molar from E15.5 (**A**), E18.5 (**B**), and neonate (**C**) were stained with β-galactosidase and counterstained with hematoxylin/eosin.

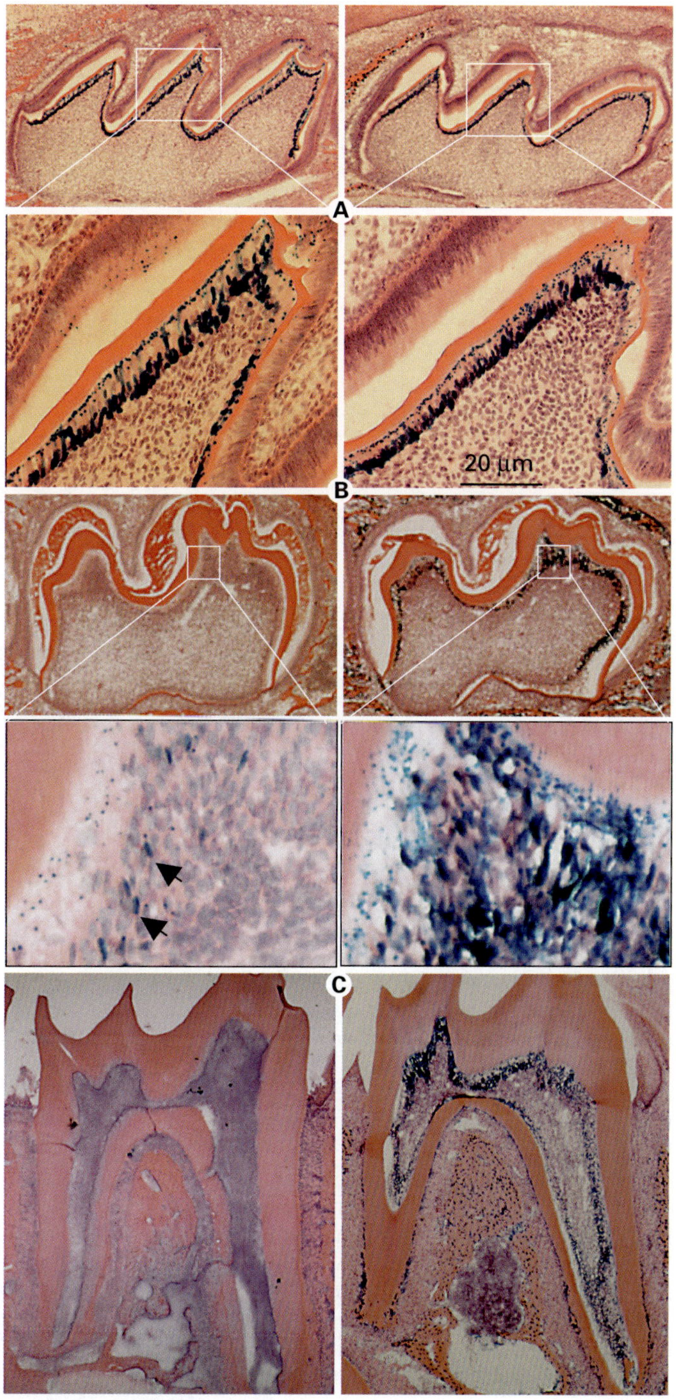

Fig. 3. The *Dmp1*-lac$Z^{2.4P}$ pups display little or no lacZ expression during later odontogenesis. Series of decalcified sections of the first molar from postnatal day 3 (**A**), day 10 (**B**), and day 30 (**C**) were stained with β-galactosidase and counterstained with hematoxylin/eosin. By day 10, the lacZ signal was sharply reduced in the *Dmp1*-lac$Z^{2.4P}$ mice (arrows). The *Dmp1*-lac$Z^{2.4P}$ is shown in the left panels, and the *Dmp1*-lacZ knock-in in the right panels.

expression pattern is similar to that of the endogenous *Dmp1* expression as determined by lacZ expression in *Dmp1*-lacZ knock-in mice. However, by day 10, the activity of this promoter fragment is dramatically reduced (fig. 3B). By day 30, the promoter is completely silent (fig. 3C). This suggests that the region controlling *Dmp1* expression in later stages of odontogenesis is located in other promoter areas, and those transcriptional factors, which were activated at the early stage, are no longer active in the later stage of odontogenesis.

In search for the region controlling *Dmp1* expression in later stages of odontogenesis, we generated the transgenic mice harboring the 9.6-kb lacZ reporter, as this DNA fragment is 7 kb longer and has higher promoter activity in vitro (fig. 1). As shown in figure 4, this DNA

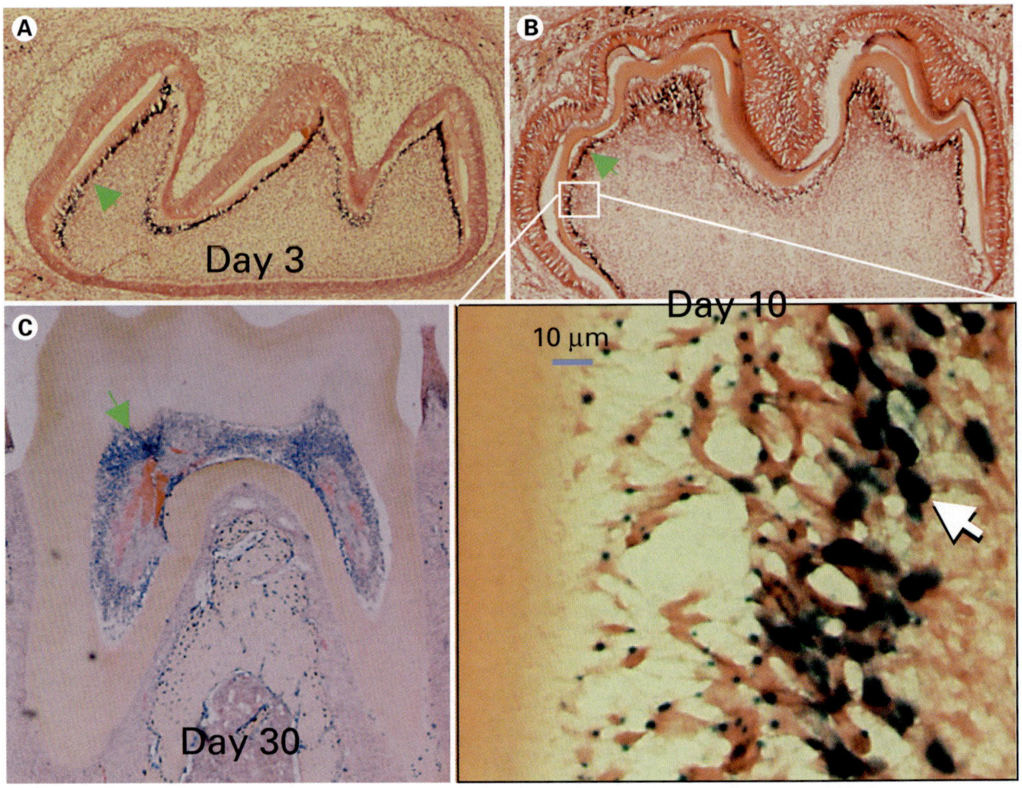

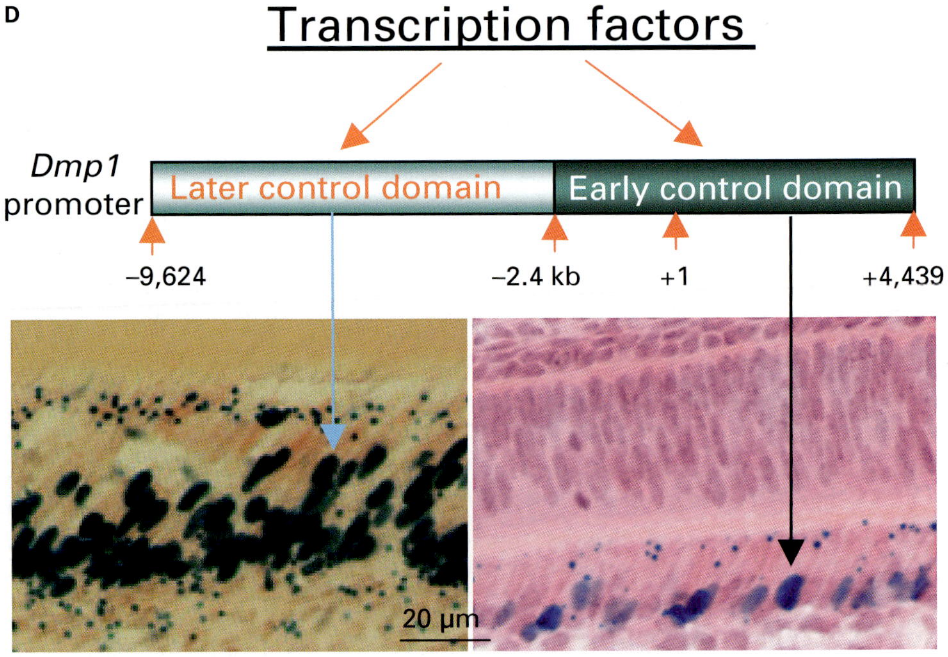

Fig. 4. The *Dmp1*-lac$Z^{9.6P}$ pups display a lacZ expression pattern identical to that in the *Dmp1*-lacZ knock-in pups during later odontogenesis. Series of decalcified sections of the first molar from postnatal day 3 (**A**), day 10 (**B**), and day 30 (**C**) were stained with β-galactosidase and counterstained with hematoxylin/eosin. A working hypothesis is presented in **D**. In this model, transcriptional factors for early and later odontogenesis are likely different. Some of them may act on the early control domain in the 2.4-kb region and the others may act on the later control domain for regulating *Dmp1* expression in later odontogenesis. The representative E18.5 incisor section stained with β-galactosidase was from the *Dmp1*-lac$Z^{2.4P}$ (right lower panel), and the day 30 incisor was from the *Dmp1*-lac$Z^{9.6P}$ (left lower panel).

fragment is sufficient to drive expression of lacZ in odontoblast cells in later stages of odontogenesis, whose expression pattern is identical to that of endogenous *Dmp1* expression as determined by lacZ expression in *Dmp1*-lacZ knock-in mice.

Taken together, we have identified two control domains (the 2.4-kb basic promoter fragment and the DNA fragment between –2.4 and –9.6 kb) for *Dmp1* expression in odontoblast cells – the proximal one at the early stage and the distal one at the later stage of odontogenesis. This finding suggests that transcriptional factors, which control *Dmp1* promoter activity, may not be the same during different stages of odontogenesis. Therefore, we propose that different transcriptional factors, which target on different regions of the *Dmp1* promoter, may activate at different developmental stages during odontogenesis (see fig. 4D for hypothesis). We believe that the current study may aid in the understanding of the control machinery for tooth morphogenesis during development.

Acknowledgments

Support for this research was provided by grants DE00455 and AR51587 (to J.Q.F.) from the National Institutes of Health. Y.L. is recipient of Dean's Fellowship, University of Missouri-Kansas City.

References

Chaplet, M., L. De Leval, D. Waltregny, C. Detry, G. Fornaciari, G. Bevilacqua, L.W. Fisher, V. Castronovo, A. Bellahcene (2003) Dentin matrix protein 1 is expressed in human lung cancer. J Bone Miner Res *18:* 1506–1512.

Feng, J.Q., H. Huang, Y. Lu, L. Ye, Y. Xie, T.W. Tsutsui, T. Kunieda, T. Castranio, G. Scott, L.B. Bonewald, Y. Mishina (2003) The Dentin matrix protein 1 (Dmp1) is specifically expressed in mineralized, but not soft, tissues during development. J Dent Res *82:* 776–780.

Feng, J., X. Li, S.E. Harris, J. Dai, M. MacDougall (2000) Genomic organization, and promoter analysis of mouse dentin matrix protein-1 (Dmp-1) gene in osteoblasts and odontoblast cell lines. J Am Acad Orthop Surg *8(suppl):* 155–159.

Feng, J.Q., J. Zhang, S.L. Dallas, Y. Lu, S. Chen, X. Tan, M. Owen, S.E. Harris, M. MacDougall (2002) Dentin matrix protein 1, a target molecule for Cbfa1 in bone, is a unique bone marker gene. J Bone Miner Res *17:* 1822–1831.

Fisher, L.W., N.S. Fedarko (2003) Six genes expressed in bones and teeth encode the current members of the SIBLING family of proteins. Connect Tissue Res *44(suppl 1):* 33–40.

Fisher, L.W., D.A. Torchia, B. Fohr, M.F. Young, N.S. Fedarko (2001) Flexible structures of SIBLING proteins, bone sialoprotein, and osteopontin. Biochem Biophys Res Commun *280:* 460–465.

George, A., J. Gui, N.A. Jenkins, D.J. Gilbert, N.G. Copeland, A. Veis (1994) In situ localization and chromosomal mapping of the AG1 (Dmp1) gene. J Histochem Cytochem *42:* 1527–1531.

He, G., T. Dahl, A. Veis, A. George (2003) Dentin matrix protein 1 initiates hydroxyapatite formation in vitro. Connect Tissue Res *44(suppl 1):* 240–245.

Hirst, K.L., K. Ibaraki-O'Connor, M.F. Young, M.J. Dixon (1997) Cloning and expression analysis of the bovine dentin matrix acidic phosphoprotein gene. J Dent Res *76:* 754–760.

Ling, Y., H.F. Rios, E.R. Myers, Y. Lu, J.Q. Feng, A.L. Boskey (2005) DMP1 depletion decreases bone mineralization in vivo: an FTIR imaging analysis. J Bone Miner Res *20:* 2169–2177.

Narayanan, K., A. Ramachandran, J. Hao, G. He, K.W. Park, M. Cho, A. George (2003) Dual functional roles of dentin matrix protein 1. Implications in biomineralization and gene transcription by activation of intracellular Ca^{2+} store. J Biol Chem *278:* 17500–17508.

Narayanan, K., R. Srinivas, A. Ramachandran, J. Hao, B. Quinn, A. George (2001) Differentiation of embryonic mesenchymal cells to odontoblast-like cells by overexpression of dentin matrix protein 1. Proc Natl Acad Sci USA *98:* 4516–4521.

Ogbureke, K.U., L.W. Fisher (2004) Expression of SIBLINGs and their partner MMPs in salivary glands. J Dent Res *83:* 664–670.

Qin, C., J.C. Brunn, R.G. Cook, R.S. Orkiszewski, J.P. Malone, A. Veis, W.T. Butler (2003) Evidence for the proteolytic processing of dentin matrix protein 1. Identification and characterization of processed fragments and cleavage sites. J Biol Chem *278:* 34700–34708.

Sreenath, T., T. Thyagarajan, B. Hall, G. Longenecker, R. D'Souza, S. Hong, J.T. Wright, M. MacDougall, J. Sauk, A.B. Kulkarni (2003) Dentin sialophosphoprotein knockout mouse teeth display widened predentin zone and develop defective dentin mineralization similar to human dentinogenesis imperfecta type III. J Biol Chem *278:* 24874–24880.

Tartaix, P.H., M. Doulaverakis, A. George, L.W. Fisher, W.T. Butler, C. Qin, E. Salih, M. Tan, Y. Fujimoto, L. Spevak, A.L. Boskey (2004) In vitro effects of dentin matrix protein-1 on hydroxyapatite formation provide insights into in vivo functions. J Biol Chem *279:* 18115–18120.

Terasawa, M., R. Shimokawa, T. Terashima, K. Ohya, Y. Takagi, H. Shimokawa (2004) Expression of dentin matrix protein 1 (DMP1) in nonmineralized tissues. J Bone Miner Metab *22:* 430–438.

Toyosawa, S., S. Shintani, T. Fujiwara, T. Ooshima, A. Sato, N. Ijuhin, T. Komori (2001) Dentin matrix protein 1 is predominantly expressed in chicken and rat osteocytes but not in osteoblasts. J Bone Miner Res *16:* 2017–2026.

Toyosawa, S., Y. Tomita, M. Kishino, J. Hashimoto, T. Ueda, T. Tsujimura, K. Aozasa, N. Ijuhin, T. Komori (2004) Expression of dentin matrix protein 1 in tumors causing oncogenic osteomalacia. Mod Pathol *17:* 573–578.

Yang, W., Y. Lu, I. Kalajzic, D. Guo, M.A. Harris, J. Gluhak-Heinrich, S. Kotha, L.F. Bonewald, J.Q. Feng, D.W. Rowe, C.H. Turner, A.G. Robling, S.E. Harris (2005) Dentin matrix protein 1 gene *cis*-regulation: use in osteocytes to characterize local responses to mechanical loading in vitro and in vivo. J Biol Chem *280:* 20680–20690.

Ye, L., M. MacDougall, S. Zhang, Y. Xie, J. Zhang, Z. Li, Y. Lu, Y. Mishina, J.Q. Feng (2004) Deletion of dentin matrix protein-1 leads to a partial failure of maturation of predentin into dentin, hypomineralization, and expanded cavities of pulp and root canal during postnatal tooth development. J Biol Chem *279:* 19141–19148.

Ye, L., Y. Mishina, D. Chen, H. Huang, S.L. Dallas, M.R. Dallas, P. Sivakumar, T. Kunieda, T.W. Tsutsui, A. Boskey, L.F. Bonewald, J.Q. Feng (2005) Dmp1-deficient mice display severe defects in cartilage formation responsible for a chondrodysplasia-like phenotype. J Biol Chem *280:* 6197–6203.

Cells
Tissues
Organs

Cells Tissues Organs 2005;181:248–257
DOI: 10.1159/000091386

Defining the Roots of Cementum Formation

T. Popowics B.L. Foster E.C. Swanson H. Fong M.J. Somerman

Department of Oral Biology, University of Washington School of Dentistry, Seattle, Wash., USA

Key Words
Cementum · Periodontium · Bone morphogenetic protein · Amelogenins

Abstract
Significant progress has been seen in research aimed at regeneration of the disease-damaged periodontium. Our own strategy has been to approach periodontal tissue development (i.e. root, cementum, periodontal ligament, and bone) as a source for the identification of key regulators of cellular processes that may be applicable to periodontal tissue repair. Specifically, enamel-like molecules, bone morphogenetic proteins (BMPs), and phosphates have been investigated for their role in altering gene expression and cell functions in follicle cells, periodontal ligament cells, and cementoblasts. Amelogenin, leucine-rich amelogenin peptide, and tyrosine-rich amelogenin peptide have been found to similarly affect cementoblast gene expression and cementoblast-mediated mineralization in vitro; however, these enamel-like factors do not increase cell proliferation as has been observed in cells treated with Emdogain® (Biora AB, Malmö, Sweden), an enamel matrix derivative. BMP-2 has been found to promote differentiation of follicle cells into a cementoblast/osteoblast phenotype, and BMP-3 is being investigated as a negative regulator of mineralization. The increased ratio of phosphate to pyrophosphate in the local region during root development has been found to significantly enhance the extent of cementum formation in animal models. Furthermore, phosphate has been identified as a regulator of cementoblast SIBLING (small integrin-binding ligand N-linked glycoprotein) gene expression in vitro. These investigations of candidate factors for periodontal regeneration have uncovered mech-

Abbreviations used in this paper

ANK	progressive ankylosis protein
BMP	bone morphogenetic protein
BSP	bone sialoprotein
DMEM	Dulbecco's Modified Eagle Medium
DMP	dentin matrix protein
EMD	enamel matrix derivative
FBS	fetal bovine serum
HERS	Hertwig's epithelial root sheath
LRAP	leucine-rich amelogenin peptide
OCN	osteocalcin
OPN	osteopontin
PDL	periodontal ligament
P_i	inorganic phosphate
PP_i	inorganic pyrophosphate
rp(H)M180	recombinant N-terminal histidine-tagged murine amelogenin
SEM	scanning electron microscopy
SIBLING	small integrin-binding ligand N-linked glycoprotein
TNAP	tissue nonspecific alkaline phosphatase
TRAP	tyrosine-rich amelogenin protein

KARGER
Fax +41 61 306 12 34
E-Mail karger@karger.ch
www.karger.com

Accessible online at:
www.karger.com/cto

Tracy E. Popowics, PhD
Box 357132, Department of Oral Biology
University of Washington, School of Dentistry
Seattle, WA 98195 (USA)
Tel. +1 206 543 5477, Fax +1 206 685 3162, E-Mail popowics@u.washington.edu

anisms regulating gene expression and cell function in cells controlling the behavior of periodontal tissues (i.e. follicle cells, periodontal cells, and cementoblasts) and offer new directions to consider for clinical repair of periodontal defects.

Introduction

Tissue engineering targeted at oral tissues has made significant advances in past years; however, there are still many unknown biological factors in the quest toward regeneration of oral tissues, and specifically, a complete tooth with surrounding periodontium. Repair of crown tissue lost by disease has been successful, such as in the application of materials to crown areas with deep decay and pulp exposure in order to repair dentin and enamel [Goldberg and Smith, 2004]. Biomimetic approaches to crown formation have also had positive results and include miniature crown-like structures derived from the application of cells from primordial rat and pig molars to biodegradable scaffolds [Young et al., 2002; Duailibi et al., 2004]. These approaches have demonstrated regeneration of enamel, dentin, pulp, and Hertwig's epithelial root sheath (HERS), but limited or no cementum-like tissue, and no tooth roots or other periodontal tissues. Experiments recombining periodontal tissues have also demonstrated the capacity for cementum and periodontal ligament to reform [MacNeil and Thomas, 1993a, b], yet regeneration of a complete tooth, including crown, root and periodontium – cementum-periodontal ligament (PDL)-bone – remains elusive. In contrast, much greater success has been demonstrated in the repair of periodontal tissues lost by disease [Kao et al., 2005]. While not predictable, it is clear that various surgical and non-surgical procedures may result in the formation of new cementum and bone, with a functional PDL. In some situations, repair/regeneration of periodontal tissues is associated with ankylosis, i.e. fusion of surrounding bone with tooth root. For example, subsequent to pathological root resorption, caused by caries, trauma, abnormal forces associated with rapid orthodontic tooth movement, and some inflammatory diseases, ankylosis is often noted [Gunraj, 1999; Helfrich, 2005]. Promising approaches toward dental tissue regeneration include replication of normal developmental conditions, identification of progenitor cells, and design of appropriate combinations of cells, molecular factors, and scaffolds to promote tissue regrowth.

Dental Development

Understanding the cellular and molecular interactions during tooth development has served as a starting point for mimicking development during dental tissue regeneration. Crown development proceeds with a series of reciprocal inductive interactions between epithelium and mesenchyme, directing the differentiation of epithelial and mesenchymal cells to enamel-secreting ameloblasts and dentin-secreting odontoblasts, respectively. These reciprocal inductions have been found to correspond with suites of signaling molecules that are used repetitively at advancing stages of tissue differentiation to modify gene expression [Thesleff and Mikkola, 2002; Thesleff, 2003]. In the case of forming the tooth root and surrounding PDL, reciprocal interactions between epithelium (e.g., HERS or epithelial cell rests) and mesenchyme (e.g., follicle or PDL cells) are still speculative. The cervical loop grows apically during the late bell stage of crown formation, encapsulates the dental papilla, and is then called 'HERS'. Zeichner-David et al. [2003] and Yamamoto et al. [2004] have identified potential molecular signals – bone morphogenetic protein (BMP)-2, BMP-4, Msx-2 – originating from HERS cells [Zeichner-David et al., 2003; Yamamoto et al., 2004], and an Msx-2/BMP-4 interaction may be involved in regulation of root morphogenesis [Yamashiro et al., 2003]. Furthermore, HERS cells signal adjacent dental papilla cells to differentiate into dentin-secreting odontoblasts that establish the root structure [Thomas and Kollar, 1989]. The dental follicle cells bordering the HERS externally are thought to contain a cell population that has the capacity to differentiate into the periodontal cell populations, including cementoblasts, PDL fibroblasts, and osteoblasts [Gronthos et al., 2000; Seo et al., 2004]. An alternative theory suggests that HERS cells may undergo a mesenchymal transformation to become cementoblasts, and are thus responsible for acellular and potentially cellular cementum [Bosshardt and Nanci, 1997, 2004]. As the tooth erupts, acellular cementum is layered on the root surface embedding the earliest periodontal ligament fibers. Subsequently, tooth function corresponds with the addition of cellular cementum (apically) and fortification of the PDL. Improving our understanding of the regulation of periodontal cell differentiation and PDL tissue formation (i.e. roots-cementum-PDL-bone) may offer keys to regenerating tissues lost by disease or to accompany tissue-engineered tooth crowns.

Progenitor Cells

Both crown and periodontal tissues have benefited from application of progenitor cells to regenerative efforts. Recombination of bone marrow-derived stem cells with epithelial cells formed enamel, dentin, and pulp structures and further expanded the scope of cell types available for use in crown regeneration [Ohazama et al., 2004]. Dental progenitor cells offer a potential resource for dental tissues, such as epithelial cells in the cervical loop of the mouse incisor that continually produce crown (labial) or root tissue (lingual) [Harada et al., 1999], or mouse and dental pulp cells capable of regenerating a dentin-like tissue [Shi and Gronthos, 2003; Iohara et al., 2004; Shi et al., 2005]. Progenitor cells have also been identified in the PDL and are capable of cementoblast/osteoblast differentiation, as well as in vitro and in vivo secretion of bone-cementum-PDL-like tissues [Buser et al., 1990; MacNeil and Somerman, 1993; Cochran and Wozney, 1999; Saygin et al., 2000; Seo et al., 2004]. Overall, progenitor cells offer an important resource for dental tissue regeneration through manipulation of cellular differentation and tissue formation [Thesleff and Tummers, 2001], and additionally, they serve as tools to enhance our understanding of the key regulators of dental tissues during development, repair, and regeneration.

Cells, Molecular Factors, and Scaffolds

Whole tooth regeneration, i.e. tooth crowns with roots and periodontal tissues (cementum-PDL-bone), calls for the adoption of key elements of development, such as cells and signaling molecules, as well as the use of biomaterial delivery system scaffolds. Epithelial and mesenchymal cells are often used as the starting point for in vivo development of both crown and root tissues and have also been used as building blocks in crown regeneration [Young et al., 2002; Duailibi et al., 2004]. In the case of periodontal regeneration studies, dental follicle cells, HERS, cementoblasts, and periodontal ligament cells are the focus of research [Saygin et al., 2000; Bosshardt, 2005]. Because of the prominence of signaling molecules in advancing dental tissue differentiation, molecular factors have been applied in vitro and in vivo to manipulate dental tissue differentiation and promote regeneration [Saygin et al., 2000; Thesleff and Tummers, 2001; Anusaksathien et al., 2004; Jin et al., 2004a]. Delivery of cells and molecular factors has been successful with the identification of appropriate scaffolds [MacNeil and Thomas, 1993b; Handa et al., 2002; Young et al., 2002; Jin et al., 2003; Duailibi et al., 2004]. Despite these successes, more remains to be defined in pursuit of regeneration of disease-damaged periodontium, as well as regeneration of whole teeth, i.e. crowns with roots and associated periodontal tissues (cementum-PDL-bone).

Our own focus has been on regeneration of the periodontium. We have identified key regulators of periodontal development for potential use in periodontal regeneration (fig. 1). Discussed below are some of the putative factors controlling periodontal development, including enamel-like factors, BMPs, and phosphates, and the progress toward their application in periodontal regeneration.

Materials and Methods

Cell Isolation, Immortalization, and Culture

Methods used to isolate cells have been published previously [D'Errico et al., 1997, 1999, 2000; Hakki et al., 2001; Zhao et al., 2002; Berry et al., 2003] and are described here in abbreviated form. Cell populations were isolated from the first molar region of CD1 mice at different stages of tooth development. Follicle cells (SVF4) were obtained from mice at developmental stage day 23–24 from vaginal plug date, set at day 0. The follicle was dissected from the first mandibular molar and digested with a mixture of collagenase and trypsin to isolate cells. Follicle cells were immortalized, using SV40, and found to be positive for expression of follicle cell markers (colony-stimulating factor 1, epidermal growth factor, epidermal growth factor receptor, and others) [Wise et al., 1992; Hou et al., 1999]. PDL cells and cementoblasts were similarly isolated from mice at developmental stage day 41 from vaginal plug date. The heterogeneous population of PDL cells were from CD1 mice and were immortalized using SV40. The PDL cells were subcloned and clonal PDL populations (SV-PDL) were selected based on lack of expression for bone sialoprotein (BSP) and osteocalcin (OCN). The cementoblasts were obtained from the root surface of the first mandibular molar of OCN large T antigen transgenic mice [D'Errico et al., 2000]. These mice contain the SV40 large T antigen under control of the OCN promoter. Consequently, the only cells immortalized were those that expressed SV40 large T antigen and OCN, enabling us to isolate cementoblasts from a mixed population of periodontal ligament cells (not expressing OCN in vivo) and cementoblasts (expressing OCN in vivo).

Clonal populations of follicle cells (SVF4), PDL cells (SV-PDL) and cementoblasts (OCCM-30) were maintained in Dulbecco's Modified Eagle Medium (DMEM) in 10% fetal bovine serum (FBS) and 1% antibiotics (100 units/ml penicillin, 100 μg/ml streptomycin, and 2 m*M* *L*-glutamine) in a humidified atmosphere of 5% CO_2 at 37°C. All cell culture products were obtained from Invitrogen Corporation, Carlsbad, Calif., USA. Recombinant human BMP-2 was generously provided by Regeneron Pharmaceuticals, Tarrytown, N.Y., USA, and was used at a concentration of 100 ng/ml. Enamel matrix derivative (EMD) was a generous gift from Biora AB (Malmö, Sweden) and was used at a concentration of 100 μg/ml.

Amelogenin Preparation

Recombinant N-terminal histidine-tagged murine amelogenin [rp(H)M180] and the recombinant N-terminal histidine-tagged murine tyrosine-rich amelogenin peptide (TRAP) were prepared in a solution of 0.1 *N* acetic acid (gift of Dr. Malcolm Snead, University of Southern California, Los Angeles, Calif., USA) [Moradian-Oldak et al., 2000; Paine et al., 2004]. Leucine-rich amelogenin

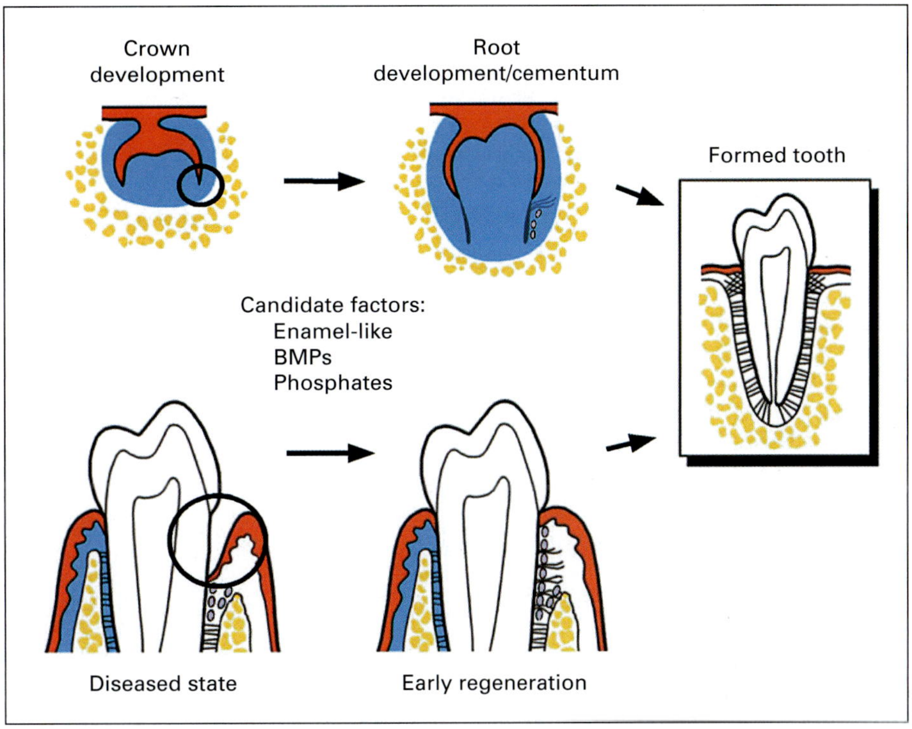

Fig. 1. Potential key regulators of periodontal development, such as enamel-like proteins, BMPs, and phosphates are being investigated for potential use in regeneration of the disease-damaged periodontium.

peptide (LRAP) was prepared in a solution of HEPES, NaCl, reduced glutathione, and DTT (gift of Dr. Carolyn Gibson, University of Pennsylvania, Philadelphia, Pa., USA) [Gibson et al., 1991]. The solutions in which the proteins were prepared were used as the vehicle controls in all subsequent experiments.

RNA Extraction

To determine the effects of BMP-2 on gene expression, cells (SVF4, SV-PDL, OCCM-30) were plated at a density of 20,000 cells/cm^2 in DMEM with 10% FBS. At confluence, media were changed to DMEM with 2% FBS ± 50 µg/ml ascorbic acid ± BMP-2 and incubated for 5 days. Media were changed on days 2 and 4. To determine the effects of enamel-like factors on gene expression, OCCM cells were seeded in 60-mm dishes at a density of 35,000 cells/cm^2. Upon confluence, media were changed to DMEM plus 5% FBS and 50 µg/ml ascorbic acid. Cells were treated with control vehicle, rp(H)M180 (10 µg/ml), LRAP (2 µg/ml), or TRAP (10 µg/ml). Total RNA was isolated 24 h after treatment using Trizol reagent (Invitrogen). Experiments were performed three times for each assay. Doses selected were based on initial studies demonstrating comparable effects of the three molecules at these selected doses.

Northern Blot Analysis

For separation, a 6% formaldehyde 1.2% w/v agarose gel was loaded with 4 µg of RNA per lane. RNA was transferred to a Hybond™ nylon membrane (Amersham Pharmacia) and cross-linked by UV irradiation. Probes for mouse BSP (a gift from Drs. M. Young and L. Fisher) and OCN (a gift from Dr. J. Wozney) were labeled with ^{32}P by Rediprime™ II random primer labeling system (Amersham Pharmacia) and purified using Probequant micro columns (Amersham Biosciences). PerfectHyb™ Plus hybridization buffer (Sigma) was used to hybridize the probes to the mRNA.

Real-Time Polymerase Chain Reaction

Cell cDNA was synthesized using the First Strand AMV reverse transcription kit (Roche, Mannheim, Germany) and 1 µg of DNase-treated total RNA. Sequence-specific primers from Invitrogen were used with the FastStart SYBR Green I kit (Roche) to amplify cDNA using real-time quantitative polymerase chain reaction (Lightcycler, Roche). Genes examined included BSP, OCN, and osteopontin (OPN), with GAPDH serving as a housekeeping/reference gene for normalization. The amplification profile used on the Lightcycler was 95°C for 0 s, 55°C for 7 s, and 72°C for 20 s (40 cycles). Primer sequences used were:

BSP: 5′-GAGACGGCGATAGTTCC/5′-AGTGCCGCTAACTCAA,

OCN: 5′-TGAACAGACTCCGGCG/5′-GATACCGTAGATGCGTTTG,

OPN: 5′-TTTACAGCCTGCACCC/5′-CTAGCAGTGACGGTCT,

dentin matrix protein (DMP)-1: 5′-ATGATAACGCAATGGGT/5′-GTAATGCCTCAATGGCAC, and

GAPDH: 5′-ACCACAGTCCATGCCATCAC/5′-TCCACCACCCTGTTGCTGTA (forward/reverse).

Primers were used at a concentration of 0.5 m*M* in 3 m*M* $MgCl_2$.

Mineralization Assay

For BMP mineralization assays, cells were plated at 20,000 cells/cm^2 and treated with factors of interest in media containing 50 µg/ml ascorbic acid and 5 m*M* β-glycerophosphate (mineralization media). For enamel-like factor mineralization assays, cells were seeded in 24-well plates (Invitrogen) in triplicate at a density of 30,000 cells/cm^2 in DMEM with 10% FBS. At confluence, cells were cultured in mineralizing media (DMEM with 5% FBS, 50 μg/ml ascorbic acid, and 10 m*M* β-glycerophosphate) with the addition of vehicle (control), rp(H)M180 (10 μg/ml), LRAP (2 μg/ml), or TRAP (10 μg/ml). Media were renewed every other day for 8 days. Mineral nodule formation was determined on day 8 by von Kossa staining.

ank Mutant Mice

Breeder pairs (heterozygote × heterozygote) of *ank* mutant mice (strain name, C3FeB6-*A/A*$^{w-J}$-*ank*) were obtained from The Jackson Laboratory (Bar Harbor, Me., USA). To determine the genotype of the mice, tail DNA was isolated. The *ank* mutation disrupts a HinfI site in the genome, so DNA from this area was amplified (37 cycles: 94°C for 40 s, 60°C for 1 min, and 72°C for 40 s) with specific primers TGCCATCCCTTGCTGATCTG and TGTCGCCATCATTTCTCACCTG. The products of amplification were then digested with HinfI and run on a gel for the determination of genotype.

PC-1 Mutant Mice

A tiptoe walking mouse (PC-1 mutant/*ttw;* PC-1 nucleotide pyrophosphatase phosphodiesterase 1), at 5 weeks of age, was purchased from the Central Institute for Experimental Animals (Kanagawa, Japan). The phenotype was confirmed by radiographs showing characteristic heterotopic ossification [Hosoda et al., 1981].

Tissue Preparation

All procedures were approved by the University of Washington Committee on the Use and Care of Animals, the Hiroshima University, and the Stanford University Institutional Animal Care and Use Committee for these respective institutions, in compliance with State and Federal Laws. Neonatal *ank* mutant, heterozygous, and wildtype mice were killed by carbon dioxide inhalation at developmental days 24, 28, 35, 45, and 52, and the PC-1 mutant mice *(ttw)* at developmental day 77 (vaginal plug = day 0). Mandibles were dissected from surrounding tissues and then hemisected into right and left halves by incision through the midline symphysis. For histological analysis, tissues were immediately immersed in Bouin's fixative (0.9% picric acid, 9% v/v formaldehyde, and 5% acetic acid; Polysciences, Warrington, Pa., USA) for 24 h, then placed in 70% ethanol. Tissues at or beyond day 27 of development were demineralized in acetic acid and formal saline (4% formaldehyde in 0.85% NaCl + 10% acetic acid) until an acceptable radiographic endpoint was achieved (generally 1–5 days). Buccolingual paraffin serial sections (7 μm) from first molars were prepared and stained with hematoxylin and eosin. For scanning electron microscopy (SEM) imaging, lower mandibles, without any demineralization, were cleaned of spurious soft tissues by tweezers, quickly rinsed by deionized water, dried by paper towel, then mounted in room temperature cure epoxy (Allied High Tech, Inc., Rancho Dominguez, Calif., USA). After curing, mandibles were sectioned sagittally by ultramicrotoming using a diamond knife (MT 6000-XL, RMC, Inc., Tucson, Ariz., USA). The block, that simultaneously revealed the interior of molars and an incisor, was imaged by SEM in the backscattered mode (JSM 7000, JEOL, Peabody, Mass., USA).

Table 1. Effect of amelogenin peptides on cementoblast behavior

Amelogenin protein	Affected cell behavior			
	mRNA			mineral nodule formation
	BSP	OCN	OPN	
rp(H)M180	↓25	↓53	–	↓46
LRAP	–	↓50	↑200	↓45
TRAP	–	↓13	↑272	↓99

Values are percentages.

Results

Enamel-Like Factors

Amelogenin, the smaller splice variant, LRAP, and TRAP were targeted as potential regulators of cementoblast function based on the reported success of EMD in promoting periodontal repair. EMD is a porcine derivative that includes amelogenin as a major component. In vitro studies have shown that EMD regulates gene expression and increases cell proliferation in PDL cells, follicle cells, and cementoblasts [Gestrelius et al., 1997; Tokiyasu et al., 2000; Hakki et al., 2001]. Additionally, EMD increased mineral nodule formation in PDL cells, but inhibited mineralization in follicle cells and cementoblasts [Berry et al., 2003]. A meta-analysis of clinical and preclinical studies of EMD application found evidence to support the use of EMD in the repair of periodontal osseous defects [Giannobile and Somerman, 2003].

Amelogenin, LRAP and TRAP have also been found to modulate expression of cementoblast-associated genes (table 1). Comparison of cementoblast BSP expression in wildtype versus amelogenin knockout mice demonstrated a marked reduction in BSP expression in knockouts, suggesting a role for amelogenin in BSP regulation [Viswanathan et al., 2003]. In vitro cell culture experiments further demonstrated an inhibition of BSP and OCN expression in cementoblasts treated with amelogenins. A reduction in the ability of follicle cells and cementoblasts to promote mineral formation was also detected in amelogenin-treated cells, although in contrast to Emdogain®, no effect was observed on cell proliferation. Both LRAP and TRAP were found to correspond with amelogenin in the ability to alter gene expression in cementoblasts. Cementoblasts exposed to LRAP and TRAP in vitro exhibit increased expression of OPN, decreased expression of OCN, and decreased mineral formation without altering cell proliferation when compared with untreated cells [Boabaid et al., 2004].

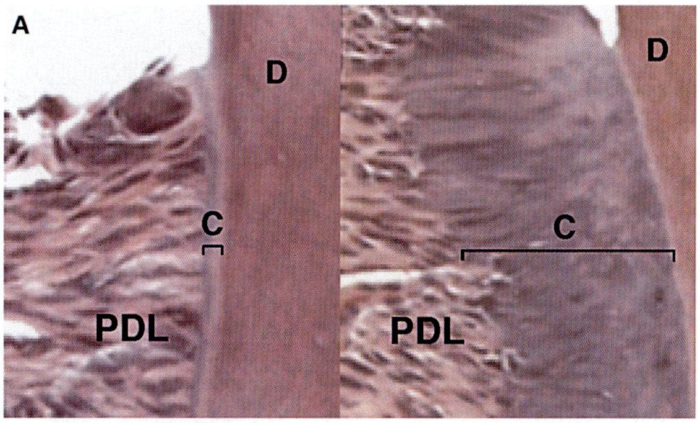

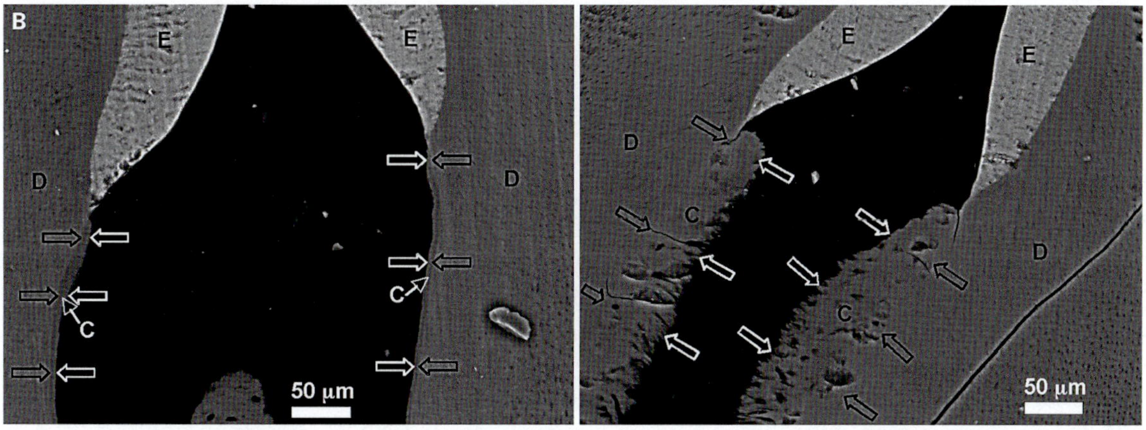

Fig. 2. A comparison of wildtype and *ank/ank* mutant mice, showing the markedly thicker cementum in mutants. **A** Light microscopy of periodontal tissues at day 52. C = Cementum; D = dentin. **B** Sagittal view of 60-day-old 1st and 2nd molars from wildtype and *ank/ank* mutant mice, imaged by backscattered mode SEM (JSM 7000, JEOL). The thickness increase in the *ank* cementum is more than 10-fold compared with wildtype mice, yet the degree of mineralization of *ank* cementum is comparable with the adjacent dentin, as measured by backscattered SEM analysis. E = Enamel; D = dentin; C = cementum.

Effects of BMPs

BMP-2 has been identified as a 'differentiation factor', capable of stimulating follicle cells to differentiate into a cementoblast/osteoblast phenotype. With the addition of BMP-2, follicle cells expressed BSP, Cbfa-1, and OCN mRNA in vitro and showed enhanced ability to promote mineral nodule formation in a time- and dose-dependent manner [Zhao et al., 2002]. In contrast, mature PDL cells showed only a very limited response to BMP-2, indicating that only a small progenitor cell population may be able to express the osteoblast/cementoblast phenotype [Berry et al., 2003]. Furthermore, exposure of mature cementoblasts to BMP-2 at a high dose actually downregulated BSP expression and inhibited cementoblast-mediated mineral nodule formation [Zhao et al., 2003]. Although the effects of BMP-2 have been found to depend on dose and cell maturity, the application of BMP-2 to periodontal defects in animal models has been found to promote cementogenesis and healing of periodontal wounds [King et al., 1997; Kinoshita et al., 1997; Saygin et al., 2000]. In contrast, BMP-3 has been found to inhibit BMP-2-mediated commitment and differentiation of osteoprogenitor cells into osteoblasts in vitro, and is a negative regulator of bone density in vivo [Daluiski et al., 2001]. Our lab, as well as others, is investigating the role of BMP-3 as a negative regulator of mineralization, allowing for maintenance of PDL between bone and root (cementum).

Phosphates

Examination of periodontal tissues in *ank/ank* mutant mice yielded surprising results. The mouse progressive ankylosis protein (ANK) controls the transport of inorganic pyrophosphate (PP_i) across cell membranes, and thus, cells derived from *ank/ank* mutant mice lack the ANK transporter function [Ho et al., 2000]. As a result, the cells of *ank/ank* mutant mice accumulate PP_i interiorly, whereas extracellular PP_i concentrations remain low. This extracellular reduction in PP_i has been found to lead to extensive ectopic calcifications in joints and an arthritis-like condition. Although similar ectopic calcifications in the PDL space were predicted, this was not observed. Instead, the cementum thickness in *ank/ank* mutant mice increased by more than 10 fold when compared with wildtype or heterozygous mice, while the adjacent dentin, PDL, and bone appeared morphologically unchanged (fig. 2) [Nociti et al., 2002]. The extent of mineralization in the cementum from *ank/ank* mice also appeared uncompromised as revealed by backscattered SEM analysis (fig. 2). A remarkably similar thickened cementum phenotype was also observed in the tiptoe walking *(ttw)* PC-1 knockout mouse. PC-1 is an enzyme that liberates PP_i from triphosphates, and in the PC-1 mutant mice, as with *ank/ank,* there is a deficiency in extracellular PP_i.

While ANK and PC-1 regulate the accumulation of PP_i in the extracellular environment, tissue nonspecific alkaline phosphatase (TNAP) is an enzyme that functions in breaking down PP_i to its two constituent phosphate (P_i) molecules. When TNAP is nonfunctional, as by mutation, the result is increased PP_i and decreased P_i (hypophosphatasia), characterized by hypomineralization and skeletal abnormalities [Whyte, 1994, 2002; Tesch et al., 2003]. TNAP deficiency also results in a tooth phenotype characterized by defective or absent acellular cementum, resulting in tooth loss [Henthorn et al., 1992; Beertsen et al., 1999]. Clearly, the cementum is sensitive to the regulation of P_i and PP_i in the local environment of the tooth root.

In addition to the role of P_i in forming hydroxyapatite, evidence has been accumulating for a role of P_i in cell signaling. It has been hypothesized that P_i in the extracellular environment of mineralizing cells such as cementoblasts and osteoblasts may serve to signal a shift in cell function or differentiation. P_i was shown to be a specific inducer of OPN in MC3T3.E1 preosteoblast cells [Beck et al., 2000], and additionally has been indicated as an apoptogen for chondrocytes and osteoblasts at high doses, possibly a mechanism for the clearing of terminally differentiated cells [Mansfield et al., 1999; Meleti et al., 2000].

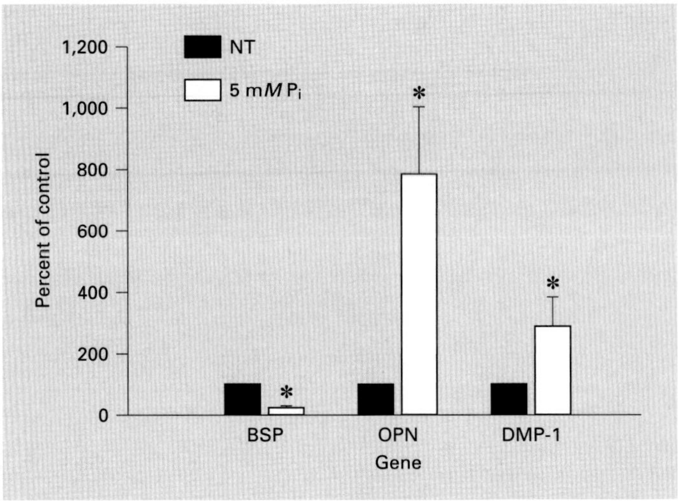

Fig. 3. SIBLING gene expression (BSP, OPN, DMP-1) in cementoblasts (OCCM-30) following 5 m*M* P_i treatment in vitro. Gene expression is shown at treatment day 6 as a percentage of gene expression in the non-treated control cells (NT). Phosphate treatment upregulated OPN and DMP-1, but downregulated BSP. * $p < 0.05$.

These accumulated results led us to investigate potential P_i regulation of cementoblast gene expression (fig. 3). We found that P_i significantly increased OPN expression in OCCM-30 cementoblast cells. Additionally, P_i upregulated DMP-1 and downregulated BSP expression [Foster et al., 2006]. OPN, DMP-1 and BSP are members of the SIBLING (small integrin-binding ligand N-linked glycoprotein) protein family. The SIBLING family is composed of extracellular matrix proteins associated with hydroxyapatite mineral initiation and growth, as well as being linked to numerous other functions [Fisher and Fedarko, 2003; Qin et al., 2004]. These three SIBLING proteins have been identified in cementum in vivo [D'Errico et al., 1997; Baba et al., 2004], with BSP and OPN localized to the tooth root surface during cementum formation. The contribution of DMP-1 in cementum formation or maintenance is currently unknown. OPN has been shown to inhibit hydroxyapatite crystal growth [Boskey et al., 1993], whereas BSP and DMP-1 are known to promote mineral formation [Harris et al., 2000; He et al., 2003]. This decrease in transcripts for differentiation/mineralization genes, such as BSP, and an increase in the hydroxyapatite inhibitor OPN, suggests that following the completion of cementum formation, mature cementoblasts may actively limit further mineralization [Foster et al., 2006].

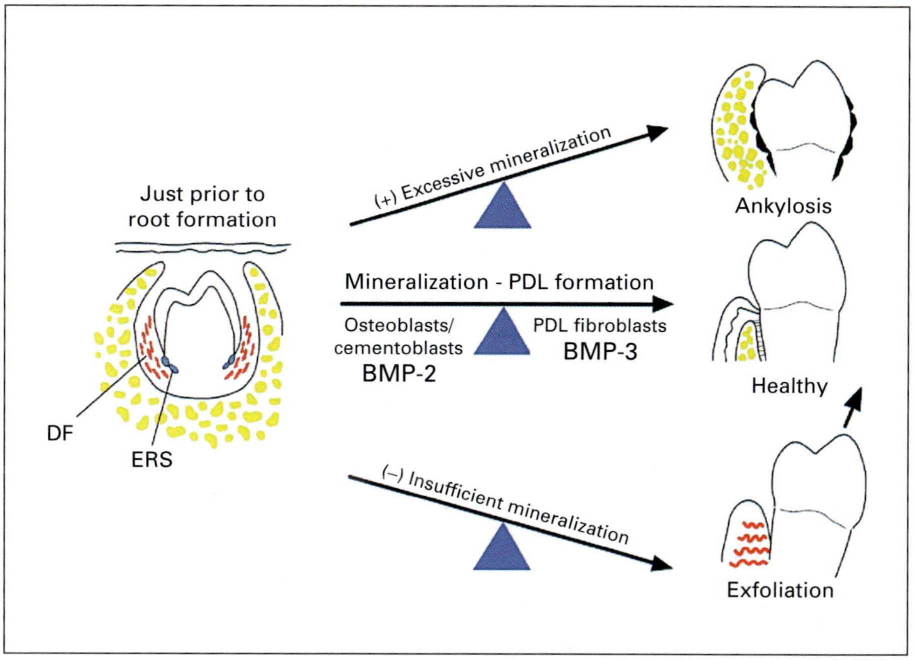

Fig. 4. Periodontal development includes positive and negative regulators, either promoting or inhibiting mineralization. If positive regulators occur in excess, periodontal ligament tissue may mineralize, resulting in ankylosis. In contrast, if negative regulators occur in excess, insufficient mineralization of cementum may occur, resulting in exfoliation. Clinical application of an appropriate balance of positive and negative regulators, such as BMP-2 and BMP-3, may promote regeneration of disease-damaged periodontal tissues. DF = Dental follicle; ERS = epithelial root sheath.

Bioengineering

Progress has been made in tissue engineering of cementum in vivo, demonstrating the capacity to both regenerate a cementum-like tissue and inhibit cementum formation. The delivery of cementoblasts or follicle cells via polylactic-co-glycolic-acid polymer sponges to periodontal defects in immunodeficient rats tested the ability of these cells and this delivery method to contribute to periodontal repair [Zhao et al., 2004]. When cementoblasts were applied to periodontal defects, a layer of cementum-like tissue covered the root surface after 6 weeks. This mineralized tissue approximated bone or cementum in its expression of BSP and OCN mRNA; however, the nature of the tissue remains unknown. In contrast, periodontal defects that received polylactic-co-glycolic-acid sponges only, or sponges and follicle cells, demonstrated less mineralized tissue formation. In fact, the follicle cells appeared to inhibit periodontal healing. Cementoblasts seeded on polymer sponges and implanted in immunodeficient mice have also been shown to induce mineral formation [Jin et al., 2003, 2004b]. In this system, cementoblasts were also transduced to express noggin, a glycoprotein that binds to BMPs and inactivates BMP signaling [Zimmerman et al., 1996]. Noggin was found to downregulate BSP and OCN gene expression in cementoblasts and inhibit cementoblast-induced mineralization [Jin et al., 2004b].

Discussion

Overall, our investigations of candidate factors for periodontal regeneration have led to a better grasp of the genes/proteins and signaling pathways controlling cell function in follicle cells, periodontal cells, and cementoblasts, and while some factors show promise, there are also limitations. Amelogenin, as well as the variant forms LRAP and TRAP, clearly alters gene expression within these cells; however, our results do not suggest that these molecules promote differentiation or mineralization in vitro. Although several groups have been trying to identify the receptors associated with the regulatory function of amelogenin, these receptors are unknown. A recent paper by Tompkins et al. [2006] reports that the 95-kDa transmembrane protein, LAMP-1, originally identified as a lysosomal-associated membrane protein, is also found at the cell surface of C2C12 mouse fetal myoblasts as an A-4 cell binding protein. Another paper by Wang et al. [2005] reported that several enamel matrix proteins interact with a large number of secreted membrane proteins and integral proteins, including LAMP-3 [Wang et al., 2005]. Thus, the application of amelogenin as a promotor of mineralization in the context of periodontal repair does not appear to be advantageous for regeneration/repair of periodontal tissues. On the other hand, observing the effects of BMP-2/3 during cementoblast development indicates potential clinical applications of these molecules in periodontal regeneration. While BMP-2 promotes follicle cell differentiation in cementoblasts, as well as cementoblast mineralization, BMP-3 may inhibit these processes (fig. 4). The application of a mixture of these molecules to periodontal defects may be useful in regulating regeneration of periodontal tissues. Lastly, the discovery of excessive cementum formation in *ank/ank* mutant mice has been exciting and has directed our investigations toward phosphate regulation of cementoblast gene expression. Limitations in phosphate delivery to periodontal defects is a challenge for us that is being addressed in order to determine whether or not enhanced phosphate levels, in a spatially and temporally regulated fashion, would prove successful for regenerating periodontal tissues.

Acknowledgments

The authors are grateful for the contributions of Jan Berry, Drs. Sahba Fatherazi, Carolyn Gibson, Eiji Nemoto, Francisco Nociti, Jr., Sunao Sato, Malcolm Snead, Takashi Takata, Hema Viswanathan, and Ming Zhao. This work was supported by National Institutes of Health/National Institute of Dental and Craniofacial Research grant DE09532.

References

Anusaksathien, O., Q. Jin, M. Zhao, M.J. Somerman, W.V. Giannobile (2004) Effect of sustained gene delivery of platelet-derived growth factor or its antagonist (PDGF-1308) on tissue-engineered cementum. J Periodontol *75:* 429–440.

Baba, O., C. Qin, J.C. Brunn, J.N. Wygant, B.W. McIntyre, W.T. Butler (2004) Colocalization of dentin matrix protein 1 and dentin sialoprotein at late stages of rat molar development. Matrix Biol *23:* 371–379.

Beck, G.R., B. Zerler, Jr., E. Moran (2000) Phosphate is a specific signal for induction of osteopontin gene expression. Proc Natl Acad Sci USA *97:* 8352–8357.

Beertsen, W., T. VandenBos, V. Everts (1999) Root development in mice lacking functional tissue non-specific alkaline phosphatase gene: inhibition of acellular cementum formation. J Dent Res *78:* 1221–1229.

Berry, J.E., M. Zhao, Q. Jin, B.F. Foster, H. Viswanathan, M. Somerman (2003) Exploring the origins of cementoblasts and their trigger factors. Connect Tissue Res *44:* 1–6.

Boabaid, F., C.W. Gibson, J.E. Berry, M.L. Snead, E. Katchburian, F.H. Nociti, M.J. Somerman (2004) Leucine-rich amelogenin peptide: a candidate signaling molecule during cementogenesis. J Periodontol *75:* 1126–1136.

Boskey, A.L., M. Maresca, W. Ullrich, S.B. Doty, W.T. Butler, C.W. Prince (1993) Osteopontin-hydroxyapatite interactions in vitro: inhibition of hydroxyapatite formation and growth in a gelatin-gel. Bone Miner *22:* 147–159.

Bosshardt, D.D. (2005) Are cementoblasts a subpopulation of osteoblasts or a unique phenotype? J Dent Res *84:* 390–406.

Bosshardt, D.D., A. Nanci (1997) Immunodetection of enamel- and cementum-related (bone) proteins at the enamel-free area and cervical portion of the tooth in rat molars. J Bone Miner Res *12:* 367–379.

Bosshardt, D.D., A. Nanci (2004) Hertwig's epithelial root sheath, enamel matrix proteins, and initiation of cementogenesis in porcine teeth. J Clin Periodontol *31:* 184–192.

Buser, D., K. Warrer, T. Karring (1990) Formation of periodontal ligament around titanium implants. J Periodontol *61:* 597–601.

Cochran, D.L., J.M. Wozney (1999) Biological mediators for periodontal regeneration. Periodontol 2000 *19:* 40–58.

Daluiski, A., T. Engstrand, M.E. Bahamonde, L.W. Gamer, E. Agius, S.L. Stevenson, K. Cox, V. Rosen, K.M. Lyons (2001) Bone morphogenetic protein-3 is a negative regulator of bone density. Nat Genet *27:* 84–88.

D'Errico, J.A., J.E. Berry, H. Ouyang, C. Strayhorn, J.J. Windle, M. Somerman (2000) Employing a transgenic animal model to obtain cementoblasts in vitro. J Periodontol *71:* 63–72.

D'Errico, J.A., R.L. MacNeil, T. Takata, J.E. Berry, C. Strayhorn, M. Somerman (1997) Expression of bone associated markers by tooth root lining cells, in situ and in vitro. Bone *20:* 117–126.

D'Errico, J.A., H. Ouyang, J.E. Berry, R.L. MacNeil, C. Strayhorn, M.J. Imperiale, N.L. Harris, H. Goldberg, M.J. Somerman (1999) Immortalized cementoblasts and periodontal ligament cells in culture. Bone *25:* 39–47.

Duailibi, M.T., S.E. Duailibi, C.S. Young, J.D. Bartlett, J.P. Vacanti, P.C. Yelick (2004) Bioengineered teeth from cultured rat tooth bud cells. J Dent Res *83:* 523–528.

Fisher, L.W., N.S. Fedarko (2003) Six genes expressed in bones and teeth encode the current members of the SIBLING family of proteins. Connect Tissue Res *44(suppl 1):* 33–40.

Foster, B.L., F.H. Nociti, E.C. Swanson, D. Matsa-Dunn, J.E. Berry, C.J. Cupp, P. Zhang, M.J. Somerman (2006) Regulation of cementoblast gene expression by inorganic phosphate in vitro. Calcif Tissue Int *78:* 103–112.

Gestrelius, S., C. Andersson, D. Lidstrom, L. Hammarstrom, M. Somerman (1997) In vitro studies on periodontal ligament cells and enamel matrix derivative. J Clin Periodontol *24:* 685–692.

Giannobile, W.V., M.J. Somerman (2003) Growth and amelogenin-like factors in periodontal wound healing. A systematic review. Ann Periodontol *8:* 193–204.

Gibson, C.W., E. Golub, W.D. Ding, H. Shimokawa, M. Young, J. Termine, J. Rosenbloom (1991) Identification of the leucine-rich amelogenin peptide (LRAP) as the translation product of an alternatively spliced transcript. Biochem Biophys Res Commun *174:* 1306–1312.

Goldberg, M., A.J. Smith (2004) Cells and extracellular matrices of dentin and pulp: a biological basis for repair and tissue engineering. Crit Rev Oral Biol Med *15:* 13–27.

Gronthos, S., M. Mankani, J. Brahim, P. Gehron Robey, S. Shi (2000) Postnatal human dental pulp stem cells (DPSCs) in vitro and in vivo. Proc Natl Acad Sci USA *97:* 13625–13630.

Gunraj, M.N. (1999) Dental root resorption. Oral Surg Oral Med Oral Pathol Oral Radiol Endod *88:* 647–653.

Hakki, S.S., J.E. Berry, M.J. Somerman (2001) The effect of enamel matrix protein derivative on follicle cells in vitro. J Periodontol *72:* 679–687.

Handa, K., M. Saito, A. Tsunoda, M. Yamauchi, S. Hattori, S. Sato (2002) Progenitor cells from dental follicle are able to form cementum matrix in vivo. Connect Tissue Res *43:* 406–408.

Harada, H., P. Kettunen, H.S. Jung, T. Mustonen, Y.A. Wang, I. Thesleff (1999) Localization of putative stem cells in dental epithelium and their association with Notch and FGF signaling. J Cell Biol *147:* 105–120.

Harris, N.L., K.R. Rattray, C.E. Tye, T.M. Underhill, M.J. Somerman, J.A. D'Errico, A.F. Chambers, G.K. Hunter, H.A. Goldberg (2000) Functional analysis of bone sialoprotein: identification of the hydroxyapatite-nucleating and cell-binding domains by recombinant peptide expression and site-directed mutagenesis. Bone *27:* 795–802.

He, G., T. Dahl, A. Veis, A. George (2003) Dentin matrix protein 1 initiates hydroxyapatite formation in vitro. Connect Tissue Res *44(suppl 1):* 240–245.

Helfrich, M.H. (2005) Osteoclast diseases and dental abnormalities. Arch Oral Biol *50:* 115.
Henthorn, P.S., M. Raducha, K.N. Fedde, M.A. Lafferty, M.P. Whyte (1992) Different missense mutations at the tissue-nonspecific alkaline phosphatase gene locus in autosomal recessively inherited forms of mild and severe hypophosphatasia. Proc Natl Acad Sci USA *89:* 9924–9928.
Ho, A.M., M.D. Johnson, D.M. Kingsley (2000) Role of the mouse ank gene in control of tissue calcification and arthritis. Science *289:* 265–270.
Hosoda, Y., Y. Yoshimura, S. Higaki (1981) A new breed of mouse showing multiple osteochondral lesions – twy mouse. Ryumachi *21:* 157–164.
Hou, L.T., C.M. Liu, Y.J. Chen, M.Y. Wong, K.C. Chen, J. Chen, H.F. Thomas (1999) Characterization of dental follicle cells in developing mouse molar. Arch Oral Biol *44:* 759–770.
Iohara, K., M. Nakashima, M. Ito, M. Ishikawa, A. Nakashima, A. Akamine (2004) Dentin regeneration by dental pulp stem cell therapy with recombinant human bone morphogenetic protein 2. J Dent Res *83:* 590–595.
Jin, Q., O. Anusaksathien, S.A. Webb, M.A. Printz, W.V. Giannobile (2004a) Engineering of tooth-supporting structures by delivery of PDGF gene therapy vectors. Mol Ther *9:* 519.
Jin, Q.M., M. Zhao, A.N. Economides, M.J. Somerman, W.V. Giannobile (2004b) Noggin gene delivery inhibits cementoblast-induced mineralization. Connect Tissue Res *45:* 50–59.
Jin, Q.M., M. Zhao, S.A. Webb, J.E. Berry, M. Somerman, W.V. Giannobile (2003) Cementum engineering with three-dimensional polymer scaffolds. J Biomed Mater Res *67A:* 54–60.
Kao, R.T., G. Conte, D. Nishimine, S. Dault (2005) Tissue engineering for periodontal regeneration. J Calif Dent Assoc *33:* 205–215.
King, G.N., N. King, A.T. Cruchley, J.M. Wozney, F.J. Hughes (1997) Recombinant human bone morphogenetic protein-2 promotes wound healing in rat periodontal fenestration defects. J Dent Res *76:* 1460–1470.
Kinoshita, A., S. Oda, K. Takahashi, S. Yokota, I. Ishikawa (1997) Periodontal regeneration by application of recombinant human bone morphogenetic protein-2 to horizontal circumferential defects created by experimental periodontitis in beagle dogs. J Periodontol *68:* 103–109.
MacNeil, R.L., H.F. Thomas (1993a) Development of the murine periodontium. 1. Role of basement membrane in formation of a mineralized tissue on the developing root dentin surface. J Periodontol *64:* 95–102.
MacNeil, R.L., H.F. Thomas (1993b) Development of the murine periodontium. 2. Role of the epithelial root sheath in formation of the periodontal attachment. J Periodontol *64:* 285–291.
MacNeil, R.L., M. Somerman (1993) Molecular factors regulating development and regeneration of cementum. J Periodont Res *28:* 550–559.
Mansfield, K., R. Rajpurohit, I.M. Shapiro (1999) Extracellular phosphate ions cause apoptosis of terminally differentiated epiphyseal chondrocytes. J Cell Physiol *179:* 276–286.
Meleti, Z., I.M. Shapiro, C.S. Adams (2000) Inorganic phosphate induces apoptosis of osteoblast-like cells in culture. Bone *27:* 359–366.
Moradian-Oldak, J., M.L. Paine, Y.P. Lei, A.G. Fincham, M.L. Snead (2000) Self-assembly properties of recombinant engineered amelogenin proteins analyzed by dynamic light scattering and atomic force microscopy. J Struct Biol *131:* 27.
Nociti, F.H., J.E. Berry, B.L. Foster, K.A. Gurley, D.M. Kingsley, T. Takata, M. Miyauchi, M.J. Somerman (2002) Cementum: a phosphate-sensitive tissue. J Dent Res *81:* 817–821.
Ohazama, A., S.A.C. Modino, I. Miletich, P.T. Sharpe (2004) Stem-cell based tissue engineering of murine teeth. J Dent Res *83:* 518–522.
Paine, M.L., D.H. Zhu, W. Luo, M.L. Snead (2004) Overexpression of TRAP in the enamel matrix does not alter the enamel structural hierarchy. Cells Tissues Organs *176:* 7–16.
Qin, C., O. Baba, W.T. Butler (2004) Post-translational modifications of sibling proteins and their roles in osteogenesis and dentinogenesis. Crit Rev Oral Biol Med *15:* 126–136.
Saygin, N.E., W.V. Giannobile, M.J. Somerman (2000) Molecular and cell biology of cementum. Periodontol 2000 *24:* 73–98.
Seo, B.M., M. Miura, S. Gronthos, P.M. Bartold, S. Batouli, J. Brahim, M. Young, P.G. Robey, C.Y. Wang, S. Shi (2004) Investigation of multipotent postnatal stem cells from human periodontal ligament. Lancet *364:* 149–155.
Shi, S., P.M. Bartold, M. Miura, B.M. Seo, P.G. Robey, S. Gronthos (2005) The efficacy of mesenchymal stem cells to regenerate and repair dental structures. Orthod Craniofac Res *8:* 191–199.
Shi, S., S. Gronthos (2003) Perivascular niche of postnatal mesenchymal stem cells in human bone marrow and dental pulp. J Bone Miner Res *18:* 696–704.
Tesch, W., T. VandenBos, P. Roschgr, N. Fratzl-Zelman, K. Klaushofer, W. Beertsen, P. Fratzl (2003) Orientation of mineral crystallites and mineral density during skeletal development in mice deficient in tissue nonspecific alkaline phosphatase. J Bone Miner Res *18:* 117–125.
Thesleff, I. (2003) Epithelial-mesenchymal signalling regulating tooth morphogenesis. J Cell Sci *116:* 1647–1648.
Thesleff, I., M. Mikkola (2002) The role of growth factors in tooth development. Int Rev Cytol *217:* 93–135.
Thesleff, I., M. Tummers (2001) Stem cells and tissue engineering: prospects for regenerating tissues in dental practice. Med Princ Pract *12:* 43–50.
Thomas, H.F., E.J. Kollar (1989) Differentiation of odontoblasts in grafted recombinants of murine epithelial root sheath and dental mesenchyme. Arch Oral Biol *34:* 27–35.
Tokiyasu, Y., T. Takata, E. Saygin, M. Somerman (2000) Enamel factors regulate expression of genes associated with cementoblasts. J Periodontol *71:* 1829–1839.
Tompkins, K., A. George, A. Veis (2006) Characterization of a mouse amelogenin [A-4]/M59 cell surface receptor. Bone *38:* 172–180.
Viswanathan, H.L., J.E. Berry, B.F. Foster, C.W. Gibson, Y. Li, A.B. Kulkarni, M.L. Snead, M.J. Somerman (2003) Amelogenin: a potental regulator of cementum-associated genes. J Periodontol *74:* 1423–1431.
Wang, H., S. Tannukit, D. Zhu, M.L. Snead, M.L. Paine (2005) Enamel matrix protein interactions. J Bone Miner Res *20:* 1032–1040.
Whyte, M.P. (1994) Hypophosphatasia and the role of alkaline phosphatase in skeletal mineralization. Endocr Rev *15:* 439–461.
Whyte, M.P. (2002) Hypophosphatasia: nature's window to alkaline phosphase in man; in Bilezikian, J.P., L.G. Raisz, G.A. Rodan (eds): Principles of Bone Biology. San Diego, Academic Press, pp 1229–1248.
Wise, G.E., F. Lin, W. Fan (1992) Culture and characterization of dental follicle cells from rat molars. Cell Tissue Res *267:* 483–492.
Yamamoto, H., S.W. Cho, E.J. Kim, J.Y. Kim, N. Fujiwara, H.S. Jung (2004) Developmental properties of the Hertwig's epithelial root sheath in mice. J Dent Res *83:* 688–692.
Yamashiro, T., M. Tummers, I. Thesleff (2003) Expression of bone morphogenetic proteins and Msx genes during root formation. J Dent Res *82:* 172–176.
Young, C.S., S. Terada, J.P. Vacanti, M. Honda, J.D. Barlett, P.C. Yelick (2002) Tissue engineering of complex tooth structures on biodegradable polymer scaffolds. J Dent Res *81:* 695–700.
Zeichner-David, M., K. Oishi, Z. Su, V. Zakartchenko, L.S. Chen, H. Arzate, P. Bringas (2003) Role of Hertwig's epithelial root sheath cells in tooth development. Dev Dyn *228:* 651–663.
Zhao, M., J.E. Berry, M. Somerman (2003) Bone morphogenetic protein-2 inhibits differentiation and mineralization of cementoblasts in vitro. J Dent Res *82:* 23–27.
Zhao, M., Q. Jin, J.E. Berry, F.H. Nociti, W.V. Giannobile, M. Somerman (2004) Cementoblast delivery for periodontal tissue engineering. J Periodontol *75:* 154–161.
Zhao, M., G. Xiao, J.E. Berry, R.T. Franceschi, A.H. Reddi, M. Somerman (2002) Bone morphogenetic protein-2 induces dental follicle cells to differentiate toward a cementoblast/osteoblast phenotype. J Bone Miner Res *17:* 1441–1451.
Zimmerman, L.B., J.M. De Jesus-Escobar, R.M. Harland (1996) The Spemann organizer signal noggin binds and inactivates bone morphogenetic protein 4. Cell *86:* 599–606.

Author Index Vol. 181, No. 3–4, 2005

Cells Tissues Organs

Subject Index Vol. 181, No. 3–4, 2005

KARGER
Fax +41 61 306 12 34
E-Mail karger@karger.ch
www.karger.com

Accessible online at:
www.karger.com/cto

Conference Calendar

Cells Tissues Organs

7.4.–10.4.2006 **Freiburg** Germany	Anatomische Gesellschaft Deutsche Akademie der Naturforscher *Leopoldina* 101st Annual Meeting	**Information:** Prof. Dr. med. Dr. h.c. mult. Wolfgang Kühnel, Universität zu Lübeck, Institute für Anatomie, Ratzeburger Allee 160, DE–23538 Lübeck, Germany Tel. +49 451 500 40 40/31, Fax +49 451 500 40 34 E-Mail Kuehnel@anat.uni-luebeck.de
21.4.–22.4.2006 **Lund** Sweden	1st European Conference on Scientific Publishing in Biomedicine and Medicine	**Information:** www.ecspbiomed.net
24.4.–27.4.2006 **Pittsburgh, Pa.** USA	Regenerate World Congress on Tissue Engineering and Regenerative Technologies	**Information:** www.regenerate-online.com
4.5.–7.5.2006 **Berlin** Germany	International Society for Cellular Therapy (ISCT)	**Information:** www.celltherapy.org
11.5.–14.5.2006 **Berlin** Germany	MDC International Conference on Epithelial Organization and Organ Development	**Information:** http://www.mdc-symposium2006.de/
12.5.2006 **Bonn** Germany	Stem Cell Research: A Challenge for Embryology, Regenerative Medicine and Bioethics	**Information:** Gudrun Mikus, Institut für Anatomie, Universitätsklinikum Essen, Hufelandstr. 55, DE–45122 Essen, Germany Tel. +49 201 723 4380/1, Fax +49 201 723 5916 E-Mail sekr.anatomie@uni-essen.de, http://www.uni-essen.de/anatomie
15.5.–16.5.2006 **Münster** Germany	3rd International Meeting of the Stem Cell Network North Rhine Westphalia	**Information:** www.stemcells.nrw.de
28.5.–2.6.2006 **Crete** Greece	1st International Conference on Osteoimmunology: Interactions of the Immune and Skeletal Systems	**Information:** www.aegeanconferences.org
31.5.–2.6.2006 **Würzburg** Germany	2nd International Conference Strategies in Tissue Engineering	**Information:** http://www.wite.org/site2006
4.6.–9.6.2006 **Corfu** Greece	4th International Conference on Innate Immunity	**Information:** www.aegeanconferences.org
24.6–29.6.2006 **Istanbul** Turkey	31st FEBS Congress Molecules in Health and Disease	**Information:** www.febs2006.org
29.6.–1.7.2006 **Toronto** Canada	4th International Society for Stem Cell Research Annual Meeting	**Information:** www.isscr.org
6.8.–10.8.2006 **Fortaleza** Brazil	ISMB 2006 Intelligent Systems for Molecular Biology	**Information:** www.iscb.org/ismb2006
7.9.–10.9.2006 **Stresa** Italy	48th Symposium of the Society for Histochemistry	**Information:** www.unipv.it/webbio/stresa2006
23.9.–28.9.2006 **Corfu** Greece	3rd International Conference on Gene Regulation in Lymphocyte Development	**Information:** www.aegeanconferences.org
24.9.–27.9.2006 **Dresden** Germany	German Research Foundation and the German Academy of Sciences *Leopoldina* International Conference Embryonic and Somatic Stem Cells – Regenerative Systems for Cell and Tissue Repair	**Information:** www.spp-stemcells.de
8.10.–11.10.2006 **Rotterdam** The Netherlands	2006 TERMIS-EU Annual Meeting	**Information:** www.termis.org

KARGER
Fax +41 61 306 12 34
E-Mail karger@karger.ch
www.karger.com

Accessible online at:
www.karger.com/cto

8.10.–13.10.2006 **Mykonos** Greece	4th International Conference on Pathways, Networks, and Systems: Theory and Experiments	**Information:** www.aegeanconferences.org
28.10.–2.11.2006 **Sant Feliu de Guixols** Spain	ESF-EMBO Symposium on Stem Cells in Tissue Engineering Isolation, Culture, Characterisation and Applications	**Information:** www.esf.org/conferences/lc06213
27.5.–1.6.2007 **Rhodes** Greece	3rd International Conference on Tissue Engineering	**Information:** www.aegeanconferences.org
3.6.–8.6.2007 **Rhodes** Greece	4th Lymphocyte Signal Transduction Workshop	**Information:** www.aegeanconferences.org
10.6.–15.6.2007 **Porto Heli** Greece	4th Workshop on Complement Associated Diseases, Animal Models, and Therapeutics	**Information:** www.aegeanconferences.org

Acknowledgement to Referees

Cells
Tissues
Organs

The Editors-in-Chief extend their gratitude and appreciation to the following reviewers whose comments and criticisms have ensured the quality of the papers published in this journal.

Dirk Adriaensen, Antwerpen
Hakan Aldskogius, Uppsala
David Allen, Boulder, Colo.
Anthony J. Atala, Winston-Salem, N.C.
Jane E. Aubin, Toronto
Francois Auger, Quebec City
Gerhard Aumüller, Marburg
Augustinus Bader, Leipzig
Kenneth M. Baldwin, Irvine, Calif.
John Bartlett, Boston, Mass.
Klaus Baumann, Aumühle
Martin Bergmann, Giessen
Lynda Bonewald, Kansas City, Mo.
Dirk Breitkreutz, Heidelberg
Bruce A. Bunnell, New Orleans, La.
Robert C. Burghardt, College Station, Tex.
Anne Grete Byskov, Copenhagen
Bruce M. Carlson, Ann Arbor, Mich.
Walter Cash, Kansas City, Mo.
Bodo Christ, Freiburg i.Br.
Constance Chu, Pittsburgh, Pa.
Anita Corbett, Atlanta, Ga.
Shuliang Cui, Parkville
Françoise Dacheux, Nouzilly
Patrick de Deyne, Raynham, Mass.
Hugh Devlin, Philadelphia, Pa.
Georg Duda, Berlin
Carlos Duran, Missoula, Mont.
Peter Ekblom, Lund
Jennifer Elisseeff, Baltimore, Md.
Allen C. Enders, Davis, Calif.
Darrell J.R. Evans, Brighton
Wahlid Farhat, Toronto
Jian Feng, Kansas City, Mo.
Wolf-Georg Forssmann, Hannover
Sally Frenkel, New York, N.Y.
Luigi Gallo, Zürich
Dave Gerrard, West Lafayette, Ind.
Stefano Geuna, Obassano
Carolyn Gibson, Philadelphia, Pa.
Jeffrey Gimble, Baton Rouge, La.
Michael Goldberg, Montrouge
Katsumasa Goto, Kanagawa
G. Granstrom, Gothenburg
Helen Grant, Glasgow
Paul Greenwood, Armidale
Stan Gronthos, Adelaide
Rainer Haberberger, Giessen
Stephen Harris, San Antonio, Tex.
David A. Hart, Calgary
Thomas Hart, Bethesda, Md.
David Hawkins, Davis, Calif.
Patricia A. Hebda, Pittsburgh, Pa.
Robert Henry, Knoxville, Tenn.
Damon C. Herbert, San Antonio, Tex.
John W. Hermanson, Ithaca, N.Y.
Susan W. Herring, Seattle, Wash.
Andreas Herrler, Aachen
Karen K. Hirschi, Houston, Tex.
Chantal E. Holy, Raynham, Mass.
Jose Icardo, Santander
Taisen Iguchi, Okazaki
Eustace Johnson, Oswestry
D.B. Jones, Marburg
Carolyn J.P. Jones, Manchester
Julian Jones, London
Thomas Jungi, Bern
Rita Kandel, Toronto
David Kaplan, Medford
Laura Kass, Philadelphia, Pa.
Jürgen Koebke, Köln
H.-W. Korf, Frankfurt a.M.
Paul Krebsbach, Ann Arbor, Mich.
Annetrudi Kress, Basel
Wilhelm Kriz, Heidelberg
Sergei Kuznetsov, Bethesda, Md.

Accessible online at:
www.karger.com/cto

Kent Leach, Davis, Calif.
Robert Levy, Philadelphia, Pa.
Gina Lisignoli, Bologna
Martin Lotz, Philadelphia, Pa.
Joachim Lübke, Jülich
Mary MacDougall, Birmingham, Ala.
Ivan Martin, Basel
Milena Mastrogiacomo, Genova
Artur Mayerhofer, München
C.D. McCaig, Aberdeen
Jürgen Metz, Heidelberg
Wilfried Meyer, Hannover
Stefan Milz, Davos
W.W. Minuth, Regensburg
Karen M. Moritz, Clayton
Joyce Morris-Wiman, Gainsville, Fla.
Peter Muir, Madison, Wisc.
Daria A. Narmoneva, Cincinnati, Ohio
Wolfram Neiss, Köln
Roberto Nicosia, Seattle, Wash.
Laura Niklason, Durham, N.C.
Roy Ogle, Charlottesville, Va.
Hajime Ohgushi, Amagasaki City
James Olcese, Tallahassee, Fla.
Michael Paine, Los Angeles, Calif.
Amit Patel, Pittsburgh, Pa.
Charles Patrick, Houston, Tex.
Lucy Pemberton, Charlottesville, Va.
Christiane Pfarrer, Giessen
Mark Pittenger, Baltimore, Md.
Tom E. Porter, College Park, Md.
Andreas Prescher, Aachen
Anthony Ratcliffe, San Diego, Calif.
Gwendolyn Reilly, Sheffield
Sharon Ricardo, Clayton
Robert Ringel, West Lafayette, Ind.
Frank Roels, Gent
Roland R. Roy, Los Angeles, Calif.
J. Peter Rubin, Pittsburgh, Pa.
Jean-Louis Saffar, Montrouge
Henning Schmalbruch, Copenhagen
Lynne Selwood, Melbourne
James Simmer, Ann Arbor, Mich.
P. Simon-Assmann, Strasbourg
Fred Sinowatz, München
Shay Soker, Winston-Salem, N.C.
Luis Solchaga, Cleveland, Ohio
G.B. Stark, Freiburg
K.M. Stürmer, Göttingen
Yoshiko Takahashi, Kobe
Emil A. Tanagho, San Francisco, Calif.
Eiji Tanaka, Hiroshima
Kang Ting, Los Angeles, Calif.
Charles Turner, Indianapolis, Ind.
Theo van Haeften, Utrecht
Ulrich Welsch, München
Jean Welter, Cleveland, Ohio
Peter Wernet, Düsseldorf
Anna M. Wobus, Gatersleben
Tim Wright, Chapel Hill, N.C.
Karl-Heinz Wrobel, Regensburg
Shohei Yamashina, Sagamihara
Ioannis Yannas, Cambridge, Mass.
Marian Young, Bethesda, Md.
Norio Yoshizaki, Gifu
Matthias Zehnder, Zürich
Yuan Yuan Zhang, Oklahoma City, Okla.
Min Zhu, San Diego, Calif.

Cells Tissues Organs

Author Index Vol. 181, 2005

KARGER
Fax +41 61 306 12 34
E-Mail karger@karger.ch
www.karger.com

Accessible online at:
www.karger.com/cto

Subject Index Vol. 181, 2005

Cells Tissues Organs

KARGER

Fax +41 61 306 12 34
E-Mail karger@karger.ch
www.karger.com

Accessible online at:
www.karger.com/cto

Vol. 181, 2005

Cells Tissues Organs

in vivo, in vitro

Founded 1945 as 'Acta Anatomica' by R. Chambers, G. Glimstedt, T. Peterfi and G. Wolf-Heidegger
Continued 1962–1974 by E.A. Boyden, 1955–1980 by A. Delmas, 1972–1980 by F. Walberg, 1945–1980 by G. Wolf-Heidegger, 1981–1988 by R. O'Rahilly, Davis, Calif., 1989–1990 by G.E. Goslow, Jr., Providence, R.I., 1981–1992 by W. Lierse, Hamburg

KARGER

Basel · Freiburg · Paris · London · New York · Bangalore · Bangkok · Singapore · Tokyo · Sydney

S. Karger
Medical and Scientific Publishers
Basel • Freiburg • Paris • London
New York • Bangalore • Bangkok
Singapore • Tokyo • Sydney

Printed in Switzerland on acid-free paper by
Reinhardt Druck, Basel

KARGER

Fax +41 61 306 12 34
E-Mail karger@karger.ch
www.karger.com

Contents Vol. 181, 2005

Cells
Tissues
Organs

No. 1

Review

No. 2

Original Papers

No. 3–4

Extra-Cellular Matrix in the Craniofacial Complex
Guest Editors:
Marian F. Young (Bethesda, Md.); Paul H. Krebsbach (Ann Arbor, Mich.)

KARGER

Fax +41 61 306 12 34
E-Mail karger@karger.ch
www.karger.com

Access to full text and tables of contents, including tentative ones for forthcoming issues: www.karger.com/cto_issues